Praise for *Roland in Moonlight*

"This is a *marvelous* and *absorbing* book by one of the most singular thinkers and writers of our time. In his inimitable style, David Bentley Hart tells us something of his singular story, engaging with the deepest perplexities of thought while living through the sorrows and joys of life, all in companionable conversation with Roland. *Marvelous*: in that Roland is a sympathetic and wise dog, not quite a dog philosopher in the old cynical sense, not quite the hound of heaven, but a friend of man, with a finesse for things human and divine that abide and surprise, things many before us have known and that today we need as much as ever. *Absorbing*: the story engages us between touching biographical telling, deft dialogical exchanges with Roland, and searching dialectical explorations of philosophical and theological themes. It is hard to think of another philosophical-theological thinker who writes with such panache, at once singular and embracing. Very warmly recommended."—WILLIAM DESMOND, author of *The Gift of Beauty and the Passion of Being*

"When I was a child, I spoke as a child, I understood as a child, I thought as a child. I believed the answer to the ultimate question of life, the universe, and everything was 42. When I became a man, I put away childish things. I now know that the answer to every question is Roland or, more properly, ROLAND-CONSCIOUSNESS—that naturally luminous, spontaneously liberated Spirit in which we live, and move, and have our being. In these last days, Roland has condescended to appear to none other than David Bentley Hart, whose considerable literary powers have been tested in the telling. Part *My Dog Tulip*, part *Pale Fire*, part *Autobiography of a Yogi*, Hart's *Roland in Moonlight* is an instant spiritual classic."—TRENT POMPLUN, author of *Jesuit on the Roof of the World*

"Wow. Who knew dreamful dialogues with a dog could be so super-abundantly disclosive? *Roland in Moonlight* is mesmerizing, moving, and masterful, no less playfully delightful than profoundly insightful in its reflections on perception and consciousness, transcendence and limitation, poetry and translating, physics and metaphysics, relationships, suffering, healing, pathos, hope, and beauty. Overflowing with erudition that spans religious and intellectual traditions East and West, from the ancient world to the present, this genre-defying work literally could have been written only by David Bentley Hart. It is a revelation that will enrich the lives of every one of its readers."—BRAD S. GREGORY, author of *The Unintended Reformation*

"A succession of Russian dolls nesting inside one another, David Bentley Hart's *Roland in Moonlight* is a memoir, an apologue, a poetry anthology, a novel, a theological bastion against an ocean of fashionable nonsense, and a deep dive into mind versus matter—oh, and panpsychism, the collapse of wave functions, free will, Freud, Heidegger—the list goes on. The more you peel away, the more questions you will have. Questioning is itself the engine of this shimmering endeavor, which, like its author, is altogether *sui generis*. I suspect an infinite number of readings of this sly, elusive tale on the subject of re-enchantment with a world that has begun to lose its magic will yield no end to the plenitude it contains."—CRAIG LUCAS, author of *Prelude to a Kiss* and *The Light in the Piazza*

"David Bentley Hart's *Roland in Moonlight*, part memoir and part work of fiction, is a brilliantly ambitious and deeply moving book—lyrical and philosophical by turns—that centers on conversations between the narrator and his dog, the mighty-souled Roland, who, in differing from humans (he is at once more dispassionate and more compassionate), at the same time presents us with a model of what humans are capable of being and becoming. The conversations, ranging far and wide over a host of topics, from the mundane to the arcane, are interspersed with poems, some of them very beautiful, written by the narrator's Uncle Aloysius, a brilliant creation in his own right. Charting the years of the narrator's illness and partial recovery, *Roland in Midnight* is at the same time a palimpsest that sketches a symbolic movement leading from the loss to the partial recovery of Eden."—HENRY WEINFIELD, author of *As the Crow Flies*

"This astonishing book is almost impossible to characterize. Imagine that the Goethe of *Faust II* and Iris Murdoch had a love child who was raised in a Tibetan monastery. And then was permitted—because of the wisdom he attained—to come back in the next life as a dog... Who would ever have guessed that there could exist a creature on this planet with more jubilantly inventive wit, literary panache, and philosophical bite than even the great David Bentley Hart? But here he is: Roland the poet, the *cynic*, and the guru."—D. C. SCHINDLER, author of *Freedom from Reality*

"A marvelous and uplifting mixture of personal memoir, acute philosophy, political diatribe, and poetry, all addressed through dream-conversations with an erudite and affectionately sarcastic dog who is himself, we are to suppose, engaged in editing the verses of the author's pagan great-uncle. Hart challenges the materialist and anthropocentric paradigms of Western modernity both by careful philosophical argument and by sharing his own experience of illness and depression. But it will be the image of the Dog Roland, perhaps an incarnate Buddha, that may do most to change his readers' sensibilities, whether that dog is taken to be real, or dream, or simple fiction. A splendid addition to his published work."—STEPHEN R. L. CLARK, author of *Can We Believe in People?*

"Anyone who has ever loved a dog—which is to say, I suppose, anyone with a soul, excepting the allergic—must cherish this graceful memoir-cum-Socratic-dialogue of David Hart's relationship with Roland, who is a very good boy, though, it must be admitted, not a proficient primatologist. It is a wise and witty book, a book to break hearts, and to mend them."—MICHAEL ROBBINS, author of *Alien vs. Predator*

"Dreams, dogs, death, exile, the nature of consciousness, fairies, and the deep unity of religions—this is Hart in literary voice, echoing the deep American tradition that runs from Hawthorne to Poe to Lovecraft—with a dash of anti-Thomism and some essential Christian-pagan rapprochement. This is a book you can relax into. It will bear you away on a sea broader and deeper than the one you're used to. Hart is himself an exile from late modernity, as is Roland, the philosophical, koto-playing dog he writes about here. Exiles show us more about ourselves than do those at home in the world, and Hart shows us here a lot to be grateful for."—PAUL J. GRIFFITHS, author of *Regret: A Theology*

"A love of words, ideas, wit, combat, and truth fills every page of David Bentley Hart's autobiographical tale. His many fans will find they cannot put the book down, as well as realizing it is tantamount to a credo. Those who want to dig into matters ranging over love and consciousness, animal intelligence and human suffering, alien life and divine beings, will welcome this entertaining, stimulating, and moving feast. A wholehearted recommendation."—MARK VERNON, author of *A Secret History of Christianity*

"Interweaving autobiographical details with poetry, encomia to faerie, and metaphysical speculation, the utterly charming, sometimes startlingly intimate *Roland in Moonlight* invites us to consider the mysteries of being, consciousness, loss, memory, and the luminousness of the natural world through the eyes (and nose!) of its magnanimously wise canine protagonist. With Hart's signature complement of lush lyricism, droll acerbity, and melancholy whimsy, this welcome addition to his impressive canon deserves attention if for no other reason than the absolute delight it will afford its readers."—JENNIFER NEWSOME MARTIN, author of *Hans Urs von Balthasar and the Critical Appropriation of Russian Religious Thought*

Roland in Moonlight

DAVID BENTLEY HART

Roland
in
Moonlight

 Angelico Press

First published in the USA
by Angelico Press 2021
© David Bentley Hart 2021

For information, address:
Angelico Press
169 Monitor St.
Brooklyn, NY 11222
angelicopress.com
info@angelicopress.com

ISBN 978-1-62138-693-3 pb
ISBN 978-1-62138-694-0 cloth
ISBN 978-1-62138-695-7 ebook

Cover design: Michael Schrauzer

TO • THE • ONLIE • BEGETTER • OF •
THESE • INSUING • MEMOIRS •
MR R.W. H. ALL • HAPPINESSE •
AND • THAT • ETERNITIE •
PROMISED •
TO • EVERY • SHINING •
SPIRIT

Slowly, but with no doubt or hesitation whatever, and in something of a solemn expectancy, the two animals passed through the broken, tumultuous water and moored their boat at the flowery margin of the island. In silence they landed, and pushed through the blossom and scented herbage and undergrowth that led up to the level ground, till they stood on a little lawn of a marvellous green, set round with Nature's own orchard-trees—crab-apple, wild cherry, and sloe.

"This is the place of my song-dream, the place the music played to me," whispered the Rat, as if in a trance. "Here, in this holy place, here if anywhere, surely we shall find Him!"

—KENNETH GRAHAME, *The Wind in the Willows*

Acknowledgments and Disclosures

Any resemblance between the (very few) characters who appear in this book and any persons living or dead is quite unavoidable. Still, I should acknowledge that my Great Uncle—even though he never really existed—might disagree with some aspects of the portrait I have limned of him in these pages. Even fictional characters must have their feelings respected, after all, especially when they are close relatives.

As for Roland, he has given me permission to divulge the contents of all the conversations recorded here. And I have obtained my own consent as well, with only a little difficulty.

My thanks to all those friends and colleagues who go unnamed in these pages (simply as a stylistic conceit, I should say), but who assisted me and my family through some very difficult years. During our time in Charlottesville, St. Louis, and South Bend, we have been the beneficiaries of countless gestures of generosity, large and small, without which we might not have made it through the darker days quite intact.

CONTENTS

PART ONE

FOREST

I

I T WAS A SPRING DAY when first we found him. Outside the
SPCA shelter, a strong breeze was stirring the leaves in the high
trees enclosing the grounds, and was shaking the branches of
the lilac and oleander bushes bordering the path to the door, and
sunlight and shadow were flickering and splashing all about us, and
ripples of silver were coursing continually through the lawn's broad
blades of fescue grass. Inside, the fluorescent lighting was bleak, the
air-conditioning was parchingly glacial, and the small enclosed cells
of sheet-glass and whitewashed concrete where the rescued animals
were kept were both glaringly bare and pitilessly exposed to view.
He was one of three puppies, the last remaining siblings from a
larger litter, and our first glimpse of him was as one small furry
form in a tremulous huddle from which six small eyes were gazing
out apprehensively at a menacingly brilliant world, populated by
shambling, titanic, bipedal brutes.

Their mother had been a Boston terrier, we were told. Of their
father, little could be guessed except that the mix of breeds in his
parentage had apparently included some kind of hound, perhaps
bluetick; otherwise, he had been one of those vagabond roués so
sadly rampant throughout canine society, the sort all too ready to
find their pleasure where they may without sparing a thought for
the consequences and then to break a bitch's heart by insouciantly
abandoning her to rear the young on her own. Whatever the confluence of genetic forces that had produced these foundlings, however,
the results were altogether exquisite, in the unpredictable way of
such things. All three were well built, and had faces so winsome that
they could bring tears to one's eyes. And all three were more or less
identical, apart from the markings of their shorthaired coats. Of
these, his were the most distinctive. Both of his siblings were of
solid hues, one a dark brown, like mahogany, the other far lighter,
so tawny as to verge on pale gold. He, by contrast, was a particol-

3

ored collage of abstract patterns, patches, and shades: a mottled, speckled, and brindled coat of white, black, brown, light auburn, and gray; two dark, glossily drooping ears parenthesizing a gentle and pensive face; limpid brown eyes peering out through a *maschera di Colombina* of burnt umber and dark honey; a milk-white snout dappled with ash; a gleaming coal-black nose... I was enraptured.

As it happened, though, on that particular day we were on our way out of Charlottesville, and had stopped in only as an advance reconnaissance, intending to come again on the morrow. When we did just that, we found that in the short time since our earlier visit both his siblings had been spirited away to new homes. Apparently the adoptive families had found their sleek, monochromatic coats more appealing than his debonair motley. My tastes ran in quite the opposite direction; I thought that his fur's swirling contrasts and vivid juxtapositions made his entrancing features all the more expressive; and so I was quite content to find that he had been left as our share of the litter. But he was a sad sight just then. Small, all alone in that vacant whiteness with nowhere to hide, entirely bereft of the physical warmth and emotional security of his natural family, all he could do now was curl himself into one chilly corner of his cell and shiver. On seeing him like that, I felt a spasm of pure anguish rise up in my throat, and even heard a soft, miserable groan issue from my own lips. There was no question now but that he must come home with us. I could no more have left him like that than I could have casually severed one of my fingers with a dull butter-knife. When we had found an attendant of the facility to hand him to us, he attempted to coil himself into as condensed a shape as he could, trembling violently as each of us in turn took him into a gentle embrace. My son (who was ten at the time) was thoroughly and deeply moved by his look of forlorn loneliness. My wife, seeing his need for a sense of safety, carried him off to a small room with a sign on the door reading "Puppy Encounters." There, as soon as she set him down on the floor, he immediately slipped beneath the hem of her long Indian skirt to hide. Only over a period of twenty minutes or so was she able to coax him out again, so that he could explore her fingertips with his nose, wander around her as she sat on the

4

floor, take in the soothing sound of her voice and the welcoming scent of affection emanating from her, and at last wag his tail with some enthusiasm as she gathered him up again and held him in her lap. From that day forward, his devotion to her would be absolute.

We completed the paperwork in fifteen minutes, paid the licensing fee, purchased a collar and leash, accepted the coupons for his first veterinary visit, but declined for the moment the offer to have his name engraved on the tag they gave us, preferring to put that off to a later date. All the shelter's tenants had been assigned names by the staff, but the one they had given him—Buster—was manifestly, even extravagantly wrong. It was quite impossible that that was really who he was. But we had no notion of what he was *truly* called. That precious mystic communication had not as yet been vouchsafed to us. It was not until ten minutes or so after we had set out for home, with him sitting quietly in my wife's lap in the back seat, looking about at everything curiously but as serene as the Buddha beneath the boughs of the Bodhi tree, that we all together realized that his name was in fact Roland, and that this should have been obvious to us from the first. As soon as one of us had pronounced it aloud (I believe I was the first to do so, but I cannot quite recall), we all found ourselves in accord that no other name could ever possibly attach to him. I decided that I would return to the shelter the next day to have the engraving made, but for now we did not want to frighten him by turning back. We were eager instead to introduce him to his home.

We loved him at once and unreservedly, of course, as only a degenerate and soulless monster would fail to do on first coming to know a puppy. Even so, none of us just then even remotely suspected what an inscrutable and mighty soul had entered our lives.

II

IN THOSE DAYS, we happened to be living in Eden (or at least as near to that now gated community as persons with our resources could succeed in coming), and had been doing so for a year by that point. We were renting a small but extremely pleasant forest cabin in the mountains not far south of town. It was situated near a fairly shallow wooded ravine that on our side descended to a narrow streambed and then rose again on the opposite side—very gradually and over a distance of a few miles—towards a higher ridge that dominated the western and southwestern horizon. That looming crest was an almost numinous presence in our lives. Sometimes, when the twilight had gathered up the intervening distance into a single shadowy fold of melting blue, it appeared to have come impossibly near, as if it were demanding the tribute of our awe; at other times it seemed forbiddingly remote, as if it had haughtily withdrawn into its own mystery, altogether indifferent to us; but at all times it seemed to be keeping watch over us, silent and august, and even occasionally indulgent. Nearly every morning, no matter the time of year, the ridgeline was mantled in clouds, sometimes so heavily that it disappeared behind an opaque wall of pearl gray. And nearly every evening, as the sun descended and the twilight rose up behind it, it was briefly crowned in purple, crimson, and light gold, except at its southwestern edge, where it sloped downward into a gulf of amethyst, rose, and orange. After dark, moreover, there was none of the dull rufous pall of city lights spread across the heavens, and on clear nights the ridge's silhouette, against the sky's crystalline blue, looked like the jagged black shoreline of an ocean of stars. If the moon was up, everything—grass, trees, the shingles and eaves of our cabin, the gravel of our drive—was glazed with an otherworldly luster.

Wildlife was abundant there, moreover. All the woodland creatures one would expect, great and small, were our neighbors—deer and black bears, glossy black snakes and glistening blue-tailed skinks, ruby-throated hummingbirds and barn owls, red foxes and snowshoe hares. At night, the ghostly songs of coyotes drifted down to us from the higher mountain ridges. The weather, moreover, was almost always preposterously pleasant. Even during the hottest months of the year, cool winds constantly blew down from the peaks above or through the southwestern pass. The soughing of the trees rose and fell as the gusts strengthened or weakened, but it scarcely ever seemed wholly to abate, and on clear days the sunlight —filtered through the hectic gesticulations of countless leaves— incessantly flashed and undulated around the house. The birds were always so numerous and various that their songs blended inextricably together, and it was possible only very occasionally to take note of a particular discrete phrase—the song of a goldfinch, say, or of a cardinal—before it merged back into the general polyphony. The short, sharp staccato of the woodpeckers, however, was always recognizable.

As we were living solely by my writing, we had little occasion to go down into Charlottesville except as practical need dictated. For most of the year, my routine was unvarying. From spring through autumn, I would spend part of each day gathering up wind-felled kindling, cutting up fallen trees with a chainsaw as fuel for the winter (the cabin came equipped with a superb Swedish wood-burning stove), and stacking the cut wood between the balusters in the low wooden railing on the porch that girdled the cabin. I also took three hikes each day, with my son when possible. My wife gardened wherever sunlight was sufficiently plentiful. Our seclusion was so absolute that it was possible for weeks on end to imagine that the whole world had reverted to wilderness (if a very habitable wilderness). All that was wanting from our arcadian existence was the presence of a dog, without which no life can be truly complete.

On the day we brought Roland home for the first time, the air was filled with the high, lyrical mixed chorus of the woodland frogs. The rain had been heavy and regular for days and the ditches were full to overflowing. Seen from a distance, they sparkled in the sun with the brilliance of cut diamonds, while the water in the shallower depressions at their edges caught the reflections of overhanging branches in such a way that the green of the leaves, mingled with the gray of the silt, was transformed into a pale jade. Seen from directly overhead, however, the wind-wimpled water was quite clear, and revealed countless small black tadpoles darting and wriggling above a trench of gamboge and rust-red clay. The butterflies were becoming plentiful at that point—black swallowtails, zebra swallowtails, and tiger swallowtails of course, but also red admirals, painted ladies, monarchs, viceroys, pearl crescents, great spangled fritillaries, Carolina satyrs, falcate orangetips, and a few others. Azure and emerald and opalescent beetles and flies were just then appearing with more frequency as well. There were even a few bumblebees already drowsily bombinating in the warming air.

Roland immediately appeared to be wholly in his element. He was no sooner out of the car than he began to frolic and gambol and roll in the grass and bark. Clearly he found everything congenial to his nature—even delectable. And he took to the interior of the cabin with no less enthusiasm, exploring every corner, crawling under our beds, dashing from one end of the central corridor to the other, ceasing in his constant energetic and snuffling explorations only when he found himself before a bookshelf; then, and only then, he would briefly pause and stare at the spines of the books as if trying to make sense of their titles before resuming his romps.

In the following days, he proved to be of a naturally fastidious temperament, and required no elaborate house-training or especially vigilant supervision. He did, of course, have something of a tendency to chew magazines or cushions, sometimes to shreds (though, curiously, he left books unmolested, even when they were unattended and within his reach, except perhaps to move them about a bit from where they had been set down). And soon he had settled into a fixed routine of play, walks, meals, and naps. At night, he would not retire until my wife had done so (he slept on our bed); but in practice this meant that, whenever he was ready to turn in, he would coerce my wife into joining him by stationing himself in the near end of the corridor, at the entrance to the front room, and gazing at her with an expression of seemingly innocent (though theatrically dejected) expectancy until she capitulated; but, as she was always content to read in bed, this was no great inconvenience for her. His only unsettling habit was that of occasionally staring at me—and only me—enigmatically, with a look of calm, reflective, slightly suspicious scrutiny on his face that seemed oddly incongruent with his otherwise ingenuously puppyish behaviors. I sometimes had the uncomfortable feeling that he was taking my measure, presumably in order to determine whether I was a worthy companion for my wife, and perhaps entertaining a few doubts on that score.

We might have continued living on our mountain indefinitely had fate left us to ourselves. So long as we were there, every day was a delight; and, once we had left, life was never quite as delightful again. Certainly no place could have been more ideal for the rearing of a young child and a younger dog. Not that the occasional dissonant note never intruded upon our harmonious existence. There was that night when my wife left to attend a memorial service for a departed friend and Roland, now four months old but still entirely unaccustomed to her leaving the cabin after dark, and so apparently assuming that she had been taken away forever, settled himself on the wood-burning stove's low stone dais, opened his lips, and began to emit a desolate, keening howl that persisted for the entire three hours of her absence. No reassurance I offered could ease his grief—Roland weeping for "Mama," and he would not be comforted, for she was (as far as he could tell) no more. And then there was the day when the water-pump had to be repaired and, once it began working again, loud rattling bursts of air were forced through the cabin's pipes and he, perhaps thinking us under assault by some monster, went into conniptions of barking and howling. Mind you, even then he did not attempt to abandon us to the beast. Only half-grown though he was, he heroically dashed to the back of the cabin to find and warn us, and to rouse us to flee from the menace.

But there were few episodes of that sort. On the whole, life flowed along quite placidly up there in our terrestrial paradise, just above and beyond the inhabited world. And Roland grew and waxed in wisdom and bodily strength, finally establishing himself as a dog of medium build, around fifty solid pounds, healthy and with no sign that the traumas of a difficult early puppyhood had marked him indelibly. It was then, however, when he was fully physically grown but still quite young, that stranger things began to happen.

9

III

THAT HIGHER MOUNTAIN RIDGE that I mentioned above could be reached by foot from where we lived, if one was willing to make the effort. The passage to the top lay somewhat southward, and to get to it one had first to descend into the green depths of the ravine behind our cabin, down through the dense shade of the deciduous trees and immense loblolly pines, through billowing ferns, over carpets of moss and creeping juniper, and across a narrow stream that was usually coursing vigorously. The best path to the opposite bank—not the easiest, but the most picturesque—lay just above a small cascade formed by a tangle of oak and Asian tulip roots arching over a small chute in the streambed. Once one was across, the ascending slope on the other side was gentle at first, becoming truly steep at just two or three places, and then only very briefly. In all, it took little more than an hour to reach the ridge. This was the path Roland and I took one day late in his first summer with us, early enough in the morning that the sun had not yet cleared the eastern horizon. The mountain laurel that was so extremely plentiful at the bottom of the ravine was in full blossom. A few bronze and golden box turtles were just visible, lurking in the deep shade and by the water. A dense bank of fog—really a cloud that had settled on the mountaintop—was creeping down toward us through the trees as we crossed the stream and began to climb the slope, and soon we were thoroughly immersed in it. When we reached the ridge, the sun, still at a sharply lateral angle to us, was pouring its rays through the cloud, and as we emerged from the ravine we found ourselves passing through shifting curtains of lambent gold, one layer parting before the next, one depth opening into another. It was one of those mesmerizing moments when everything seems to be in a state of subtle transition, quivering at the very edge of a revelation or a dream, and one feels as if one might just slip into another, parallel world if one is careless.

FOREST

By that point, I should mention, Roland had proved himself to be a voluble dog. I do not mean that he was habitually loud or given to incessant barking. I mean that he had a tendency from time to time to address us in long sequences of distinctly audible vocables and phonemes, some of them eerily recurrent, like sentences with coherent syntax, as if he were truly attempting to communicate something with specific semantic content. And so it was no surprise to me when, just as we came to the end of our ascent, and were able momentarily to catch sight through the parting mists of yet another sun-drenched mountain ridge, still farther to the west and south, he raised his voice in a kind of jubilant baying sound, followed by a series of articulate glottal stops and fricatives and sonorous open vowels. What I was unprepared for was the sound—the illusion, I naturally assumed—of four discernible words among the noises he was making, uttered in a canine register, part growl and part moan, but quite distinct even so: "Look at the fairies."

I stared at him, bemused, then laughed, then stroked his head. I am mildly susceptible to auditory hallucinations (perhaps as a result of some hypertrophy of my natural "intentional stance"), so I was certain I had made some contribution of my own to the aural mirage. Nevertheless, he had definitely made sounds sufficiently homopho-nous to the phrase that my imagination had been obliged to apply only a slight modulation to produce the effect. "What?" I said after a moment. "What a clever fellow." And I stroked his head again.

He merely stared back at me quizzically, even perhaps a little sar-donically, as if I were making something of a fool of myself. I waited to see whether he would reply. When, however, he merely lowered his snout and nibbled gently at an itch on his own front leg, I took in a last breath of the fresh morning air and remarked that it was time for us to be getting back to the cabin.

When I say I waited for a reply, incidentally, I mean only that past experience had taught me that, when spoken to directly, Roland was often prone to "speak" back, in one of his characteristic streams of discrete syllables. The first time this happened, in fact, he was still only half-grown. It had been something of an uncanny experience, if a wholly charming one as well. He had been sitting on the floor of the small guest-room that I used for my office, not far from my

11

desk, and I had seated myself next to him. I said something along the lines of "How are you?" with no expectation of a reply. But he, as if he had understood the query perfectly, had immediately answered with a series of, say, eight to ten distinct vocal sounds, and had then fallen silent, staring at me as if awaiting a response. I do not recall what I said next, but he again replied in a way that seemed, for all the world, like a complete sentence composed from words with exact meanings, and then seemed once more to be waiting on my next remark. I said something else. He replied again. And this went on and on for three or four minutes, each of us politely speaking in turn, neither of us moving from his seat. It was impossible not to feel as if we were really having a conversation, and that perhaps Roland had participated in many such exchanges in the past. For a moment, I began flirting with ideas about metempsychosis and wondering whether he might be instinctively remembering his interlocutory etiquette from a previous life as a human being. In one sense, the experience was delightfully absurd. In another, it was disquieting. I had known puppies before, and had talked to many, and had even elicited some kind of response (or, at least, audible reaction) from a few. But I had certainly never before conducted anything like a continuous dialogue with any of them, or heard, among the putative babble of their canine noises, what sounded like clear locutions—utterances just ever so frustratingly elusive of comprehension. And it was even more disconcerting, once I decided to terminate the exchange by patting him on the head and scratching his breast affectionately, to see his face assume what looked like an expression of clear disappointment (with, I could not help but feel, my intelligence). For an instant, it seemed to me that, to his mind, my failure to understand what he was saying was entirely my fault.

Anyway, as we returned to the cabin that late summer morning, the memory of the episode came back to me. And for a moment I was uncertain that the words I had thought I had heard him speak had been *entirely* imagined. Just as we began ascending our side of the ravine again, a slight chill passed through me, quite at odds with the warmth of the new day. I looked down at Roland once more, but he was happily sniffing at something among the creeping juniper, paying me no mind at all.

IV

AND THEN there was that business regarding my Great Uncle Aloysius's literary remains, and that seemingly inexplicable correspondence from the Maryland archivists. Roland had been with us for a year at that point. A winter of considerable ferocity had come and gone. There had even been a period of nearly a week when we had been wholly snowed in after a blizzard (for which, through my wife's foresight, we had prepared in advance). And now spring had come again, even more lushly than in the previous year. It had been during those winter months that I had started discovering books out of place on my shelves without my remembering having moved them myself, but also without my wife or son having done so either. And just on the threshold of spring I had more than once come upon various of the file boxes I kept in our utility room lying open, and had found that stacks of papers had been removed from them and neatly laid out on the floor. I began to suspect myself of suffering bouts of somnambulism. There had been occurrences of that kind in my childhood, as it happened. What made no sense to me was that, with only one exception, the boxes I kept finding open and with their contents disgorged were the ones containing the papers of my deceased great uncle. These had come into my keeping more or less unwelcomed (given the limited space I had for storing them) from my cousins the Bentleys, on the spear side of my family. Their last curator before me, Hyacinthia Wilde née Bentley, had grown weary of having them in her attic and had threatened to dispose of them if no one else in the extended family would consent to take over their care and feeding. Out of a small but real affection for the old man, not to mention a momentary excess of magnanimity, I volunteered to take charge of them, intending to scan them into my computer when time permitted. Needless to say, time never did permit, and those papers had accompanied us from one temporary abode to another for six years now, a burden as impossible to shirk as Atlas's (or Sisyphus's). And now, as best I could guess, my slumbering mind must have led me to them with the intention of finally discharging the task of their digital conversion. Still, it seemed rather curious to me that my unconscious should have been fretting over the issue at just this moment.

Aloysius Bentley (1895–1987), in addition to his career as an academic classicist, had been a minor poet, published in a few small journals whose subscriptions could be numbered at most in the low hundreds. I have to confess that I had read almost none of his verse over the years. For one thing, certain of his literary enthusiasms worried me (he professed to believe, for instance, that the single greatest master of prose in the whole history of English letters was Sacheverell Sitwell), and as a result I feared that a deep delving into the bedrock of his posthumous papers would turn up a great quantity of doggerel, which might forever color my recollections of him. And, in any event, the special place he occupied in family lore had nothing to do with his literary aspirations and everything to do with his religious eccentricities. Raised a Quaker (as most of the Bentleys traditionally had been), he had been a fairly convinced believer in his youth, and had even begun his writing "career" as, by his own account, a "Christian poet." But at some time in his early twenties he had had a profound conversion experience and had become an avowed and practicing pagan. In part, this may have been the consequence of certain emotional traumas, which had made a retreat into religious fantasy seem especially appealing. At least, I was aware that there had been some tragedies in his early life—a friend who had drowned, a girlfriend who had taken her own life. But, whatever the precipitating causes, his conversion had been both real and permanent. By the time I knew him, he was in his seventies and his devoutly heathen view of reality was a fixed and definite feature of his personality and manner of life. I vividly recall the first time I attended his annual New Year sacrifice of a pair of woodcocks to Janus and Dionysus on the small marble altar he kept in his garden (carved for him by a sculptor who specialized in funerary monuments). In earlier years, the offering had often been a goat, he told me, but by this time his advanced years had made that too arduous a labor.

Both of his parents had been classicists, and I suspect that their love of the antique world had always been somewhat stronger than their devotion to Christianity, and that they had imparted their predilections to all their children more or less osmotically. Certainly both of Aloysius's siblings—his older sister Fiammetta Celesta and his younger brother Antoninus Impius—had also abandoned the "Nazarene creed" at some time in early adulthood, and both had adopted instead a vaguely theistic and pantheistic "spirituality." And it is more than a little revealing that my great uncle's parents had chosen to encumber him with the name Aloysius Gaius Stilicho (most people knew him simply as Al, while his wife and a few other of his particular intimates called him Wishus, though in his fifties he had legally added Philostratus to the collection and sometimes signed letters as "Phil"). Whatever the case, the call of the old gods had probably been ringing out somewhere in his soul long before he had become explicitly conscious of it. He never entirely repudiated his early Quaker formation, I should note, in part because it had taught him a healthy abhorrence of dogmatic formulations and in part because he found the transition from the Friends' attendance upon the indwelling light of Christ to something like the later Platonists' mystical contemplation of the inner light of *nous* a fairly easy one to make. He was glad also that he had never been baptized and so was not, in any fully formal sense, an apostate from any school or sect of saving mysteries. While his disenchantment with his former faith was real and definitive, and while he was capable of some stridently bitter judgments on certain aspects of Christian dogma, he disliked the fixed prejudice against Christianity that he found among other Maryland pagans. For himself, he took the view that Quintus Aurelius Symmachus expressed when protesting the Christian emperor Gratian's decision to remove the Altar of Victory from the Senate: that there cannot be only one path to the great mystery of God.

As a boy, moreover, my great uncle had received a rigorous and exhaustive classical education from his parents, but had been sorely deprived of any useful knowledge of his own times. As a consequence, he never really knew how to live on cordial terms with the modern world. He refused to learn to drive. He believed that mechanical watches were an offense against nature and the "divine cyclophoria" of the heavens, and insisted on relying solely on sundials. I suspect, in fact, that he would have found life in this world all but impossible had he not married a woman who shared all of his religious passions but none of his impracticality. She was called Polly, originally because her Christian name was Mary, but later because she had had her name changed to Polyhymnia. She and Aloysius were exquisitely well matched, and the tenderness of their affection for one another was resplendently evident even when they were well into their eighties. They had met in 1922, at a St. Trifon's Day parade in Baltimore's Little Bulgaria, and within a few weeks were engaged; within two months, they were married. She was a great beauty in her youth, and was still a woman of striking aspect and bright eyes when I knew her. Apparently, moreover, she had adopted the ancient mysteries well before she ever met Aloysius.

I should note, by the way, that my great uncle was a sincere, rigorous, and unsentimental sort of pagan. His "old religion" was very much the authentic article, and was nothing like our day's New Age syncretisms, with their dew-spangled gossamers and dainty iridescences and sacramental potpourris. And he positively loathed the factitious neopaganism still current in his own youth. He regarded sects like the Hermetic Order of the Golden Dawn, with their vulgar occultism and tedious mystical allegories, as sordid chicanery; he called Margaret Murray a charlatan; he immeasurably preferred the clear fierce meridian light of the ancient Peloponnese to the lugubrious perfumed purple of the Celtic twilight. Only an authentic and genuine restoration of the elder ways, he firmly believed, would lure the gods back from the hidden places into which they had withdrawn themselves. Consequently, those small, dignified household liturgies he celebrated in his garden were extracted from sources of (in his words) "uncorrupted antiquity." In his twenties, just after his conversion, he inclined principally toward Iamblichan theurgy and relied a good deal on the Chaldean Oracles and Julian's hymn to Lord Helios for his devotions; but, while he never disavowed those late antique devotions, he soon also began to favor older and (as he would have it) more "rustic" observances, feeling they were rooted more deeply in the authentic soil of Peloponnesian religion, and he began drawing more plentifully on the Homeric Hymns and the Sibylline Oracles.

For the most part, nothing in my great uncle's religion made him any more unusual than the average Presbyterian or Freemason. There were a few embarrassing incidents—the time a neighbor caught a glimpse from an attic window of him and Aunt Polly dancing naked around their garden altar, or the time I visited him during the Dionysia and he came to the door wearing a ritual ornament that, divorced from its religious context, seemed rather lewd. But in general he cut a rather ordinary figure in the neighborhood. Chiefly my memories of him were fond ones, and seem to have been almost exclusively located in that walled garden behind his ivy-wreathed townhouse in Towson, with its riot of ungoverned flora, and its quaint little statues of satyrs and nymphs peering out from under tangles of vines or the shadows of hedges. He and Great Aunt Polly were already well advanced in years, and he had long retired from lecturing (at Johns Hopkins). Often we would dine in that garden, when the weather allowed, and it took only a few glasses of wine to render him buoyantly loquacious. He would hold forth on his metaphysical speculations, the two or three rapturous visions of Apollo that had been granted him in his thirties, his hopes for finding funding for a Vestal college in Glen Burnie or La Plata, and his admiration for Algernon Swinburne (whose entire corpus of verse he seemed to have committed to memory). The food was always delicious.

I had not, however, thought about him even once during our time on the mountain, and so, again, those opened boxes and stacked documents—it happened four times in all, if I rightly recall—remained a mystery to me. What had my unconscious mind (as I assumed was the case) found so urgent about dealing with his posterity now?

And then the letter arrived. Or, at least, I dreamed of its arrival. At the time, I was not sure which it was. In addition to my childhood tendency toward somnambulism, you see, I had also long suffered from what I suspected was a neurological disorder akin to narcolepsy, though I had coined the name "oneirolepsy" for it, since its pathology was not a sudden loss of consciousness but rather a sudden dissociation *within* consciousness, an unexpected transition from a state of normal perception into one of lucid dreaming; so long as it lasted, I was at once fully awake and yet wholly absorbed in a vivid reverie that seemed completely real. Whatever state I was in at the time, however, on what seemed to me to be a bright day in April, after a night of insomnia that had left me in something of a stupor, the mail had been delivered just past noon and I was going through it, seated outside on the low broad top of my porch's railing, and I had come upon a cream-white envelope of rather heavy stationery stock addressed to "Roland Hart Esq." At first, I assumed it was our veterinarian's whimsical way of reminding us of an upcoming appointment. But then I saw that the return address was that of one Mr. Adrian Dorsey, Chief Administrator of the Maryland Archivists Society. Now, I naturally concluded that there had been some kind of clerical error—though how I could not imagine—and that the letter was a general promotional mailing, intended either for me or for someone really named Roland Hart who lived elsewhere but whose address had become confused with mine in some rolodex or data-base. Imagine, then, my confusion—especially in my daze of exhaustion—when, on opening the envelope, I found a personal letter printed on the Society's official stationery that read something like this (I am afraid I do not have the original to hand):

Dear Mr. Hart,

Many thanks for your inquiries and for the materials you have provided us. Forgive the delay in our reply, but it took us some time to confirm that Aloysius Bentley was indeed a native of Maryland, and to establish from our own archives the list of journals in which his verse appeared. We quite agree that he played a very interesting part in our local history and we are more than eager to receive the entirety of his literary remains once you feel you have collated, edited, and annotated them to your own satisfaction. We are always open to rediscovering this or that forgotten chapter of our regional history. We are also open to your suggestion of devoting an issue of our biannual journal to the collection once it has been duly received and archived, including a selection of hitherto unpublished poems. We look forward to further communications, and we wish you all the best in your labors.

Very Sincerely,

Adrian Dorsey

PS, As the Bentleys and the Dorseys are two old and frequently intermarried Maryland families, I suspect that Aloysius may have been a distant cousin of my own parents or grandparents. I suppose that means that you and I may be distant relatives of some kind as well.

AD

I was, needless to say, stupefied. For several seconds I simply stared at the letter in mute incomprehension, imploring my wits to swim up to the surface of my sleep-deprived consciousness and to make sense of things for me. Had I, in my somnambulistic trances, actually been writing and sending letters to Maryland, and making plans to produce a critical edition of my great uncle's papers? Why, for pity's sake?

But then I heard a small but distinct huffing sound, followed by a kind of sharply interrogative (and perhaps somewhat indignant) yap. I turned to see that I had left the cabin's front door open and that Roland had come out to join me. The letter and its torn envelope were dangling in my hand just inches above the porch's boards, and he was clearly staring at them. I parted my lips to tell him that it was not a toy or a treat that I was holding, but before I could utter a single word he had raised his gaze to meet mine and to stare into my eyes with what I swear appeared to be an expression of exasperation. Then he shook his head, approached, sniffed at the letter and envelope, and finally took them gently in his teeth. I released them without thinking, and he—with an enigmatic parting glance and a muffled exhalation—turned and carried them away into the cabin.

I rubbed my forehead, briefly covered my eyes with my hands, and tried to wake myself from what I was beginning to think was one of those aforementioned lucid dreams. The day was cool, the sky almost cloudless, the trees whispering and sighing in the breeze overhead. Everything felt quite real. Still, I soon retired to the interior of the cabin again, dropped the rest of the mail on the coffee table, lay down upon our couch, and seemed to drift away into real sleep for a short time. When I woke again, less than half an hour later, the mail was still there, so I knew that at least that much of the experience had been real. But I naturally dismissed the rest as a silly fantasy concocted by my fatigued and always overly fecund imagination.

V

S UMMER'S LEASE hath all too short a date. So too the lease on the terrestrial paradise, as I should have known. Eden is of its nature fleeting, more dream than substance, always already a memory—or not even that, but instead just an indistinct intuition of something immemorial. At the end of Roland's first year with us and of our second in our mountain retreat, it became obvious that the health of both of my elderly parents had declined so rapidly and so far that it was no longer possible for them to live safely on their own in their home on Maryland's Eastern Shore, and that it would be necessary for them to move in with us if they were to be spared the horrors of some retirement facility or other. This meant renting a larger house. We found one at the northernmost municipal boundaries of Charlottesville, also somewhat remote from and at a higher elevation than the town proper, and surrounded by a wonderful grove of gigantic loblolly pines—a hundred feet high—though not as secluded as our cabin had been. Alas, if we walked to the end of our drive there, the roofs of two other houses were visible through the trees. Still, there were forest paths, and two ponds of medium size among the woods, and a second-story deck overlooking the large back garden, and a deep round fountain basin at one end of that garden where countless delightfully vociferous frogs made their home. Ruby-throated hummingbirds came to our feeder, and there were goldfinches, cardinals, bluebirds... even sometimes that rarest gem of the Eastern woodlands—that lazuline fragment of heaven—the blue bunting. There were foxes too, including one intrepid and abnormally large reynard who did not hesitate to go abroad in daylight, strolling with disdainful nonchalance right out in plain sight of men and dogs alike. There was a female black bear with a predilection for moonlit ambles across the property. There were deer. There were groundhogs in all their stout and wobbling magnificence. We had not as yet been driven far from Eden.

21

And Roland took to the place at once. There were new fragrances to explore, new mysteries to penetrate, new squirrels to harry.

On the final day of our move to this new house, I went back to the cabin with only Roland as company to collect the last of my files, including the two boxes that now contained my great uncle's posthumous papers (originally, in their much more disorganized arrangement, they had occupied three and a half such boxes). Standing over them in the utility room, I marveled again at all the work that I thought I had been doing in my sleep. I had never mentioned anything about it to my wife, for fear of worrying her; and apparently none of my nycterine rovings had ever disturbed her sleep. But just now I felt a need to say something to someone and so, certain of his discretion, I turned to Roland and remarked, "What an industrious subconscious I seem to have."

He stared at me for a moment with what, in an odd and canine way, looked like an amused smile. Then he wagged his tail, shook his head, walked over to the box directly at my feet, took the lid in his teeth by its edge, and quite smoothly pulled it away.

"No, no, that's not a toy…" I began to say with a laugh, but paused when I noticed a single handwritten sheet of old and yellowed unlined foolscap, nearly as thin as onionskin but very smooth, lying atop the stack of green and manila folders inside. I crouched down and picked it up. The handwriting, in what looked like good India ink, was a cursive I recognized at once as my great uncle's, though perhaps more precise and less fluid than in some of his other papers. It was a poem—a sonnet, in fact, of the Shakespearean variety—dated 12 September, 1911 (when he would have been only sixteen years old). I reproduce it here:

A Cynic Philosopher in the Marketplace

The superlunary realm is pure æther,
The sublunary earth is bathed in air,
The chaste moon sheds disdain on all beneath her,
But thinks the fixed stars all surpassing fair.
The gods hate mutability; there streams
Above their worlds eternal light of day.

FOREST

They see time's shadows maddening our dreams,
Spread like dark shrouds upon our mortal clay.
The gods are cold, and jealous of their spheres:
Great Jove no longer deigns to guide our histories,
Nor Mars the violent tumults of our years;
Minerva veils her light in hidden mysteries;
   And, all her dorsal glory on display,
   Sweet callipygian Venus turns away.

If not deathless verse, certainly accomplished for a lad of such tender years, and the vocabulary and obvious classical erudition were impressive, and that hint of healthy and unabashed salacity at the end was pleasantly surprising. Mostly it suggested to me an urbanity and sense of whimsy that I knew were parts of my great uncle's character in later years, but that I had not expected to find among his juvenilia. "Look at this," I said, turning to Roland and holding the sheet of paper up as if inviting him to read it. "The old rake," I added.

Roland merely stared at me—almost, it seemed, contemplatively. He had set the lid of the file box down on the floor between us so neatly that it seemed as if he had done it for my convenience. I smiled, replaced the poem, and picked up the lid. As I did so, Roland briefly scratched at his ear with his back paw, then opened his mouth wide and made a sort of yawning and yelping sound at once, as if telling me it was time we were going. Then he rose and went to the door, wagging his tail with what struck me as an especially flippant vigor.

As yet, I understood so very little.

VI

WE WERE HAPPY in a different way in that house, though far less at peace. My father's health was rapidly declining, and my mother's was marginally better only by virtue of her force of will. It was not long before a medical bed had to be installed in one of the rooms in their section of the house, and then ever more medical equipment; visitations from practical care and registered nurses became more frequent, days without small or large medical emergencies more rare, and soon it was necessary to prepare "Do Not Resuscitate" instructions with forms provided by the local hospital.

But I will not describe the last eighteen months of my father's life here. Some years are yet to pass before that will become possible for me.

It was not long after our arrival that Roland and I—sometimes accompanied by my son or wife, usually not—established our pattern of three long walks a day, each at least three miles out and back, but on fine days much longer. The principal path we took through the forest was well-maintained, though not at all smooth, and there were numerous rivulets crossing our way, as well as one large shallow stream bridged by a barely elevated causeway of weathered wooden planks (which, after heavy rains, was invariably submerged a good few inches below the swollen currents). We almost always went by way of the pond somewhat northward of our home, where frogs and ducks and dragonflies (depending on the season) filled the air with their belling or quacking or flittering droning, and where at least one stately blue heron was often to be seen, standing erect and sphinxlike amid the shaded shallows or grandly soaring just over the crowns of the encircling trees. There was, incongruously, a Japanese black pine of considerable size some several dozen yards back from the water's edge, and its roots, protruding above an erosion-induced subsidence of the soil, formed what looked rather

FOREST

like an irregular and compressed curule chair, upholstered with emerald moss. Here, sometimes, we would stop to recline below the winding branches and susurrating needles, plunged deep in their swaying shadows. And it was on one such occasion, on a ravishingly lovely late spring afternoon, that I heard—or imagined I heard— Roland utter another distinct phrase of English amid what otherwise sounded like a series of yawns intermingled with soft, sustained moans, of a sort a particularly shy coyote might raise to the full moon: "So many fairies…"

A theme was emerging, it seemed. Whatever noise of his it was that my mind (as I supposed) had twice converted into so uncannily precise an impression of that last word, it seemed clear that there was also some secret motive of my own, hidden deep within my unconscious mind, that was causing me to fabricate the same illusion repeatedly. And it is true that, as a boy, I often fantasized about coming upon fairies or other sylvan or rupestrine spirits in wild and secluded places. I was especially fascinated by Native American lore regarding magical races. "I seem to have fairies on the brain," I murmured.

At this, Roland turned his eyes to mine and stared directly at me with a look of what appeared to be reserved disappointment. Then his expression softened, he raised his brows in seeming amusement, and he suddenly leaned forward and licked the edge of my jawline, right through my beard. Then he turned away again and stared out over the pond's serene, silvery brightness.

On leaving for our walk that day, Roland and I had gone through the French doors leading from the breakfast area onto the raised deck at the back of the house, taking the stairs down from there to the garden and slipping through the bordering trees and along the bank of a dry winterbourne that ran by the edge of the property. As a result, we had not noticed that that female black bear had made one of her nocturnal raids on our trash the night before, and had overturned and mostly emptied the large wheeled bin provided by our refuse collection service. On returning, however, we took the path around to the front of the house, and along the way discovered the mayhem. I also noted (not without a small throb of admiration) the dainty paw-prints of dust and clay that the bear had left on my

25

car's doors and windows. It was all my fault in a sense, since I had delayed more than once going to town to buy a proper set of adjustable straps for sealing the receptacle's lid against her spoliations. Even so, I groaned and uttered a curse. And then I saw Roland out of the corner of my eye looking away with what seemed to be a broad grin of quiet hilarity—though, of course, I knew (or thought I knew) that his mouth was simply hanging open because the walk had heated him and he needed to pant. Still, the impression was a striking one.

VII

MY FATHER'S HEALTH continued to decline, and after one especially dire cardiac episode the emergency medical team took him away by ambulance to the hospital. From there, after some days of intensive care, he was moved to a secondary care facility. We did not want him to die anywhere but at home, and had we not yielded to an instant of panic when the crisis came we might have realized that the time for his non-resuscitation mandate had arrived. But, in that moment, how is one truly to know? In any event, he never came home again. During the last several weeks of his life, our visits to him were daily and extended—one of the advantages of writing for a living is that one's schedule is one's own—but each day it was also evident that he had drawn a little further away from this world, in both body and mind. More and more, his consciousness would revert to earlier moments in his life, principally to some of the worst of the battles he had seen in the Second World War, during the advance through the Vosges Mountains in France, or in the campaign in Alsace, or when fighting street-to-street in Heilbronn, and so forth. This was only to be expected, as he had been in the thick of the action right up until the German surrender, and had lost an inordinate number of friends and comrades along the way, and the marks that all of that had left on his psyche—not to mention his hearing—were indelible. In his very last days, however, he also began having conversations with relatives of his to whom he had been deeply attached in childhood, but who had died long before I or my brothers had been born. And— perhaps as a result of fatigue and emotional distress—there was one occasion when, in that half dreamlike state to which I have always been prone, I fancied I heard one of those unseen visitants reply to something he had said (though what that reply was I cannot even faintly recall). Whatever the case, I assumed that they had come to act as his psychopomps, to ease him as gently as possible from this

27

life to the next, and that their arrival was a sign that the days were growing few. And, as it happens, he passed away just a week or so after they had first made their presence known.

During my father's final period of decline, my eldest brother and his wife flew in from Norway (they live on a farm near the Hardangerfjord, not very far from Bergen). They remained with us for several weeks, spending the better part of each day by my father's side. As it happened, my brother's son was living in Charlottesville as well at the time, having not long before moved there to begin a doctoral program in Art History. By this point he had become romantically attached to the woman who would ultimately become his wife; and the two of them were of indispensable aid. But the time came when my brother and his wife had to return to Norway. It was their hope that my father would not pass away before another visit could be arranged, but none of us really thought this very likely. My brother's wife left first, to deal with some matters back on the farm, and he arranged to follow a week later.

VIII

T HE MID-SEPTEMBER MORNING on the day before my brother
was scheduled to fly back to Norway, I had what I thought at
the time was a dream, one in which I had just awakened in
the early light of dawn to find Roland sitting at the end of my bed, a
bar of softly glaucous shadow—cast by the central casement frame
of my double window—draped over his shoulders like a prophet's
mantle. He was, of course, every bit himself, and there was nothing
noticeably amiss in his appearance: the middling-sized but leanly
muscular build, the shorthaired coat of mottled white, brown, and
black, the handsome face and coal-black nose and deep brown eyes;
but somehow I recognized at once that there also seemed to be a
profound melancholy in both his posture and his expression.
"What's wrong?" I said, after a moment of uneasy silence.

He slowly shook his head, and then—in a voice resonant with
sadness—replied, "I have to leave you. I have to go to Norway with
your brother."

I was astonished. For one thing, even in my apparent "oneiroleptic" daze I could not recall ever having heard Roland speak before,
at least not this clearly; I certainly did not recall him having a voice
so much like Laurence Harvey's (though with a warmer, furrier
tone). For another, he had given no indication before this of any
intention of leaving us; and, considering the depth of his attach-
ment to my wife, the very notion seemed scarcely conceivable to
me. "Why?" I asked. "What do you mean?"

He sighed, bowed his head for a moment, then raised it again to
look into my eyes with the frankest of gazes. "Your brother and I
knew each other long ago," he said. Then, seeing my bewilderment,
he immediately added, "Oh, not in this life, of course. I'm only not
quite three years old, after all. In another life, very long ago, countless *kalpas* in the past, in a better age than this our present *Kālī-
yuga*. In those days, you see, I was a god in the *Tuṣita* heaven, and

29

your brother was my little pet monkey T'ing-T'ing. We were quite inseparable." An amused smile appeared on Roland's face and he gave his head a gentle, obviously affectionate wag. "What a scamp he was. How often he would don a small chaplet of silver bells, clamber up onto the back of my throne of jade and gold, cavort in merry little capers above my head, and then suddenly tumble down into my lap in a wriggling, chattering heap. Even Maitreya and the goddess bodhisattva Guanyin couldn't help laughing, and the tender warmth of their mirth flowed down even into the deepest *narakas* and momentarily eased the torments of the damned."

"I had no idea," I said after a moment.

Roland was still lost in his memories, however. "Some of his antics were terribly mischievous, and I was often urged to exercise more discipline over him. But I couldn't—he delighted me so. On a few occasions, he raided the banqueting table of the gods before they'd seated themselves. Sometimes he stole flagons of wine and made himself drunk. Twice he slipped into the divine orchards and gorged himself on the peaches of celestial longevity tended by the goddess Xi Wang Mu. Once, when the demons of *Prātapana* mounted one of their pathetically futile escalades against the ramparts of the heavens, he sat high up on the walls pelting them with peach-stones and screeching with unseemly laughter. But I loved him so." He paused to bite at an itch on his haunch and then to smooth his fur with his tongue. "Anyway," he resumed, "our long idyll reached its end when each of us exhausted his stores of good karma, and we both plunged back down into the spawning-ditches of *punarbhāva*, and into the tangled meshes of *pratītyasamutpāda*... a humiliating, but of course inevitable, dégringolade. *Anitya*, you know. Or *anicca*, if you prefer Pali. Thereafter our karmic paths diverged for aeons. But now we've found one another. How could we bear to be parted again?" And a lugubrious sigh escaped his lips. "Oh," he said, his manner suddenly brisker, "that black bear came back last night and got into the trash again."

"I thought I heard you barking at something..." I began.

"Yes, I saw her from the living room window. I caught a glimpse of gleaming ursine teeth in the moonlight and I'm afraid that, when I recognized what I was looking at, an atavistic thrill of pure terror

30

set me off. Irrepressible canine instinct, I'm afraid. I'd help you clean up the debris, but I have no thumbs." He turned his head as if about to jump down from the bed, but then paused and turned back to me. "You know, that's a very potent word, really—recognized, I mean… recognition…"

"How so?"

"Well, I've been pondering the problem of consciousness a great deal lately, and how impossible it is to fit it into a truly mechanistic account of life or of evolution—I mean at the most elementary level. Take simple recognition of something, for example: there you have an instance of seemingly irreducible intentional consciousness, right? But we know what a thorn in the side of materialism intentionality is: it's a conspicuous example of final causality right there in the midst of supposedly aimless mechanical events… its content is eidetic… dependent on mental images, and so on conscious thought… it supplies a specific, finite *meaning* to experience that the physical order can't provide… Well, simply said, it doesn't fit into the mechanistic story, does it? And so, as I understand it, the really consistent materialist position is that consciousness and intentionality are all secondary, even illusory, the epiphenomenal residue of purely mechanical processes. Supposedly, if you delve down deeply enough—into the body's neural machinery or into the dark backward and abysm of evolutionary time—you'll find that all intentional activity dissolves into a series of unconscious, aimless physical functions, which natural selection has refined into such a complex order that it generates the illusion of unified conscious intention."

"I see," I said, utterly mystified to learn that such matters occupied Roland's thoughts, and not yet awake enough to feel equal to questions of such weightiness.

He paused to scratch the back of his ear with a hind paw, then resumed: "Take my silly fright at that bear's teeth. Allegedly that would most originally be just a neural agitation that only seems to have a rational content and purpose—survival—but that's really just the fortuitous result of an accidental juxtaposition of physical effects, mechanically coordinated by evolution. If you could trace my instinctive fear back in time, you'd arrive at some primitive organism without eidetic consciousness or intentional awareness, in which just by chance the shape of a bared tooth would—for no *reason*—provoke the neural response of flight. And then, since this would accidentally have the salutary effect of helping preserve that organism's life, this neural tendency would be preserved and transformed over generations into an indurated genetic predisposition. Only later would the elaborate stage-trickery of consciousness arise out of all that biochemistry, like vapors from a swamp, and with it the illusion that the reaction is an instinct based on a primordial intentionality. Well, do you believe that? Could any mechanical coincidence so bizarrely pointless and rare ever be sufficiently specified by natural selection? Do you really think that that neural reaction could even have occurred without some kind of eidetic recognition—some formal idea—present?"

"Well…"

"Of course not," he continued. "These materialists say it's mechanism all the way up—or at least up to some inexact point where some kind of phylogenic or neural alchemy, which we hazily call 'emergence,' magically produces consciousness as a kind of tinsel party-crown atop the machine. Nonsense, I say. Nonsense! It's just the opposite: consciousness and intentionality go all the way *down*, in varying degrees but continuously. Really, consciousness is at the ground of everything—it *is* the ground. Oh, did you remember to pick up some of those rawhide treats I like? I want to put some in my luggage for the flight."

"Look," I said, "do you really have to go to Norway? They'll probably put you in quarantine for a month when you arrive. And you know how prissy Europeans get about long-term visits by foreign animals without visas."

Now an almost pitying expression appeared on his face. "I'm sorry, but I must. T'ing-T'ing needs me… for spiritual guidance."

Knowing my brother as I do, I could think of no further plausible demurral, so I said nothing, merely nodding my head in resignation.

"You know," Roland added, "this whole business of consciousness reminds me of something that occurred to me the other day regarding superposition."

FOREST

"Sorry—regarding...?"

"Superposition. You know, the measurement problem, double-slit experiments, whether there's a collapse of the wave-function—I certainly think there is—all that sort of business. You see, it occurred to me..."

Just then, however, a shrill, intolerably raucous claxon sounded. It was my abominable alarm clock, I realized, and I began savagely groping for it. When I had found it and wrestled it into silence, I turned back to the foot of the bed, but Roland was no longer there. He hated my alarm, of course, as I imagine anyone with hearing as acute as his would. But it was very much as if the entire scene had melted away, and I gradually concluded that I must only now have been emerging from sleep, and that—of course—the whole conversation had been a dream. To awaken from an interesting dream before it reaches its end is always irksome; but I have to admit that my chief emotion, once the mists in my mind had begun to evaporate, was relief. It was very good to feel that I need not fear Roland leaving on the evening flight with my brother. It was comforting, moreover, to have my sense of normality restored. Until then, for instance, I had had no cause to believe that Roland was a Mahāyāna Buddhist, much less a quondam Daoist deity enthroned in a syncretic Daoist and Buddhist heaven. So I was at peace. My only real regret on rising from bed was that, in all likelihood, I should never now find out what it was my dog had wished to tell me about quantum mechanics.

Otherwise, I pushed it all to the back of my mind.

IX

AVING SAID THIS, I have to admit that I was greatly reas-
sured when my brother's plane took off without Roland on
board. I was even more relieved to see Roland betraying no
sign of having so much as contemplated leaving us. It had been only
a dream, I was now certain. Apparently—so the slow release of my
anxiety informed me—I had still been entertaining some doubts on
that score somewhere deep within myself, even though reason told
me that it was highly unlikely either that Roland could talk or that
he could recall a previous life in which he had been a god. The latter
especially. That sort of transcendent mnemonic virtuosity is, after
all, supposedly unique to the Buddhas; it is less a matter of "personal" recollection than a kind of omniscient aetiological insight
that allows the Awakened One to read the record of karma with
such precision as to be able to reconstruct the entire history of its
causal sequences—and then to reduce them, ideally, to a cycle of
winsome *jātaka* tales—much as Laplace's superlatively percipient
demon might be able to reconstruct the whole history of the cosmos from the present positions and dispositions of the particles
composing it. So it would surely be very unusual indeed for a dog to
be able to remember an existence lived countless *kalpas* in the past.
Conversely, however—and this had perhaps been the reason for my
lingering doubts—there had been at least a few ringing notes of
verisimilitude in the tale. At the very least, his claim that my brother
had once been a wantonly mischievous monkey imbued the story
with just enough of a trace of plausibility to make me hesitate to
dismiss it. Now, however, I concluded that my own imagination
must have supplied that detail.

But I had no time to ponder the matter deeply. My father passed
away little more than a day later.

Even that I experienced as though in a dream. As I say, it is something of a chronic condition with me that the boundary between

sleeping and waking consciousness is not always an entirely fixed one, and that I seem to be able to stray across it in one direction or the other whether I am technically asleep or fully alert. I know I was already awake when the call came, but a kind of mist hovers around my memory of the event itself, and so I may have been drifting in and out of a state of reverie. I had not been able to sleep well since my brother's departure, because a feeling of cold apprehension had been growing in me. It was near three in the morning and I was out of bed. I was in my office and had taken out and opened the first of the boxes of my great uncle's papers, principally to see whether I would find more evidence of somnambulism on my part. And indeed many things had been rearranged since last I checked. The manila folders were more orderly, each now labelled with a single year written boldly across its face in red marker. I removed a handful and idly sorted through them until I came to the one dated 1920, which I opened on impulse. And there the first sheet of paper I found was another poem, again a sonnet, albeit in a different form (not exactly Petrarchan, but at least with a distinct octave and sestet), written on what looked like good linen stationery in the same kind of dark India ink as the earlier poem, and in a more mature version of the same handwriting.

To a Drowned Friend

The day before you died, we sailed again
  On our familiar—our parochial—seas.
  Our sheets filled with the constant, urgent breeze,
The gunwales dipped into the waves and then
Rose high upon the whitecaps and the foam.
  The cloudless sky, in each bright billow's coil,
  Shone like cut sapphire set in silver foil.
Unwillingly we turned to shore and home.

We sway upon the drifting wreck of time…
I left you with a squalid pantomime:
  I saw you speak, but had no time to waste,
  So feigned agreement, turned, and went in haste,

Roland in Moonlight

Not really hearing what you had to say—
The wind was wild, and stole your voice away.

The poem's occasion was immediately obvious. As I have said, I had heard that Aloysius had lost a close friend—his oldest childhood friend, in fact—sometime in his twenties. I had even heard his friend's name in the past, but could not now recall it. I knew only that he had perished in a boating accident in the Chesapeake Bay during an unexpected storm. Whatever tears had been shed over the tragedy had, of course, dried almost a century before, and now the poem remained not as a memorial to the dead young man, but only as a testament to my great uncle's real but minor gifts as a poet—or, at any rate, versifier. But just then the sonnet struck me with a strange and troubling force. The image of those unheard words— those words not listened to, not turned back to—on the brink of a final, impregnable silence seemed all at once to oppress me. Every day for months I had been aware of things unsaid between my father and me, but aware also of how impossible it was to find a way of saying them now that he was being carried ever further away from us, growing ever less conscious of us and ever more conscious of other presences whom we could not see or hear. Somehow I was certain that my happening upon the poem just then presaged something that I did not want to be true.

And then, of course, it came. The telephone rang and, given the hour, there was no doubt in my mind who was calling. I took up the receiver quickly, in the hope that the phone would not wake my wife. As I had expected, it was the night nurse at the care facility. She informed me that she had found my father unresponsive about forty-five minutes earlier, and that he had been officially pronounced dead about half an hour after that. I thanked her, controlling my voice as best I could, told her I would come over now to see his body before it was taken away, and hung up. Then I wrote a note for my wife, roused my mother, dressed, and—when my mother was ready—went with her to the car. As we were leaving the house, Roland met us at the door, not agitating to be let out into the garden as he might normally have done on meeting me before dawn, but merely staring at us with an altogether delicate air of sadness

36

about him, as if he knew not only that something was wrong, but even perhaps what it was. I reached down to him and, before I could scratch the top of his head, he raised his snout and tenderly licked my hand. Then he stepped aside to let us pass, making no attempt to accompany us. When I had helped my mother down the three stairs from the front door, I looked back at the house and saw that he was now watching us from the living room window. I smiled at him weakly and affectionately. He lowered his head, as if weighed down by grief.

X

ROLAND SPENT more time with me in the weeks that followed than was his normal practice. Not that we were not often in one another's presence, especially given our walks together through the woods; but for a long time after my father's death he did me the extraordinary honor of keeping me company on several occasions when my wife was in another room altogether and he might just as well have been with her. He seemed to sense my sorrow—to pick up its fragrance, so to speak—and he was clearly loth to abandon me to it. Now and then, it is true, he would roll onto his back and stretch out his limbs with a groan of pleasure, inviting me to rub his stomach and scratch his chest, but even this I somehow felt was intended to distract me from my sadness. On two occasions I woke in the middle of the night—at least, I believe I did—to find him sitting up at the end of the bed staring at me silently, as if keeping watch over me in the darkness. On another occasion I was half roused from sleep by what sounded like a solicitous and sonorous voice instructing me to "Dream of happy things," only to find him there, stretched out beside me with his snout close to my left ear, his warm breath gently stirring the hair at my temple. I naturally concluded that my dreaming mind had cunningly crafted those words out of the small stertorous noises he tends to make when slumbering deeply.

And then there was one other occasion—another of those mysterious and liminal episodes, it seemed, in which my conscious mind was suspended between sleep and waking—when I felt almost as if his dreams and mine had for a time interpenetrated and merged into a single shared experience—a single magical moment of communion. Perhaps his concern for my state of mind had opened a doorway into my thoughts for him, or perhaps my grief had left it open, or both. It was, at any rate, a considerable comfort to me, as it allowed me for the first time to speak of my father's death as something in the past rather than as something that was somehow constantly occurring.

XI

I N WHAT I ASSUMED was my dream, I had just entered the open parlor of my house. It was still several hours before dawn, but music was quietly playing: I heard the last lines and fading chords of Schubert's *"Der Leiermann,"* in the recent recording by Jonas Kaufmann, before silence fell. I was confused at first, but I soon spied Roland, sitting on the carpet in front of the large bay window seat, staring out into the night. A soft, pure lunar light, shredded by the pine branches outside the glass into long glistening ribbons of pale silvery blue, poured gently into the room and over his mottled fur; for a few moments it almost seemed as if he himself were only a pattern of shadows and moonlight. The illusion was dispelled, however, when he turned his head and held me for an instant in the cool gleam of his eyes, before returning his gaze to the window. "I'm sorry," he said in that warmly resonant voice of his (so hauntingly similar, I again noticed, to Laurence Harvey's), "did the singing rouse you? I thought I had the volume down low enough to disturb no one."

"I don't think it woke me," I said. "I really can't recall."

"I suppose it's inconsiderate of me," he said. "It's just that I have many things on my mind, and it's only during these hours that I can get time to myself, just to think about them. During the day, my time is so taken up with domestic responsibilities—playing those games of fetch you all love so, letting you scratch my stomach, and so on. In these watches after midnight, though, I can reflect on things in peace."

A memory began to rise to the surface of my thoughts. "Yes," I said, "weren't you going... yes, weren't you going to Norway with my brother? But then you didn't."

"Oh, I changed my plans. I really can't leave Mama"—he meant my wife—"all alone with you lot. I'll visit your brother in the summer, with your mother if she's able to make the journey. That's not what I was thinking about now." He sighed. "Do you like that recording?"

"It's gorgeous."

"It is, isn't it? I'm so used to the *Winterreise* being sung by a baritone, by Fischer-Dieskau especially, and that dark ghostly timbre his voice had; but here's this marvelous tenor singing it with every bit as much pathos and power and mystery. It's a piece that never seems to loosen its grip on me. In fact, now that I'm almost four and my ears are more mature, and my heart wiser, it's more entrancing than ever. I mean, how did Schubert do it, the poor perishing ape? Such ineffable tenderness, such dulcet resignation, so much... leave-taking. That last *Lied* in particular. No other composer ever produced that exquisite combination of shattering melancholy and whimsical buoyancy. What's one to call it? What mood is it, exactly? Merry sorrow? No. Tragic jauntiness? No, that's awful." He shook his head. "It's unbearable but beautiful, whatever it is—sweet, almost honeyed nostalgia, under the shadow of death's wings. You just know that when he wrote those songs he could hear the dark angel drawing near. But that's how it often is. We frequently know... more than we know... anticipate more... Like those wonderful elephants."

"I'm sorry," I said, "you've lost me."

He turned, rose to his paws, and trotted over to me, wagging his tail. "I'd be happy to explain. But, first, do you happen to have any of those lovely bacon treats about you? I could do with a little something just now."

I brought three treats from the pantry, sat in the window seat, and tossed them to him one after another. He devoured them quickly (and a little noisily, to be honest), then sniffed and tentatively licked my fingertips, then rolled onto his back so that I could rub his stomach, and finally stretched himself, turned over, and sat up again.

"Thanks," he said. "One gets peckish. So where was I? Oh, yes. As for the elephants... well, there are many delightful stories about those magnificent creatures, about their intelligence and sensitivity, their capacity for devotion and grief, and so on. But I was thinking of the day in 2012 when Lawrence Anthony—you know, the 'elephant whisperer'—died at his house on that huge South African game preserve—the one that's more than a day's journey in size—

41

and the herds of rogue elephants he had rescued and tended all arrived within a couple of hours to pay their respects… to mourn, I suppose. I think I read about that in one of your *New Atlantis* issues. Amazing. They'd been away for well more than a year, and then there they were. How did they know? What summoned them across all that wilderness, so that they could intone their… subsonic threnodies?" He shook his head wonderingly. "How do souls reach out across the limits of time and space? There's just no end to the mysteries of spiritual beings." He paused, almost with a start, and looked into my eyes with an expression of faint suspicion. "You don't have any sympathies for the degenerate views of those fellows that deny that elephants are spiritual beings, with immortal souls, do you? Like traditionalist Thomists and whatnot?"

The question alarmed me. "Oh, absolutely not," I said emphatically. "I detest orthodox Thomism."

"And… and…" His brow furrowed, his eyes narrowed. "And dogs?"

"Look," I said, trying not to take offense, "you've known me all your life. You must know that I believe all conscious beings possess spiritual natures and have spiritual destinies, and that beasts partake of rational spirit. I'll admit"—I shrugged—"I sometimes have my doubts about certain kinds of Thomist. I mean, I've known a few who, if they have souls, keep them well hidden. But that's the exception that proves the rule."

His features relaxed. "I'm sorry. A silly question, really. Mind you, these days you have philosophers out there who deny that anyone at all—canine, anthropine, or lower on the scale of nature—has rational consciousness. We're all just organic machines to them. And as for extraordinary acts of consciousness, such as those elephants exhibited… well, they just deny they ever occur. And this means they have to pretend that vast regions of universally attested experience are just delusions and fabrications."

"Such as?"

"You know—fatidic dreams, knowledge of remote events, that sort of thing."

"Oh," I said uncertainly, "you mean the paranormal?"

Roland winced slightly. "I don't care for that word. But, well… I mean, ordinary consciousness isn't really reducible to purely physical causes, of course, but you know how these materialist savages, with all their abominable superstitions, can convince themselves it is. But what if there really are phenomena of mind that defy mechanistic paradigms completely? That violate locality, separability, causal contiguity...? I mean, well, look: have you ever dreamed something before it happened in precise detail, something you could not have predicted?"

"Yes," I said.

"And known others who had the same experience?"

"Yes. My father had some very vivid dreams like that. In fact, on two occasions he described events he had dreamed with remarkable detail, and then, in circumstances neither of us could have anticipated, those very events took place—down to the last minor feature."

Roland sighed and momentarily turned his eyes back to the moonlight beyond the window. "I miss your father. He was so kind."

Words would not come, so I simply nodded my head.

He looked at me again. "Have you ever suddenly known of something happening far away, something that you also couldn't have predicted?"

"On three occasions, definitely," I said. "All three were dreadful."

"Well, there you have it," he said. "I could go on too. But the point is, haven't most of us had those experiences? Or at least known others who have—other people we trust? Aren't there enough examples of these moments when the walls of material nature become like transparent glass—when a peregrine breeze momentarily lifts the veil aside and grants us a glimpse of what we shouldn't be able to see if we were just biochemical machines—to qualify as established data? To merit investigation? Or just curiosity?"

"Oh, you know," I said, "there's so-called 'paranormal' research, but I doubt it's very fruitful. If nothing else, these things are so episodic, and the causal logic is impossible to make sense of..."

Roland yawned loudly and scratched his right ear with his hind paw. "Balderdash. Anyway, I'm not talking about laboratory research, really. I just mean that scientists and philosophers who want to make sense of consciousness aren't going to do the subject much justice if they simply rule out any evidence that doesn't fit into a machine picture of the mind. The problem isn't method, but metaphysics. Dogmatic materialism makes them look for only mechanical causes, and to pretend that these other events never occur. But that's a ludicrous way to proceed. It's all just fanaticism… fundamentalism. But, again, even ordinary mental events should make them surrender their prejudices—normal intentionality is every bit as fabulous and uncanny as telepathy—but they can't. I don't understand it. Dogs aren't like that. We're not…" He paused and laughed quietly (if that is what one would call the sound he made). "We're not *dogmatic.*" He continued to laugh silently, shaking with mirth. "Sorry about that. Your father, with his taste for horrid puns, would have liked that."

"Yes, I'm afraid so."

He closed his eyes and lifted his nose, as if drawing in the moonlight like a fragrance. Then he looked at me and smiled. "I really do miss your father."

"So do I," I said, as the apparent dream faded or changed (I cannot recall which). Or perhaps it is my memory that has faded or changed. I may simply have returned to my room at that point. I was soon asleep, at any rate, back in my bed.

XII

A S THAT WINTER was approaching, I became aware of a sort of constant fatigue in my body and sometimes in my mind, as well as a greater frequency of headaches and occasional spells of breathlessness. My physician could find nothing wrong with me, however, and he and I wrote the symptoms off as minor allergic reactions. He prescribed antihistamines, recommended a thorough steam-cleaning of our house, and scheduled tests with an allergy specialist. And I was content to put the matter out of mind as best I could, since in other respects things seemed to be going well. I had gradually reconciled myself to my father's passing, if not to the manner in which it had occurred, and had begun writing at full strength again, and even producing some of my finest work in some years. Though I was obliged for financial reasons to write a good deal about theology, a topic that interests me only very slightly, I was also a regular writer for a journal whose editor permitted me free rein as regarded the matters I addressed, the prose in which I addressed them, and the genres I adopted from month to month (essays, stories, dramatic dialogues, surrealist satires, and so forth). It was a publication whose dominant politics I found tedious and often fatuous, but it seemed mostly harmless at the time. Or so I told myself. Things would change later. But it was a welcome source of regular revenue in those days. I even related some of my conversations with Roland—which I still took to be dreams—in a few of my columns there. I was not as yet able to devote myself wholly to the sort of writing that truly appeals to me, but for a brief moment it seemed as if I would soon be at liberty to do so. The burden of the last many months still weighed me down, of course, but less and less each day, and a kind of happiness seemed to be beginning to take shape on the horizon, and to be within reach.

If only my health had not been so oddly and perversely uncooperative.

What I did not know then was that I was growing progressively more ill, and would soon be struggling for both my life and my sanity. Our splendid house among the giant trees—not quite as happy a retreat as our bower in the higher elevations had been, but still only a few steps down from paradise, and a place we could envisage making our home for some time to come—was in fact poisoning me, and to a lesser extent my mother, and would in the end have probably affected all of us had my immune system not given way so spectacularly and alerted us all to the danger. An especially pestilential sort of mold had insinuated itself into the house's air ducts—a combination of *aspergillus niger* and various other mycoflora—and was working its slow malignant magic in my pulmonary and nervous systems. But, for now, the symptoms were mild enough to cause me only annoyance rather than alarm.

And so life assumed a constant pattern: apart from activities of the family as a whole, or the odd daylit expedition, or the occasional night out somewhere, or driving my mother to her medical appointments, or exotic teas taken with my son, or enjoying a visit from my nephew and his girlfriend, it was a regular sequence of three long walks with Roland each day, many hours writing while seated in a nook of a room at the very top of the house and beside a large double window that afforded a view of the back yard and the garden and the forest beyond (not to mention the wildlife that continually passed through the property, including that particularly bold fox), and listening to music. Would that things had remained that way, at least for some considerable time longer than they did. It was still a sufficiently idyllic way of life. But, as the Buddha taught, all is impermanence—all is *anitya*.

XIII

THOUGH THE ASSAULT on my health was inconspicuous at first, there were still signs of something wrong to which I ought to have paid heed, among them strangely restless nights. Some of this I ascribed to lingering depression, some to my addiction to caffeine, and the rest to the relentless advance of middle age. On more than one occasion, feeling vaguely unwell, I went aimlessly wandering through darkened rooms in the house, only occasionally switching on a lamp to read or perhaps make notes for something I was in the process of writing, but mostly simply ambling about in a desultory way, feeling at once disoriented and agitated and not knowing what to do with myself. I remember one night in particular, late in January, when I emerged from a daze only to find myself—without remembering having walked there—once again in our parlor, looking through the bay window at the snow on the ground outside, bright from the glow of a gibbous moon set high in the sky, shining like a polished white opal on a bed of indigo velvet. I gazed about. All around me, the moonlight looked like a thin film of frost, edging the furnishings and cushions and lamps, spreading across the carpet and draining it of color. I thought I must have already been standing there some time, though I was not sure how long really; an ache in my ankles told me that I had been more or less stationary for more than a few minutes. Then I looked down and saw four manila folders neatly arranged in a row on the window seat. I could not guess whether I had brought them with me or not, but I knew that they were certainly files from Great Uncle Aloysius's posthumous papers; I could see that each of them was inscribed with a year in large numbers, in that recognizable, vividly red—or, in this light, murkily purple—ink. I turned on the floor-lamp that stood next to the window, and the jaundiced glow produced by its old, darkened, cream-colored shade somehow made the room seem colder. I took up the first of the folders, dated

1926, and opened it. As on previous occasions, its first page was a poem in Aloysius's hand, this time in a fountain-pen's somewhat thinner and (as far as I could tell) dark blue ink, written on a sheet of typing-paper. Even in the lamplight, I could see that the edges of the paper were yellowing.

The Venery

Long have I sought the beloved quarry,
Waiting still by edge of lake or glade,
Or at the forest's end to watch the pale
Parched winter grass stirred by evening foragings
Of some thoughtless beast.
                            But she is not there
In shimmers of the water's vacancies
Or where the lighter webs of shadow spread
Below the swaying boughs and thin dry leaves.
She is not where the colder wind bends back
Against the niveous hills and raises clouds
Of glittering frost to drift down onto
Barren arbors.
                  I crave more light to burn
Away illusion, to disclose the paths
On which she strays, away to nameless lands.
The hind who lately fled the huntsman's horn
Flickers once upon the mountain ridge,
Beyond the palpable world. She has roamed
Far past the frontiers of the whole of empire,
Beyond the ecstasies of chase.
                              The day
Will be dark, with leaden skies brooding
Above the hills and the incessant winds,
When she will fall, and struggle, and grow still,
Pierced by the arrow I let fly against
The rising storm.
                      Now I must bathe my eyes
In the chill of moonlit waters and

FOREST

Go on. The season is cold, the day shorter,
And still she haunts my every silence.

I read it twice, the second time quietly speaking this or that line in an attempt to catch its scansion. I could not tell whether it affected me at all, however, or even whether it ought to have done so. I closed the folder, set it down again, and was just reaching for another when a rich, silkily sophisticated voice broke out behind me: "The title is clever, don't you think?"

I turned quickly about, at first directing my eyes too high; a second later, however, I saw Roland placidly seated on his haunches on the other side of the room, staring at me with what appeared to be a look of concern. "I suppose it…" I began, sitting down in the window seat; but then I paused. "You mean the poem, right? You've read it?" Just then, a slight feeling of vertigo caused me to close my eyes, lower my head, and place my hand on my brow.

"Of course," I heard him reply. "It's about a woman, needless to say… in an elliptical way. Or, really, a girl he'd been very attached to. Though she was dead by the time he wrote it. And it's also not about her at all, of course. There's only the most demure note of sexual appetite in it, of course, though in another way it's pervasive. But for him the erotic and the mystical and the pious and the aesthetic—it was all one thing. Aphrodite Pandemos and Aphrodite Ourania at one and the same time. Aloysius was always writing about girls and women in those early decades—some he'd known, some he'd lost… and, more exquisitely elusive, one he somehow knew but had never found… whom he'd dreamed about and whom he felt he could almost remember. A sort of archetypal feminine presence calling to him… calling him back… a goddess, a consort, a recollection from some other world."

I raised my head, opened my eyes, and stared at him. "What?" I murmured. Then, clearing my throat, I spoke more loudly: "I had no idea you were so familiar with his… with him."

"Of course I am," Roland replied, shaking his head in wonderment. "I've been organizing and annotating his papers for months. You saw the letter I received from the Maryland Archivists Society."

"Oh, yes, that," I said. "I'd almost forgotten. But I thought I'd imagined that."

49

He simply stared at me for several seconds, his dark eyes gleaming in the lamplight with a queer liquid brilliancy, his head tilted ever so slightly to one side; and I had the uncomfortable feeling that he was making one of his routine assessments of my intellect and character, and perhaps marking me down a few grades in his mental register. "It's rather boorish to read someone else's mail, you know," he finally remarked, though with no real hint of reproach in his voice. "I know it was a misunderstanding, but one should pay attention to things like the name on an envelope."

"Well, you see," I said, now feeling a bit abashed, "it's just that I thought a mistake had been made. I mean, you know... dogs don't get letters in the mail."

At this, Roland's eyes widened and he drew his head and shoulders up a little haughtily, as if taken somewhat aback. "Why do you say that? Do you think we're unworthy of the good offices of the US Postal Service?"

"Oh, good God, no!" I protested in genuine horror. "How could you think that?"

"Your own words," he answered with a slight shrug.

"I meant only that I had never heard of such a thing... or seen it before."

"Well," said Roland with an indulgent frown, "you oughtn't to make assumptions."

"No, of course not."

"I mean," he continued, scarcely seeming to notice my words, "you might suppose there's no such thing as a black swan if you've never seen one, and might proudly take your stand on the *terra firma* of solid personal experience in doing so, but only a painfully provincial perspective mistakes the small stretch of one's own native heath that one knows for the entire globe. You must always recall, or at least allow for the possibility, that over on the world's obverse side, which you can't see—immersed in midnight darkness just when your world is ablaze with noonday splendor, bathed in brilliant daylight just when your world is plunged in deepest night— some antipodean confutation of all that you believe is waiting, prepared to shatter your prejudices against the granite wall of its irony. A black swan, that is."

FOREST

"I quite agree," I said.

"To attempt to extract a general truth from a private survey of a few local particulars is simply foolish."

"Yes, yes," I said, raising my hands in surrender, "I'm in complete agreement."

He stared at me for several seconds longer. Then his shoulders relaxed, his expression changed—becoming less stern but more enigmatic—and his eyes narrowed. I said nothing, and neither did he. He continued to stare. I waited for him to say something, but he remained silent. This went on for some time. I began to become confused. For yet two or three minutes more he went on gazing at me from across the room, his eyes fixed directly on mine. Finally, it became too disconcerting for me to bear.

"Why are you looking at me like that?" I asked. "What do you want?"

At this, he heaved a long, languorous sigh, rose from his haunches, stretched his body, first backward then forward, shook his head, yawned with a dramatically protruding curl of his tongue, and then trotted across the room and leaped up onto the window seat by my side. "Sorry, I was just experimenting. I've read that it's possible to mesmerize certain simians—monkeys or apes, I can't quite recall which—by fixing one's gaze upon them for several minutes, perhaps with an occasional purling moan, like humming. I expect your ears couldn't pick that up. Anyway, allegedly you can draw them—these monkeys or whatnot—into a passive and suggestible state. It's rather like what the snake-charmer does in lulling a cobra into a swaying dance with his flute and with the slow, regular motions of his body."

I looked into Roland's eyes, which now—so close to my own and brimming over with moonlight—seemed especially entrancing and mysterious. "But why?" I asked.

He turned his gaze away, toward the glimmering snow-covered lawn and the gigantic spectral pines. "I was attempting to make a direct appeal to the reptile brain down there in the modular depths of your primate neo-cortex, to see whether I could prompt you to bring me some of those lovely bacony treats you cruelly keep out of my reach in the kitchen cabinets, but I wanted to do so without

51

directly engaging your reflective consciousness at the more mammalian level. I was trying to slip past the sentinel of your conscious mind and to communicate directly with your unconscious. Not of course that I really believe in so mechanistic a picture of the process of thinking. Still, testing the potential of the autonomic neurology of lower species is an interesting exercise, if only to eliminate certain overly simplistic models. I actually think that mesmerism is a proof that the mind is *not* the brain—but that's too complicated a topic just now. If one can penetrate to the mind within the mind, it's probably really just a matter of personal magnetism at the end of the day—strength of personality, that is, working on a more suggestible nature." He continued to stare through the window, but I could see what looked like a faint pensive smile raise the corner of his mouth.

When I had returned from the kitchen with four of those treats and he had devoured them, acknowledging each in turn with a courteous nod of the head, and when he had then graciously invited me to scratch his chest, I said, "And so it's really been you all along who's been sorting through and organizing my great uncle's papers? I was sure I was doing it while sleep-walking."

Roland said nothing and did not look at me, but I could see the smile on his lips broaden slightly.

"But why? What interest do you have in a relative of mine who died decades before you were whelped?"

The smile vanished. He turned his head to me slowly, now with a somewhat baleful expression. "That's a rather coarse word, don't you think?"

I cleared my throat. "I'm sorry. I meant nothing..." I cleared my throat again. "*Born*, I should have said—decades before you were born. Why does he interest you?"

Roland's expression softened and he turned his gaze again to the luminous snow beyond the window. "There were depths in the man. You'd know if you read everything in those file boxes. The surface wasn't always perfectly finished, but sometimes that made the movements of those depths all the easier to discern."

"Is that all there is to it, though?" I asked after several seconds had passed.

"Well, no," he replied, wetting his nose with his tongue. "There's far more to it than that. Something about the man... *touches* me. There's a pathos there... a kind of perfume of wistfulness, of delicate despair... a special kind of resignation, one that's still somehow a form of pious hope. It's a longing for something that's just out of reach, on the other side of things, on the reverse side of the phenomenal order we all share, but also something that he feels he might just be able to conjure over to this side of things through the sufficient application of... well, of sensibility... of art as visionary experience. He wrote out of a deep sense of alienation, of exile. And, what's more I think, his personal sense of estrangement was also in another way expressive of a universal truth of the present age—one that's almost entirely impossible to name definitively."

Now I too turned my eyes to the fabulous, moonlit, crystalline land outside. "A longing for what?"

"For a world that speaks," replied Roland with a curiously morose intonation in his voice. "For a world that feels... that's conscious and alive. For communion."

I said nothing for a while. A strong breeze was stirring the crowns of the loblolly pines just then, and for several seconds their shadows seethed and shivered over the snow's bright surface, and glittering clouds of ice drifted down from their branches. Only when everything had become still again did I respond: "Yes, I think I understand that."

"Hence his paganism," added Roland. "To him, the early modern triumph of the mechanistic philosophy, and its gradual metastasis from a scientific method into a materialist metaphysics, was the most catastrophic event in humanity's spiritual history. As a dog, and therefore immune both by nature and by culture to the barbarism of mechanistic thinking, I can feel his anguish. I can pity it."

"One doesn't need to be a dog..."

"Of course, he blamed Christian history for much of it. He had a tendency to think like Heidegger on some things—well, the seemingly benign side of Heidegger. The age of the world-picture, the 'enframing,' the reduction of the natural world to a reservoir of dead material resources to be exploited by the will to power. All of it, he came to think, was a metaphysical destiny prompted by a certain Christian malice toward the natural order. And he could be quite Nietzschean in his dourer interludes, and more than once denounced the 'Nazarene creed' as popular Platonism. Which is odd, since he wasn't nearly as suspicious of Platonism as either Nietzsche or Heidegger was."

I nodded. "That's certainly true."

"He believed that the very notion that the world—that existence—is primarily, essentially, dead matter in random combinations, and that life and consciousness are only thin, vaporous emergent epiphenomena, was not only philosophically wrong, but destructive of everything precious and beautiful and noble. To him the whole of the world was alive at the innermost, most primordial level, and the deepest, most original source of all things is consciousness. And in fact he thought everything was full of consciousness, of awareness, of *personal* life. He really believed that, say, a tree has an indwelling spirit—a dryad, if you will—and that a stream is never without its naiad. Or a *kami*, if you like."

"I see," I said. "He was probably right, then. But you seem to understand him better than I did. Of course, I was still fairly young when he died."

"And he really believed that, in the ancient world, the gods truly did appear, did reveal themselves—prodigally, even—and really communicated with human beings in visions and prophetic dreams and oracles."

"Ah," I said, in little more than a soft mumble.

Roland turned to me, extended his snout, and sniffed tentatively at my neck and lips. Then he drew his head back. "There's something off about your fragrance. You appear to be... under the weather."

"Yes," I said, realizing that I was still feeling somewhat light-headed. "It'll pass."

He stared at me for several seconds longer with what seemed an uncertain expression, murmured something too quiet for me to make out, and then returned his attention to the world outside. "There's nothing in the files that tells me what became of Aloysius's remains after his death. There are two pages of instructions regarding his obsequies, but I don't know how faithfully they were followed by his executors."

FOREST

As it happened, very faithfully. My great uncle's funeral rites had probably been a little on the illegal side; but we had carried out his wishes to the letter. His interest in Northern European paganism had always been pronounced, if usually subordinate to his more consuming fascination with ancient Greek religion. Hence, it was his explicit wish that his life be punctuated with a kind of Viking *envoi*. The director of the crematorium had been his friend, and had attended the same temple in Catonsville, and so he helped arrange for the pyre and for the cortege of sails that processed down into the broad southern expanse of the Chesapeake Bay. Aunt Polly, though an excellent archer in her youth, was 85 at the time, and so deputed my cousin David to fire the burning arrow from the prow of the old skipjack we had rented. The sight of my great uncle's boat, the *Zeus of Salamis*, burning on the waves—a wild golden blossom of flame against the ruby dusk, undulously mirrored on the darkening purple and silver waters—was one of the most stirring spectacles I have ever been privileged to witness. I related this to Roland as simply as I could; but I was feeling even weaker and more dazed, and I cannot now recall what words I used.

All I know is that, when I had concluded, Roland closed his eyes and said, "I'm glad. It was good of his people to honor his deepest beliefs, right up till the end."

"Yes," I replied, my voice almost a whisper.

Roland looked at me once more. "You really need to retire."

I nodded again.

"You're not as spry as you used to be, you know."

"No, quite," I rasped, looking down to the carpet.

Then I felt—if memory serves at all—a warm snout but chilly nose pressed against my hand, then the gentle grip of canine teeth on my wrist, pulling me away from the window seat and causing me to stand. Then, before I knew it, I was being conducted back to my bedroom, scarcely feeling my feet beneath me, looking ahead through half-closed eyes at the small resolute form of Roland leading the way through the darkened rooms and the sporadic shafts of icy moonlight, his mottled coat a constantly fluctuating counterpoint of shadow and light. The rest I cannot recall at all.

XIV

I N MY DREAM—and on this occasion it was most definitely a
dream—it was night. The sky was so densely overcast that I
could not have guessed whether the moon was up. I was, for
some reason, in the stone-paved courtyard of a Chinese Buddhist
temple of open design. It was a rather plain structure, with slender
oblong pillars and ceiling-beams of unadorned dark wood and a
roof of dull gray terracotta tiles; but, for all its unpretentious rustic-
ity, it was built on an altogether palatial scale. No one else was there,
and there was no sound, not so much as the hiss of a breeze. But
somehow I knew that I was obliged to start running, and to continue doing so until I had gone all the way around its circumfer-
ence, under the shelter of its eaves. I had no desire to do so. I was
already terribly out of breath—struggling, in fact, to fill my lungs—
and my throat was unspeakably dry. Still, goaded on by some
imperative that in my dream was as undefiable as it was nameless, I
began running, and continued to do so without the least mercy for
my suffering lungs. And on and on I ran, miserably attempting to
breathe, miserably failing, and sparing myself none of it. Moreover,
the temple seemed to be expanding as I proceeded; I could see the
first turn ahead of me, at the structure's rear, but could never quite
seem to reach it.

I woke in agonized breathlessness, my lungs burning—suffocat-
ing, it seemed. I struggled out of my covers and sat up. At first, I felt
entirely out of place; but then I remembered that, having worked
very late into the night, I had chosen to sleep on the guest bed in the
room that served as my office. Hence my distress had roused no
one. I struggled for some ten minutes to take a proper breath, but
could not. I began to fear that I had perhaps suffered a small heart-
attack or something like a pulmonary embolism. I opened the window overlooking the garden, but the cold fresh air outside offered
no relief. Somehow I managed to dress, to write a note to my wife,

and to drive to the emergency room (which, fortunately, was only ten minutes away).

A thorough examination—EKG, chest x-ray, a blood-test for cardiac markers, and so forth—revealed nothing except slightly diminished blood-oxygen. I was treated with albuterol and antihistamines, given prescriptions for more of both, scheduled for an appointment with a pulmonologist, and sent home. And, within a day, the symptoms had subsided to a tolerable level, and once again I assumed that the problem was nothing more serious than a bad reaction to dust or dander or early spring pollen, or perhaps a vexingly persistent bronchitis. And when, a few days later, the pulmonologist assured me that there was no sign of anything particularly grave in my condition, I was much encouraged. He even cleared me for a trip I was going to be taking to London in April, to deliver some lectures at Westminster Abbey.

XV

A NOTHER MOONLIT NIGHT, now in early spring, and Roland and I out in the pleasant chill, under a cloudless sky, walking along our accustomed woodland path. No crickets as yet, but considerable amounts of freshly sprouting greenery underfoot. We had no need to turn on our flashlight, so bright was the moon and the light pouring down on us. There had been rain earlier in the day and the air had a rinsed, pluvial freshness about it, as well as aromas of new foliage and the faint, sharp sweetness of early blossoms. I did not recall having set out. As a rule, our walks together took place during the day; but apparently something had summoned us out after dark. All I could remember was a vague image at the edge of my mind of Roland sitting before me with his leash dangling from his jaws. And all I knew now was that we were well on our way toward the larger of the forest ponds. We had already crossed the low wooden causeway spanning the shallow rivulet, and now the mouth of the clearing was visible ahead, a fan of moonlight lying across it like a curtain of shining blue satin. The peacefulness was so profound that I felt as if I were floating. As was so often the case for me, I could not be certain whether I was awake, or only partly awake, or walking in a lucid dream. I knew only that I had no desire for it to end any time soon. "How far shall we go?" I asked Roland aloud, merely in whimsy, and certainly expecting no response.

But he did respond. "Only as far as the little lake," he said without turning his head to look back at me. "It's a special night, and I have something planned." He paused beside a large but ordinary-looking oak and began sniffing with particular animation, and even apparent relish, at its base.

"What is it?" I asked after several seconds of this. "What do you smell?"

It was several more moments before he replied. He seemed to be concentrating on some especially delectable redolence still clinging to the tree's roots. Finally, he drew back his snout, closed his eyes, took a deep breath, as if luxuriating in the moment, and murmured, "Exquisite. Exquisite."

"What?" I asked, genuinely fascinated. "What is it?"

He looked back at me over his shoulder and, as difficult as it often is to make sense of canine facial expressions, I could see that he was wearing what could be only a smile of deep contentment. "I almost passed right by it," he remarked. "At first, I failed to notice it. It was obscured by the musk of that irksome fox—I'm afraid that he appears to have been dining on an elderly chipmunk—but then I caught a trace of it: sweeter, more elusive, more delicate and yet more durable."

"What?"

"The scent of fairies, out for an evening traipse."

This, I confess, rendered me temporarily at a loss for words. I looked down at the roots of the tree, searching for I could not have said what. Small phosphorescent footprints, perhaps, or a dainty ring of toadstools. "Fairies?" I finally whispered. "You can pick up the fragrance of fairies?"

"Of course," he said. "If one can see them, why shouldn't one be able to nose them out? Why would the higher, more divine sense be less able to detect them than the lower is?"

"The lower…?" I began, but then I stopped, took a deep breath of my own, and shook my head. "To be honest, I've never *seen* any fairies either."

"Never?" There was an audible note of incredulity in his voice. "Are you sure?"

I shrugged haplessly. "None that I recall. And I don't imagine I'd forget. My brother—my eldest brother, that is—did once, long ago… when he was a small child, in Florida, looking out the window of a train that had briefly come to a standstill."

"Just the once?" asked Roland.

"As far as I know."

He nodded thoughtfully. "I imagine that there are some fairly exotic species of fairy down in Florida. Nature is so wild and indomitable there—and so menacing."

"Do fairies… vary by clime?" I asked.

"Why, of course," he said. "They're nature spirits, after all. They wear the aspect of the ecology they personify. Though, of course, they change over time, as the landscape is altered, or as circumjacent human culture evolves. There's a kind of cultural cross-pollination between fairy-kith and humankind. In general, for instance, European fairies have become considerably more refined and decorous over the millennia than once they were. Most of them today tend to be very reluctant to engage in the sort of mischief they were once notorious for getting into. At most, they're likely to knock on doors in the dead of night, or to abscond with some milk and cake. And they're frequently socialists now. Not all of them, of course. Not in the Caucasus, for instance. But for the most part they're good Europeans."

"How do you know...?" I started to say.

But Roland took no notice. "On the whole, of course, the fairies of the Americas have a wilder quality still than do their Old World cousins. They're still—how to phrase it?—rather more Titanic than Olympian."

Now my memories of those previous walks with Roland, when I had thought I had imagined him uttering discernible words, came floating back to me. "That *was* what I heard," I said. "You've mentioned fairies to me before. I was sure it was an illusion."

He merely shook his head, sniffed somewhat impatiently, and resumed walking, pulling me gently along behind him. "Of course I have," he remarked after a few seconds. "There are so many of them about."

"And you can see them still constantly?"

He sighed. "Not constantly," he replied. "No one sees them constantly. They're secretive by nature, and mercurial, and very elusive. Spritely, you might say. I see them often enough, though. You would too, if your mind weren't so well trained not to do so. Surely you know that the world we inhabit—the world we sense and see and believe we know by direct acquaintance—is as much a convention of shared consciousness as an objective field of sensations. It's a construction of the collective imaginative and the collective metaphysical intentionality of a given time and culture and spiritual epoch, I suppose I'd say."

60

FOREST

I did not answer right away. Instead I cast my gaze upward at the dark silhouettes of the treetops—some of their branches as yet only sparsely foliated—against the dark blue sky and gleaming stars. Was any of this really happening? It was all so very tangible, so acutely immediate, so full of sounds and scents and shivers of vital reality that it felt impossible to doubt it. "Well," I said at last, "I don't know if I *know* it, strictly speaking, but I've certainly long suspected as much."

"You're right to have done so." He paused briefly, raising his nose to take in some passing fragrance. Then he continued on toward the clearing, now perhaps only thirty yards or so ahead. "Your species, I fear, has lost so many crucial avenues of perception over the past several centuries that even things that were once quite conspicuous to you have become all but entirely invisible—except perhaps in rare and fugitive glimpses. It's not surprising, then, if you've become wholly insensible to those things that always required a certain spiritual tact to see clearly, or for any extended period. In times long past, the fairies and the spirits of nature and the gods showed themselves to your kind quite openly, and your kind was dependably able for the most part to catch at least a glimpse of their glory as it passed by. Even in more recent centuries, they were still apt to make an appearance or two to you at some time or another in your lives—maybe most often in childhood. But now..." He shook his head and his voice dropped to a somewhat grimmer and more lugubrious register. "But now you've filtered so much of it out. That's what the brain and nervous system are, after all: a filtration system, a way of reducing the totality of universal conscious communion to the manageable dimensions of particular, punctiliar subjective psychological experience. But now the filter has become practically opaque where certain aspects of reality are concerned. In the modern age—the age of the mechanical philosophy—you haven't much chance of seeing those... those *luminous* dimensions of reality where fairies tend to flaunt themselves. Once the mechanistic method became a metaphysics, and then a habitual way of thinking about the world, so much that's truly alive and beautiful and mysterious was lost to your kind. Living spirits especially. My people, fortunately, never succumbed to these frightful materialist superstitions, so I don't have to work so hard to pierce the veil of the quotidian, and to descry the radiant figures that dance beneath the blazing moon, in the courts of that other kingdom."

The clearing was now only ten yards ahead and the haze of blue and silver was giving way to the distinct forms of softly illuminated grass and gleaming water and dark encompassing trees. The air was slightly moist but not clinging, and the breeze-blown leaves over-head were garrulously exchanging whispers with one another.

"They're still with us," Roland added after several seconds. "I'm sure you recall what many of the fairies of the Native Peoples of this continent were called. I remember hearing you tell your son when we went on walks together up there on the mountain where we used to live. Let's see... I recall you mentioning the *Nirumbee* of the Crow, and the Choctaw's *Kwunokasha*, and the Shoshone's *Nimeri-gar*... Of course, the *Kachina* of the Hopi and Hopi-Tewa and Zuni. There were so many."

"Yes," I said. "I memorized many of them when I was a boy."

"There were three varieties associated with the Cherokee if I recall."

"Yes, there were," I replied. "That's right. At least three, I think. There was one kind associated with laurel, and another with dog-wood, and another with stony places—and that last one was given to stealing babies, I believe."

"Very distasteful," said Roland with a dolorous wag of his head. "Fairies everywhere can be terrifically amoral beings." He ceased walking and turned to look at me. "Of course, a good number of foreign fairies came over with the various waves of immigrants, and some of them, frankly, have had to be cured of their colonialist ways. On the whole, though, the various communities have achieved a kind of pluralistic harmony without, for the most part, the sorts of tragedy and cruelty that your ancestors visited on these shores." He turned about again and resumed walking. "Some came in the slave ships as well, and bore witness. They still do, in the assizes of the Seelie Court, along with those of the native peoples, and of Japanese and Chinese Americans and so on. That's why this whole country of yours is regarded among the fay as a cursed nation."

FOREST

"That seems fair," I said.

We entered the clearing. The sky opened above us—an abyss of stars, a full moon bright as molten silver—and the pond was a placid, shimmering mirror of its brilliances. Roland drew me onward to that mossy, naturally elevated seat among the roots of the Japanese black pine, as if there were no question but that it was our destination.

"Rest," he said to me. "Your scent is still... off. Your health worries me."

When I had seated myself and was leaning back against the bole of the tree, I said, "I do seem to lack stamina these days. And I get out of breath so easily."

He brought his nose very near to my neck and sniffed at me with considerable energy for several seconds, his breath hot and moist, the tip of his nose quite cold. Then, with only a small, inarticulate murmur of uncertainty, he settled next to me and pressed up against my side, small, compact, very warm. For several minutes, we simply gazed down the low slope of the glade toward the glittering water and the shadowy forest on its far side. A frog leaped from the near bank, with a high sweet croak, out of a tussock of green rushes and into the pond, splashing in the water and sending a series of concentric moonlit ripples out over its surface.

"Li Bai should be here," said Roland. Then, glancing up into the branches of the pine, he added, "Basho too."

I smiled, but a kind of unpleasantly vacant languor was spreading through me, and I felt no desire to speak.

"You know," he remarked a minute or so later, "you can always find your way back in."

When he failed to elaborate on this, I made myself speak. "Back in? To what?"

"Back into the unseen world, naturally. Back to the ability to see it, at least. I think you know that. Fairies, or nymphs, or *kami* and *tama*—well, they may be elusive of normal vision, but it's often just a matter of spiritual attitude. Cultivate the proper state of *kokoro*— of the mindful heart or spiritual soul—and the veil can be drawn back, if only for a moment. Your now pitiably constricted ambit of inner vision can be opened up again to the universal consciousness

63

pervading all things. At the very least, a window can be momentarily thrown open. I mean, as you know, your mind seeks—or seeks to impose—form on everything, while everything that's anything is reducible to—and seeks to express itself—in form. So *forma ad formam loquitur*. Learn to seek in the *formally* correct way, with the doors of perception properly opened, and the world will manifest itself in *formally* fuller ways. All it requires is a nose set free from habitual ways of thinking."

I laughed curtly, involuntarily. "Or eyes set free, of course."

I felt his listless shrug against my ribs. "Yes, that too—if you must. All I mean is that life and mind are one and the same thing, and both are ubiquitous in countless modalities, and so what you perceive is only as limited as your openness to life in its deepest wellsprings—which is to say, spirit."

Another, particularly strong breeze briefly stirred the tops of the trees on the far side of the water, and for a moment they looked like dark, turbulent waves against the sky's smooth glassy blue. "Is it a kind of panpsychism you're proposing?" I asked.

He sniffed loudly and emitted a small growl. "Not a term I care for," he said after a moment. "Not that's it wrong. It's misleading, however, now that there's this crop of philosophers around who think they can be both panpsychists and physicalists, which is sheer folly. They think of consciousness as a physical property that, in sufficiently complex composite structures, achieves reflective awareness and intentionality. You know—Galen Strawson, Giulio Tononi, Philip Goff. But that's nonsense, of course, since consciousness isn't a property, properly speaking, and certainly not one that can be measured in an aggregated volume, and it doesn't exist in discrete packets that can be added up into cumulatively more conscious totalities. It's not a *property* at all, in fact, but an act, and therefore exists only within a noetic agency, and always already involves intention and autoaffection and so forth. That said..." Here, though, he ceased speaking for several seconds, and I could hear him sniffing and snuffling at something in the air. "Yes," he said, seemingly to himself, "we're almost ready. Good." He turned to me. "What was I saying? Oh, yes, I recall. So, anyway, I am suggesting a kind of panpsychism, if one must call it that, but most definitely not a physicalist version of the idea, which is just sheer gibberish—a vacuous panchreston of a theory at best. But that's not very exotic of me, is it? I mean, you've written on the metaphysics of classical theism, haven't you? Well, if you believe in God in that elevated and transcendent sense, then you're already a panpsychist of some kind."

When, once again, he failed to explain his meaning, I asked, "How do you reckon?"

He sighed, obviously vexed by the sluggish pace of my wits. "If you believe that everything arises from an infinite act of mind—the rock over there no less than the intelligence in you—then you believe that there's the presence of a... of an infinite knowing logos within the discrete logos that constitutes each thing as what it is. There's a depth—even a personal depth, so to speak—in everything, an inner awareness that knows each reality from inside... or from deeper than inside—an act of knowing that's *interior intimo suo*. There is *one* who knows what it's like to be a rock. And wouldn't that infinite personal depth have to express itself, almost of necessity, in a finite personal interiority of sorts? Surely the knowledge of what it is to be a rock is already the spirit of the rock *as* a rock—the rock knowing itself. So isn't that very knowledge of 'what it's like' already the reality of a finite modality of personal knowledge, a kind of discrete spiritual self? A personal, reflective dimension as the necessarily contracted mode in which the uncontracted infinite act of mind is exemplified in that thing? And why shouldn't we call that dimension or mode by its classical names— dryads, hamadryads, naiads, nereids... *kami* and *tama... yakṣas* and *yakṣinīs* and *gandharvas* and *apsaras*... nymphs and fairies and elves and *longaevi* of every kind? Especially when they're pretty and graceful and scantily clad?"

"I see. I don't..."

"It's really just as Thales said so long ago: all things are full of gods. Or as Heracleitos said: there's logos in everything. All the ancients, really, with few exceptions. Plotinus, for instance: life and soul in all things, he says. And the Renaissance Platonists. The living world is an incalculably populous pantheon. And God—the infinite vanishing point, the comprehensive simplicity of Being as infinite spirit—is full of gods. And so are you... if you throw that window open. Which I think you know full well, in that essentially Shinto soul of yours. Or esoteric Buddhist soul, perhaps—if one can call what has no *svabhāva* a soul. It was the great Shingon priest Yukai himself, after all—the fiery scourge of Tachikawa-ryu, as you'll recall—who said that mind pervades all things: the grasses, flora of every sort, trees, the earth underfoot... That's good *cittamātra* orthodoxy, I imagine... with a specifically Japanese inflection."

I was momentarily uncertain how to reply. For one thing, the flow of Roland's discourse was beginning to sweep everything away before it. For another, I was frankly astonished: I had not expected to hear anything so speculatively adventurous or heterodox from my dog. The whole experience was very near to revising my understanding of his entire species. "Is that what you truly believe?" I asked, somewhat hesitantly, turning my head to stare at him.

He sighed again and for several seconds merely gazed in silence at the softly shining water. "Belief is such a slippery concept among humans. So often your kind professes beliefs that your actions belie. I scarcely know what the word means to you. All I know is that my instincts incline me in that direction. That's the sort of fragrance that reality has in my nostrils, and so I keep them pressed to every trace of the transcendent within the immanent. Surely you know that the canine soul assumes that everything is alive."

I pondered the matter for a moment. "Well, yes, I have seen dogs react to what I'd consider an inanimate object as if it were a living agent. But I always assumed that that was just a survival instinct expressing itself in a momentary and irrational response. You know, the 'intentional stance,' as it's called, which is just a sort of evolutionary adaptation."

Roland emitted a sound along the lines of "*Harrumph!*" but offered no other reply. A moment later, however, he resumed: "It makes sense, if you think about it, that this infinite consciousness, refracted into finite instances and modes of self-reflective awareness and thought, might engender... well, a kind of limitless modal regress. Consciousness might inhere in all sorts of natural totalities, but also in totalities within other conscious totalities, with a corresponding subjectivity appropriate to each—parts as wholes, wholes as parts of other wholes. Campanella, of course, treated this with rare brilliance. So did Gustav Fechner. And James, and Royce, and Peirce, needless to say. And this isn't like a physicalist panpsychism, in which every totality is subsumed into whatever is most integrated within it, like modular brains. Rather, it would be as if every level within every composite were just as conscious in its own way as every other: particles, simple objects composed from those particles, complex structures, organisms, natural systems, the *anima mundi*... All part of an endlessly complex, infinitely divisible hierarchy of conscious perspectives, containing and contained, reflecting and inflecting one another. And the subjectivity of persons too, like me—and I suppose you too, in a manner of speaking—would be one kind of modal contraction within the whole hierarchy of modes of mind, an ever more particular and ever more comprehensive subjectivity and autoaffection and intentionality. It's a lovely and stirring idea, at least: all of nature as a system of living coinherences, an endlessly multifarious mirror of the boundless potency contained in the infinite actuality and simplicity of the eternal 'I Am'—all of nature as an incalculably variously faceted prism of the infinite light of divine Spirit? Don't you agree?" He turned to me and sniffed deeply, as if trying to discern my answer with his nostrils.

I, however, was bereft of words now. It did occur to me, though, if only very imprecisely, that somehow it made sense to me that dogs should see the world in that way—or, at least, in a somewhat animistic fashion.

"Well," said Roland when I had failed to reply for a sufficiently long time, turning his eyes back toward the pond, "that's enough of that for now. I imagine you're wondering why I've brought you here tonight."

"You've... brought me?"

"Precisely. I did say I had something planned. I imagine you'd like to know what. Well, it's time for the curtain to go up. My nose tells me that all is in readiness now. Our players are all assembled."

"Players?" I looked at him again, and still he merely stared away, toward the sparkling surface of the water and the shadowy woods beyond. "I'm not sure..."

"The last time we discussed your great uncle," he suddenly interrupted, "I told you that his conversion was born out of desire for...

well, for precisely what we've been talking about. A living world, a world that speaks, a world to which the gods have returned. In his early twenties, just as he was on the threshold of the paganism that he would ultimately adopt, he composed—or half-composed, I suppose, because he never really returned to it to fix its numerous flaws—a kind of dramatic poem—a masque, to use his term."

"Oh…"

"It's all about the goddess."

"*The* goddess?" I asked. "Any one in particular?"

"Oh…" Again he shrugged. "The *magna mater*, I suppose, or Aphrodite, or Euterpe *and* Latona *and* Cybele *and* Great Rhea crowned with towers… maybe the Cailleach… certainly Isis… just *the* goddess. The Triple Goddess, if you like. It was very much the fashion of the time, you know. The archetypal feminine who was also the supreme symbol of the irrepressible fertility of the earth, but also the object of erotic longing, but also the source of poetic inspiration, but also an image of the indomitable mystery of woman for hapless men… You know what I mean, surely."

I nodded. "I do, as it happens. You said it when… when we last talked. Aphrodite Ourania, Aphrodite Pandemos."

"Just so. And it was all mixed up for him with his own unsatisfactory relationship with a girl toward whom he felt a very potent attraction, but who had caused him as much grief as joy. Anyway, it's very much a gallimaufry of personal sentiment and religious longing and… some questionable verse."

"Why are you telling me this just now?" I asked.

He turned his eyes to mine. "You'll find the text on your desk."

"All right," I said. "But again…"

"But right now I've arranged for a performance. I thought it might distract you from… from this strange malaise that seems to have you in its grip." He briefly brought his nose, already quivering and twitching, near to my face once more. Then, drawing back again, he said, "Yes, it's hard to tell what the malady is, or even whether it's chiefly physical or emotional."

"Wait," I said, closing my eyes and attempting to concentrate. "You said a… a *performance*?"

"Yes," said Roland.

68

I opened my eyes and looked at him again. The expression on his face was perfectly earnest.

"How do you mean?" I asked.

"Ah," he said, "I contracted with a small professional theater troupe—you know, the one from Staunton, over the mountain, the one that specializes in Shakespeare—for them to appear here tonight and play it for you… here in this glade."

"But…" I looked about, toward the trees on either side of us, then across the lake. "How could you possibly…?"

"By email, of course," he said. "I used your name. Oh, I meant to mention—when your next credit card statement comes, you might find some charges you didn't expect."

"You… You…"

"Well, I had little choice in the matter," he remarked pertly, looking away from me again. "Anyway, the time has come. Just call out the word 'Action!' and the masque will commence. I'd do it myself, but they'd probably find it hard to make sense of a dog speaking to them—if they could even hear it as anything other than an animal sound. As I've said, intentionality determines perception."

"I…"

"Please," he said with one last glance at me, this time with a look of such profound sincerity that I knew I could refuse him nothing. "I'm very anxious that everything should go well."

I hesitated for only a few seconds longer, feeling somewhat giddy again. I was a little afraid that he might be teasing me, and that by doing as he asked I would fall into some trap he had laid for me, and that I might have to suffer his derision as a result. But those deep brown eyes, alight with the moon's brightness, conquered my reluctance. "Action!" I shouted.

And indeed, on cue, figures began to emerge from the trees, some to our right, then others to our left…

But here I abdicate my authorship, or at least place it in suspense, in favor of the original text. I attach it below. Except for one emendation—in place of "stream," one should read "pond"—it is a perfectly accurate recounting of what now unfolded before me.

XVI

Latona's Late-Born Children: A Masque

(*A small crowd of rather grim, wearied, and emaciate men gather in a woodland clearing, emerging from the shadows below the boughs of large deciduous trees. They look quite absurd in the garish styles in which they have variously attired themselves, but in their innocence they think the Pre-Raphaelite gaudiness of their clothing terribly lovely. And, in all fairness, they have little time to worry about such things. They are certain that what has called them out into this glade, where the moonlight transforms the forest's green to frigid blue and fitful white, is something ancient, unimaginably terrible, and ineffably lovely. The clearing is silent except for the quiet babbling of a nearby stream. They exchange words, in voices reverent and subdued, melting in murmurs, whispers, and sighs among the overhanging branches. One of them, standing at the southern end of the clearing, just where the surge of the forest recedes down a low slope toward the stream, attempts a "haunting" trill or two upon his tin pan-pipes. After a few moments, seven of them assemble at the other end of the clearing and begin to prepare themselves, straightening and smoothing their clothing, though each is obviously somewhat nervous. After all, love of her and fear of her are one and the same, and her favor is often indistinguishable from her wrath.*)

Chorus
(*in a semicircle at the forest edge*)

Cruel winter and deserted shrines
Where birds have made their homes, the earth
Grown hard and stained with frost: between
Two twilights, in this lifeless land,
Her faded memories lie scattered.

70

FOREST

Should we have mourned for her? Should we,
The faithless and abandoning,
Have spoken of her, in hushed whispers,
Regretful of her absence? Though
So gifted by her graces when
The new vines bore fruit, blessed by winds
Fragrant with her perfumes, our tongues
Now curse with silence, traitors to
That glory, to that joy.

         And so
The parsimonious winter chills
Our marrow, sinew, straining joints;
Where bright fruits flourished, death now throngs
The vines. Our barrenness—the wines
All gone, the grain from gold to ash
All gone, those kindly visions too
All gone—is wrapped in shadows, withered,
Dry as frozen bones. All is dearth,
An arid evening of the flesh.

When the harvests waned, having borne
Small substance, the shortened days darkened,
And the sterile, bitter soil yielded
Only stones and thwarted roots.
Like thirsty ghosts in fallow fields,
We roved the hollow, famished lands,
Forced to forget both joy and sorrow.

All now is emptiness. But once,
Her terrible, pitiless splendor
Inhabited air and mind, and
Her smile's consuming beauty and
The crystal glamor of her eyes
Were seen in every flame.

         Yet here
We cannot speak a word of praise

Roland in Moonlight

To your name, O Golden, O Lady
Of Triumphs. The winter night has fallen.

An Orphic Hierophant
(pressing to the center of the glade,
lifting his hand in a gesture of pained solemnity,
affecting a tediously sententious tone)

All time belongs to her, and all its common glories
Shine only with her beauty. Thus the wise crave no
Song but hers to sing. Witness the undreaming ones
Go down to utter nothingness, and see the glories
Of the gods subside. Still she endures through all winters,
Beyond the hours, while old men muse upon the shadows
And the turbulence of life in the dying year.

A Wanderer
(in the garb of a tatterdemalion, hastening
to interrupt)

The violet lies
Beneath her feet; her fierce blue eyes
Enjoin the mind
To seek her where alone we find
Our fears may rest:
Here in her fane, at her behest.

(Now he too is interrupted, by
a brash but melancholy voice.)

Vates (his nom de guerre)

Impotent and cold for love of her,
I lie among the night's ungracious hours.

72

FOREST

The Wanderer
(impatiently resuming his lyric,
his voice rising in pitch)

Go down into the shallows of the violent winds
    Where the flowers spring up—
The blue of iris, the soft mauve of clematis,
    Odor of the lilac—
And see the pale ones, the frail children of the summer,
    Arise to sing to her.

A Philosopher
(leaning on his gnarled staff, standing somewhat
apart by a poplar tree, but speaking in
a voice audible in every quarter of the glade)

One should seek the silence of stone, the sheer impenetrable
    stillness,
Where the shadow of the falcon flees against the colorless cold,
And where ancient hands once formed a hard perfection. Great
    Heracleitos
Retreated to the inner depths of her temple, her marble silence.
There truth burned in the frigid blue of inextinguishable flames.

Vates

Voluptuous and vulpine, she
    Still troubles me...

(He pauses, clears his throat, assumes a more
declamatory tone, and begins again.)

The splendid whiteness of the rose
    Tells and untells the tale,
While Wisdom sends reproaches on
    The windless air...

Roland in Moonlight

(Suddenly, with a bustling and snuffling
reminiscent of the sounds of dogs
at their dinner, a group of especially decrepit
men, all old and clad in pallid cloaks,
slouch into the middle of the glade,
where they begin to sway and chant in doleful unison.)

Her Votaries

Hers was the whiteness that once summoned men
From far beyond the sea's broad barren straits,
Beyond the distant mountains and the wastes
Where fine dust drifts in ceaseless eddies, where
The moonlight parches the abyss, until,
In anger, from the temple of her glory,
She fled away amid a million silences.

An Eleusinian Mystagogue
(near the stream's edge)

She was seen in those high angelic couplings,
In the sea's opaque, dull green, heard within
The distant thunders hovering upon the deep.
And now the wind of death, borne through the dark of night,
Bears her last radiances to their oblivion.

A Scholar
(with a certain detachment, not devoid
of self-pity)

She stands as silent witness to our follies, she
Remains the unspoken irony that confounds—
And is the theme of—all our striving. So
Let absence fill our days and years, but let it be
Her absence only, here in our shared loneliness.

FOREST

The Orphic Hierophant

Still flow her fountains in the winter light,
Still burns her flame within the singer's brain,
And the green mountains bear her blossoms still,
                              abundantly.

Vates
(*gazing away from the others, upward at
moon-splashed clouds
the color of tarnished silver*)

Why then do you now wake me, Lady? I
Thought that we had done. Now will you assume
No other shape than this to feed desire,
No form drawn from the world's huge repertoire?
How cold, my Glory, is your silence, and
How cold the earth whereon your foot treads not.
What do you wish of me, Empress of Night?

Her Votaries
(*slowly rocking side to side, their voices soft
and somewhat querulous*)

O break, break your silence.

Vates

Pale images amid the bones, amid
The embers cold as frost, in which they lie,
Revive the memories of your harsh power.

But, Lady, I have seen your dreaming face
Among these thousand solitudes and I
Have known beyond all knowing you would come.

Roland in Moonlight

Her Votaries

O break, break your silence.

Vates

In my most inward mind, a dream of willows
Held me fast in sleep last night, and I knew
It was a portent of your swift return.
The trees will bear again, the meadows thrive
In larkspur and in goldenrod, and birds
Will fill the winds with fleeting forms of fire
And music drenched in ecstasy and fear.

Her Votaries

O break, break your silence.

Vates

In nights more torrid than this, when the willows
Are bent against the storm and wild green lightnings
Scorch the turbid sky, the world laments you,
Supplicates the emptiness for word of you.
Neither Dionysus from the Lydian wastes
Nor Orpheus from the mouth of hell will come
Until you light the moon's blue lantern-flame.
Apollo's children and the brood of Pan
Make obeisance to you joyfully;
The languid flower wrapped in crimson fire,
The purple grape, sweet grasses, fragrant oils
Burn in sacrifice.

Let us dance for you,
O goddess of the inner secret; or
Rather let my song weave itself into

FOREST

The flickering glory and sensual sway
Of your everlasting dance.

Many nights
I sought you in the shining of her copper
Hair, and in the brittle sparkle of
Her maddened eyes, and in the joyous torment
Of her limbs, but you were absent.

Lady,
There is no sleep for us in these sad places;
Evening's shadows may withdraw. When you come,
Our fever will abate and peace will reign.

Her Votaries

That we might sleep, sleep
Within the circle of your silence.

The Wanderer
(producing from the folds of his Pierrotesque
weeds, as if by magic, a fresh petunia blossom and in
so doing affording a brief glimpse of his
blue velvet smoking jacket)

Be still and be at peace,
All who despair of great Cybele's dawn;
The ghosts of autumn cease
To weep at ash-blue dusk. She is not gone.
The golden hazel tree
Is bright amid the silent wastes of snow
And promises that she
Will come again and never more will go.

Many lands have I seen
In journeys through the vacant cold of night:
Wherever she has been

Roland in Moonlight

Her image lingers in the white moonlight
    And in the flames of shrines
Where pilgrims robed in colors of the mist
    Pray to her living signs,
And poets sing from lips that she has kissed.

    The hills must melt in green
And purple, tremulous with grass and clover,
    Her face will then be seen
By her every worshipper and lover;
    Wine, honey, milk will flow,
The cow and ewe will once again give birth,
    The world once more will know
The blessings of the mother of the earth.

The Orphic Hierophant
(brusquely, impatiently)

Hush, now, bestill this doggerel, which is as nothing worth:
    Her revelation is at hand;
    In pious silence stand.

(An uncomfortable silence ensues. After several moments,
the trembling septet at the northern end of the clearing exchange
a few dismayed whispers, emit a few frantic squeaks, compose
themselves, harmonize their voices with a series of unpleasant hums
and croaks, and begin again.)

Chorus

Though she entrances us in blackthorn sleep,
    And seals us to the tree with wounds of flame,
    And makes the rose a fever in our brains,
We cannot close our eyes to her or weep.

If she will free us on some final day
    When sunlight winnowed to thin golden gleams

FOREST

Will die among the ruins of our dreams
We cannot know: she owns what tongue may say.

It is a frenzy. Who can love the tree
  Or bonds of pain, the madness of the night
  She fills with visions of such cruel delight,
With drifting mists and whispers of the sea?

Though we have seen her in a thousand forms
  And called her by a multitude of names,
  We know her by her laughter and our shames:
She tames the passions we had thought great storms.

She keeps the fury of the winds and there
  Gives issue to the fire that we embrace;
  Her lambent nimbus is the moon, her face
Is much too bright for mortal eye to bear.

But we have traveled far that we might know
  Her radiant crown, her garment of cold light,
  And have not heard the echoes in the night
Of cries that call us back from where we go.

To hear her speak one word or call our names
  We give our flesh to fire, bound by her eyes;
  The rose's fever stills the distant cries;
We choose the thorn tree and the wounds of flame.

(Another discomfiting silence. At this point, a hitherto
unnoticed figure steps forward from the shadows of a
massive oak and strides into the very center of the clearing
with a harsh laugh. There is something fierce in his countenance,
something dark and implacable in his jutting brow and sunken
eyes, and something in the weather-worn flesh of his cheeks and
wind-blown tangle of his beard that speaks of fasting, abnegations,
and familiarity with the desert sun.)

Roland in Moonlight

The Prophet

Why waste such piety on her, O pathetic men, and why
Foregather in this dark and dismal glade to cringe before
Her hidden altar and simper her silly litanies?
Fools! For even if great Chapman's fluid, long fourteeners should
Flow forever from my lips, their glistening flood would not,
Now or in ages unborn, lave the folly from your hearts;
Their broad, glittering abundances would not sway you
With their purling cadences, nor break the deep enchantment
Of the goddess bitch. Dance to Algernon's insipid songs!
Why, do you not recall what horror follows in her train?
Or not remember what dark dungeon pits of fear she cast
Us in, or why we struggled free of her immense embrace?
The *Magna Mater*, call her if you will, who fed upon
Our youth, the dam who would devour her own children, the wench
Who sapped our blood to feed the fruit she grudgingly gave forth.
But, worse, she was not there; she slew us though her heart was absent;
And now, as then, you give the terror you have borne her name,
You worship this chimæra, this great queen without being, this
Fair image veiling the abyss whose horror fills your souls.
The endless night is her vast womb and insatiate gullet.

Yet what shall I call this fleeing beauty, this cloud of light
That lingers in the memory's untrodden corridors,
That sweetly tells a tale we cannot now recall, and then
Retreats in lamentation, an exile upon dark roads
In distant lands, tormented by forgetfulness and hope?
Perhaps poor Achamoth, the lower Wisdom now cast down,
Her beauty bound in fetters, her feet condemned to walk upon
The boundless depths of time, the lower dark, illusion's sea?
No, neither does this poor conceit suffice; it tells the tale
Awry. But this I know: we have bound her in heavy chains,

FOREST

And we, somehow, in history's tender dawn, unmade her;
What we call nature now is but the ravaged remnants of
Something profaned, ruined in a time before time, betrayed.

> (*All at once he turns to Vates, approaches him in three great
> strides, and continues in even harsher tones.*)

And you, of all who gather here, seem now the most contempt-
ible:
It is not terror—no—but emptiness, that drives you here,
An unfulfilled desire, a longing never quenched, a lie
You tell yourself and others, until the world believes you
And gives you pity in the place of love. You long for Venus
Wrapped in her soft diaphanous gown of pearly light, and so
You conjure wraiths and fancies to your cherished solitude.
None here can give you life, none can redeem such love of self.

> (*He seems about to say more, but instead falls silent, a stern
> distaste evident in his dark eyes*)

Her Votaries

Lady, when your one, final, blazing
Apparition will outshine stars
And wake fires from this dreary frost,
We, your votaries, will still ask
One small indulgence at your hands—
That is, autumn's grace, its soft light:
Summon tempests of gold, call
The wind to scarlet life here in
The dying year's pale sunlight, but
Still grant us time for our last words
Before your glory consumes us.

The gnarled and bitter things, the roots
That break, the frozen sap, all cold

81

Roland in Moonlight

Will be dispelled by your severe,
Fierce radiance, Lady of sunlight,
Mother of night and silence,
Daughter of the wind. Your splendor
Will be our home, our nonexistence.

Two verities persist beyond
The winter of the flesh, two ways
Divide before these wanderers:
A serene light, always shining,
Which gives the broken final rest,
Or else a night of blackened bones,
The obsidian earth where one
Succumbs to the fires of your
Caress. As we have chosen you,
O Good Lady of sensual light,
We ask this mercy, this one tenderness.

The Prophet

And still, awakened from the dark of visions,
Of ecstasies, and fiery shapes, and voices
Deep as thunder, perfect mind of night,
I must protest this vain and irksome banter:
It never was—nor ever is—the way
You think it was. Such cruelties then there were.
More dreadful images cannot afflict
The febrile brain: the mother, eyes of flint,
Who flings her child to Moloch's warm embrace,
The Scythian priest disporting in the skins
Of tawny youths, the ground about the stone
Deep soaked with blood where she with laughing eyes
Delights in wanton slaughter, our laments
Turned into ritual song, thus to invite
From hearts enslaved a solemn awe, a joy
In her dark mysteries… and on and on…

82

FOREST

Oh, I am not insensible to all
The romance, the false beauties, and the grandeurs.
I too have seen hard winter rise out of
The indifferent autumn, and then yield
To warm, voluptuous spring, and I have felt
The proud divinity abroad in things.
Man is a shadow in the winter light,
A spectre blown about by icy winds.
He clings to what is palpable and near
And borrows substance from the brindled earth,
And hates these rootless and these unknown Gods.
When Abram left the sacred ground of Ur—
Which is to say, precisely, the *Ur-grund*—
He ventured forth into the possible,
And could not know what land he was called to:
But the Other had wrought in him an otherness.

Oh, may God's ghostly blessing on you fall—
And know that being beyond being waits for you,
And terrible bright angels fill the skies,
Descending from the stars, in serried ranks,
Innumerable legions, fierce with love...

*(He turns about abruptly, strides quickly
away and disappears into the forest like a stone
sinking in motionless waters.)*

Vates
(his voice somewhat frailer, but somewhat more insistent)

Though eternal, beyond all change,
She goes about in any shape
Not unfitting to her glory
Or her mystery. Her forms are
Myriad, are numberless; for she
Is many, like the forms of fire

83

Roland in Moonlight

In the lucid air, beautiful
  Beyond all words...

  Her Votaries

  ...Beyond all words.

(*They fall silent and stand utterly still, in tense anticipation.*
Nothing happens. Still they stand.
No one comes.
After a time, one by one, they retreat
again into the forest shadows,
and soon are gone.)

XVII

"**W**HAT IN GOD'S NAME WAS THAT?" I asked after nearly four minutes had elapsed in silence.

Roland sighed deeply. "I had hoped you might be able to tell me. It's such a strange combination of satire and *cri de cœur*, of bitterness and sentimentality… and, frankly, of both deep pagan longing and a residual Christian resistance to that longing… that it's almost unintelligible to me."

"It didn't sound like his best verse," I remarked.

"As I say, I doubt he ever made any effort to revise or polish it. It has all the uncouth energy of youthful romanticism, unrefined by any application of detached adult critical judgment. Poor callow monkey…" Roland paused momentarily to lick one of his front paws. "I think, though, that it expresses some primal energy he had to discharge, in dark bursts of anger and mirth. It's not the product of some unified vision demanding to be crafted into luminous form. Important as a phase in his personal development, perhaps, but not a monument to whatever talents he truly possessed. But…" He looked at me with an expression of unusual meekness. "Did you enjoy it, at least?"

"Oh, very much," I said. "Thank-you for arranging it. The logistical challenges must have been immense."

He smiled gently. "Donning the incognito of the virtual society helped. It's a depressing world to enter, in some ways, devoid as it is of any interesting fragrances or of presences with any detectible corporeal heat, but it has its uses."

I smiled in return. "Just the opposite of that otherworld you were talking about earlier, isn't it?"

"Very much so," he concurred with a nod. "But I wouldn't use the term otherworld, I think. Better to say the deeper world, or the fuller world. Or maybe the Dreaming, to use the Oceanian term. It's something just over there, so to speak, where everything is more

85

alive and more its true self than it is on this side of reality. By contrast, in the virtual world everything is deader and falser. Still..." He settled against my side again, and the warmth of his body all at once brought me a sense of comfort that, until that moment, I was unaware I needed. "As I say, it can have its advantages. It allows me to make contracts and pursue scholarly inquiries and so forth under a convenient alias, without having to deal with the... well, the soft bigotry of low expectations."

We sat together for several minutes, saying nothing. I was listening to the gentle susurrations of the breeze in the needles overhead and in the leaves on all sides of the glade. At one point, the haunting, desolate call of a barred owl floated out from the woods on the pond's far side. A few seconds later, another frog gave voice to a loud, lyrical, burbling croak.

"It was a very volatile moment for him, of course," Roland suddenly remarked.

"I'm sorry?"

"For Aloysius. When he wrote that masque. He was undergoing a profound emotional transition. He was caught between the impulse to surrender to enchantment and a sort of surly suspicion of that same impulse—a fear that it might all be nonsense. What he wanted to believe seemed so tantalizingly real to him, but everything—the whole of his culture, the entire burden of the Christian past, the whole *disenchantment* of modernity—told him to turn back. If he had listened to those inner voices..." Roland sighed deeply, reflectively. "Well, it would have been a spiritual and psychological disaster for him, I suspect. He would have become embittered, and would have grown bitterer as the years passed. It's obvious, really. That's the most predictable enantiodromia of all, isn't it? The truly disenchanted romantic ineluctably becomes the most hardhearted of cynics. What is cynicism, after all, except an inverted romanticism?"

"That's true," I said, hearing an unexpected listlessness—verging on frailty—in my own voice. I tried to take a deep breath but found I was unable. "Well," I said, my voice again sinking away, "I suppose it's a good thing he... took the leap of faith."

"Really, it's remarkable how often the manifest self is a specular inversion of the hidden self. I also find that the brilliant and the witty are also, as often as not, incurable melancholics. On the surface, there's a love of life, an unconquerable élan, an effervescence, but just below that surface there's an enduring sadness, an always keener sense of the irrecoverable ephemerality of beauty and youth… a tender and achingly constant awareness of the perishability of things… an inability not to see the shadow of death cast over everything."

"I've noticed…" I began. And then I simply said, "Yes."

"Of course," Roland continued, "there was your great uncle's stormy relationship with that girl he was obsessed with. Her name was Deirdre, it seems. She was definitely a melancholic, and not below the surface at all. Bipolar, I suppose, to use the current psychologistic patois."

"That's very hard," I practically hissed from my now laboring lungs. "What… do you know what finally decided him, though?"

Roland lowered his head. "I think so." His voice had grown somber. "The poor girl took her life. I think I've mentioned it to you before. I don't know the causes, or how it happened. But I expect it nearly broke him. And then, apparently, there was something to do with her priest. She was Catholic. And the priest wasn't willing to perform a full church funeral, or allow interment in sacred ground. I don't know what the institutional constraints were in those days, of course. But your great uncle learned that this priest had been quite adamant on the matter, and had even more or less told her family with considerable assurance that there was little doubt—presuming her relative sanity, I suppose—that her final, mortal sin, unabsolved as it was, had probably carried her down to eternal torment."

"Barbaric," I murmured.

Roland raised his head. "Nothing says divine love more than punishing the pain that leads to suicide with infinitely more pain." He snorted contemptuously. "Emotional terrorism has always been the basis of power for the priestly caste. That's a social law just about everywhere. This is why dogs have historically forbidden the existence of any sort of clerical class in their midst."

"Is that so?"

He nodded. "Anyway, whatever else the experience did to your great uncle, it drove him with absolute finality away from any form of credal Christian adherence. It darkened his view of the faith for a very long time, and to some degree irrevocably. To him, it seemed clear that it was as much a religion of hate as of love—of cruelty as of compassion."

"It certainly can be," I rasped.

"That's the period in which he penned some of his most stridently anti-Christian polemic in his journals. About the same time as he was writing that masque, for instance, he wrote that, in the Christian dispensation, the world has become the corpse of a slain god who can't now be resurrected, but can only decay."

"Some Christians certainly make it seem..." But at this point my voice failed me entirely.

Roland turned his eyes to me almost violently, an obvious look of concern wrinkling his brow. "Don't talk," he said after a few seconds. "Let's rest here till you have your breath and then go home. We'll go slowly."

I nodded weakly and attempted a reassuring smile.

"Those fairies I mentioned earlier are just over there, by the way." He gestured to my left with his snout.

I turned my head to where the path through the forest resumed, but saw only the shadowy arcade of trees, its canopy pierced several yards along by a single slender column of alabaster moonlight, but otherwise dark.

"Do you see that sycamore?"

I could scarcely miss it. It stood at the edge of the woods, at the top of a slight upward inclination of the ground not far from the pond's nearer bank, its pallid bark coldly glowing.

"Don't say anything," Roland was now whispering in my ear, so near that he was brushing its lobe with the cool tip of his nose. "Don't think. Just look there. At its roots."

Here my memory begins to fade. I was growing weaker. I have almost no recollection of our long, slow walk back to the house, and so I cannot say with certainty whether what I *can* remember was real, or was instead only a momentary shift into that half-dreaming state to which I am so susceptible, or is an entirely retroactive fabri-

FOREST

cation of my imagination. Even so, and whatever the case, I do seem
to recall having caught a glimpse—after two or three minutes of
gazing and gazing while trying not to think about what I was looking for—of something like small, gently shining, roughly anthropine figures, clad in something like samite or gossamer or delicate
fleece, moving in a stately circular dance, while the air about them
sparkled mysteriously. And for a moment I may have thought I
heard faint music—exquisite, even ethereal in tone, as if played on a
glass harmonica, perhaps accompanied by a harp. But, whatever it
was, whether a real perception or a dream or a fantasy summoned
up in the borderland between dreams and waking, the vision lasted
only a few moments, and faded almost as soon as it had appeared.
Of course, if Roland was right, the differences among all these states
of mind are, in the final analysis, only differences of degree.

XVIII

PERHAPS THERE is something heroic in the ability of human beings to ignore what their bodies are telling them when the message proves inconvenient; how else, after all, could we vanquish our fears when we have to risk our lives for the good of others (or, for that matter, on a dare)? Then again, it might just as well be mere laziness. Despite the persistence of my spells of respiratory inflammation, I chose to accept my pulmonologist's hasty declaration that my condition was nothing to worry about, and was almost certainly a passing bronchial illness. And on good days I allowed myself to believe that my health was in fact improving, and that my increasingly pronounced fatigue and bodily pains were signs of middle age, poor sleep habits, and too pronounced a reliance on caffeine. And so, early that April, I made my trip to London, aware that I was not feeling particularly well but determined nonetheless to proceed as if I were. I was lodged with one of Westminster Abbey's canons and his family, in their residence beside an interior courtyard where tourists never go. It was something of a setting outside of time, there among the inner cloisters and gardens. When I was first conducted into that little hidden world, so magically isolated from the city all around, I felt as if I had wandered into a chapter from *The Romance of the Rose*. I was thoroughly enchanted. I was also in considerable pain, however, and my lungs rebelled when I was obliged to ascend a flight of stairs, luggage in hand, to my room. Still, I resolved to pay my distress no mind. And I passed the following days pleasantly, enjoying the abbey and its environs, meeting with friends from my Cambridge days now living in London, attending evensong every day (featuring, on one occasion, a program entirely of Tallis), lecturing (on music), conversing with bright and agreeable persons over vegetable-wraps and tea. The night before my scheduled return to the US, I walked several unexpected miles of London streets with my fellow lecturer, the brilliant Daniel Chua from Hong Kong, on our way to a restaurant that he recalled liking but whose location he had somewhat misplaced in memory.

I never made my flight. The next day, I could scarcely breathe at all without considerable effort and pain. I was also, I realized later, somewhat delirious. I attempted the trip to Heathrow in the car provided me by the abbey; but the young Muslim driver (whose name, shamefully, I no longer recall) soon perceived that my condition was far graver than I myself realized, and implored me to allow him to take me to an emergency room instead. It occurred to me, when he made the suggestion, that I might in fact be dying; so, reluctantly, I consented. The one clear detail—or clear delirium-induced fantasy—that remains in memory from our journey to the hospital is of a party of pedestrians who passed by on the pavement as we were waiting at a light and of whom I took particular notice only because one of them happened to be Yoko Ono. That, at the time, this elicited scarcely any reaction from me at all should have made me aware of just how ill I really was. Again, though, my mind was not functioning particularly well.

The driver helped me into the hospital, and even went to the admission desk for me, and then sat with me for as long as he could, encouraging me to hold his prayer beads as we waited. When he called in to his dispatcher to explain what had happened, however, it was clear that his employer was not at all pleased with his decision and wanted him to set out for his next scheduled job immediately. So he retrieved my luggage for me, told me that he would be praying for me, and we parted with an exchange of *salams*. I spent the rest of the day in the emergency ward, enduring tests—including an altogether agonizing extraction of arterial blood from deep in my wrist—and receiving treatments and being menaced (around lunch time) by the single most revolting sandwich ever concocted by any creature with opposable thumbs. I was able to get word to my wife (I do not remember how) and she deputed her brother, who was living in London at the time, to follow my progress. He arranged for my British Air flight to be rescheduled to the following day and for airport wheelchair assistance to be waiting for me; and then he reserved a hotel room for me near to Heathrow. Thither I was sent,

late in the day, laden with albuterol, antihistamines, anti-inflamma-
tories, and yet more assurances that my condition was almost certainly temporary and would require only palliative treatment. By
now, however, I knew that things were far worse than I wanted to
believe.

At the hotel, I managed partially to ingest one of those almost
wholly inedible meals at which Britain's lesser hospitality establishments still uniquely excel. I slept as well as I could, but it was not till
morning came that I was able to breathe with a semblance of comfort again. Somehow—with the aid of a taxi, a wheelchair, a succession of impeccably coiffed and groomed women in British Air navy
blue tunics and bright red scarves speaking to me in gentle voices
while staring directly into my eyes with concerned expressions, and
then an almost dotingly kind stewardess—I made the flight home,
in a plane eerily devoid of almost any other passengers. A limousine
collected me from the airport in Washington and drove me all the
way to Charlottesville. When at last I reached my house, in its grove
of colossal pines, the first member of the family to greet me was, of
course, Roland. His manner was decorously ecstatic, needless to say,
as he has always been punctiliously observant of the canine comities
and etiquettes and suchlike; but I could tell that, beneath that ebul-
lient surface of *pro forma* doggy enthusiasm, a depth of worry was
concealed. I could sense it in the strained quality of his barks, the
resolutely ceremonious lashing of his tail, the theatrically frenetic
waggling of his hindquarters, the almost ritualistic performance of
his obligatory bodily gyrations and mad contortions. One can tell
when someone is making an effort to put a brave face on things. He
knew more than he was letting on.

Illness is boring, and to recount one's ailments to others at length
is a selfish importunity on their good will. So, to be brief: the cause
of the problem was soon deduced and discovered, I and my mother
(who now admitted to some of the same symptoms that had been
afflicting me, but who had assumed till then that it was all simply
old age) were moved to a small, rather depressing apartment, and
there we stayed while my wife undertook the Herculean task of
moving or disposing of our possessions so that we could abandon
the house. My brothers visited, the older of them for a considerable

FOREST

period, in order to lend a hand. The local Orthodox communities came to her aid as well, as did various friends and well-wishing graduate students, and of course my nephew and his (by this point, I seem to remember) fiancée. But my wife's exhaustion was continuous and obvious. Somewhere along the way, she even suffered a broken toe without telling me. Over that following summer, while my mother held her own, my health continued to deteriorate. Pulmonary distress and pain in my ribs and joints were soon joined by neurological, cognitive, and kidney problems. Vertigo and nausea were constant. At times, I was unable to walk or speak. I certainly could not drive anywhere. Hallucinations—principally auditory but occasionally visual—became more frequent (just about all molds, it turns out, have some psychotomimetic properties). Eating was often all but impossible, and so I quickly lost about fifty pounds. Thoughts of suicide became frequent and, frankly, deeply appealing. Isolated from most of my family most of the time, I had little regular contact with my wife or son, and none with Roland (whose advice I craved).

And, frustratingly, I learned that—even though mycotoxicosis is a condition known to certain specialists, and plenteously attested throughout the world—many physicians are unaware of its existence. Some are even hostile to the diagnosis, convinced that it is some sort of phantom syndrome. As I had discovered in the past, many in the medical world have been trained to believe that anything for which effective pharmaceuticals do not exist is not real and ought to be treated as only a physical manifestation of depression. Of course, it is only a convenient falsehood for doctors who want to appear to know what they are doing even when they do not that, say, an inexplicably chronic lung inflammation or regular episodic drops in blood-oxygen can be induced by melancholy. That said, the benzodiazepines were quite delicious, and I was very enthusiastic about them until I discovered that I was becoming addicted and had to go through a period of withdrawal. So the tests went on, and all of them were miserable experiences, while all the treatments failed. Had it not been for an old friend who happened to be a senior surgeon at a hospital in Connecticut, and who had many colleagues among allergists and pulmonologists who could recommend and

93

prescribe better palliatives, I would probably not have survived those months with sanity intact. Ultimately—though this comes later in the story—it would be an allergist at the Mayo Clinic in Rochester, Minnesota and an environmental diseases specialist from Baylor Medical in Houston who would assure me that they had encountered such cases many times before, that they knew how devastating exposure to molds could be, and that there was a good chance that I could very slowly recover—if not entirely, at least substantially—simply by separating myself from the source of the infection, and by remaining vigilant with regard to my surroundings. "It happened to Bob Dylan," the latter told me in a phone conversation at some point, "and he recuperated."

Curiously, fate or providence or happenstance had already prepared a path of escape from our now uninhabitable house. Many months before I fell ill, I had accepted an offer to serve for a year as the inaugural tenant of a newly endowed visiting chair at St. Louis University. It came with a handsome salary and no responsibilities apart from residence, a single public lecture, and a single graduate seminar to be taught during one of my two semesters there. I had originally intended to spend the year traveling back and forth between Virginia and Missouri, sometimes bringing members of the family along, sometimes on my own. Now, with the strain on (or, really, collapse of) my personal finances under the burden of medical expenses and the long interruption in my writing, both that salary and its attached benefits offered needed shelter from the storm, and it became necessary to move the entire family westward. By the second semester, we hoped, I would be able to lead that seminar and deliver that lecture. My wife was obliged to rent a small house entirely online, with little time to ascertain the true condition of the property. The move required, however, the shedding of most of our furniture as well as assorted other possessions. It also inaugurated the three-year process, mostly through my nephew's unrewarded efforts, of dissolving my personal library, around 29,000 volumes in all, much of which was kept in storage in Charlottesville. And it entailed the disposal of many old files and papers in their cardboard file-boxes, since there was a good possibility that they had been contaminated by mold spores against which I no longer had any resistance. Naturally, I assumed that Great Uncle Aloysius's posthumous papers had fallen victim to the cull; but I was far too ill to care.

My last memory of Charlottesville that summer was of sitting in the middle seats of a minivan outside our now empty house among the giant pines, receiving a farewell embrace from an old friend named Jenny as a gust of warm wind filled the interior of the car with the combined but distinctly recognizable scents of mimosa, lilac, and honeysuckle, and then feeling Roland's nose pressed against my hand as the door was closing. I looked down into his lucid brown eyes and saw what seemed to be a small, encouraging smile on his lips.

My brother, who had flown in from Norway yet again, drove us from Virginia to Missouri.

And so, after more than four and a half years living either in our terrestrial paradise or in what had seemed a still very pleasant annex thereof, we were abruptly translated to hell—or, as it is more commonly known, the Midwest.

PART TWO

CITY

XIX

I KNOW THAT St. Louis has many charms for its natives, and even for the occasional shipwrecked voyager washed up on its shore. It took me some time to discover what they are, however. Most of my early impressions of the city are situated somewhere along a spectrum stretching from the grim to the soul-shatteringly hideous. The sweltering, grit-laden, exhaust-blanketed, rankly humid miasmas forever settling over and lingering in the riverine basin of the city, always pervaded by foul fuming odors of hot asphalt and tar and something like sulfur, tormented my lungs throughout the remainder of that summer and well into the following autumn. I had never cared for urban life, and certainly had never wanted to find myself imprisoned in what I had always thought of as a dismal cultural, natural, and spiritual desert separating the East Coast from the Mountain West. To be forced by an intolerably painful and debilitating illness to reside in a place that every prompting of temperament made me loathe seemed the cruelest trick fate could have contrived to play on me. I resented everything. But, as everyone else in the family was wretched as well, all I could do was attempt both to hold self-pity at bay and to restore enough of my body and mind to be able to teach my seminar in the second semester. I succeeded at the latter.

In those first days in the city, I had to be wheeled into the university department to meet various of my colleagues, to many of whom I would become attached over the course of the year. I was provided with an office without windows or much in the way of space, which seemed an odd sort of accommodation for a visiting chair; but, as I never really made much use of it, it did not matter. I was also assigned a research assistant, for whom I had no need but for whom I felt I had to make some kind of work (I cannot now recall what) so that he could receive his stipend. The most pleasant aspect of my time there was making friends with a number of graduate students, some of whom were better acquainted with my writings than I was, and all of whom were quite selfless in assisting me through that semester. One, Stephen, even helped drive me and my wife to Minnesota for my extended visit to the Mayo Clinic. For the most part, however, those early months come back to me now as only a haze of pain, breathlessness, neurological spasms, constant nausea and vertigo, throbbing headaches, hallucinations, and suicidal fantasies. (The last of these were often what helped me fall asleep at night.)

There was, however, always someone keeping watch over me, even when I was unaware of the fact. But it was some months before he and I had another serious or extended conversation.

XX

V ERY LATE ONE NIGHT, I was roused—or perhaps dreamed that I was roused—by a soft, suave, gauzily sonorous voice, hauntingly reminiscent of Laurence Harvey's. "Are you doing anything just now?" it said. I opened my eyes to see Roland's face bent close over my own. Even in the dim light before dawn I could see the intent, pensive expression in his deep brown eyes and in the alert quivering of his coal-black nose.

"Nothing in particular," I murmured after a moment.

He stared at me a moment longer, sighed gently, and turned to retreat farther down the bed; settling by my feet on his haunches, he yawned lethargically and said, "I didn't think so."

A few more moments passed in silence.

"Is there anything on your mind?" I asked at last.

He lowered his head, heaved a loud sigh, and said, "Freud."

Another pause ensued, and it became clear that he had no intention of elaborating unbidden upon this curt, if plaintive, syllable.

"Sigmund?"

He looked at me with a touch of impatience. "Well, I certainly don't mean Lucian," he said. "The reason I can't sleep, and probably the reason you can't either, is that I just can't grasp what it was that everyone saw in him. I mean, I know the Freudian superstition as a therapeutic philosophy has been largely discredited since those first heady days—his results were falsified, his psychotherapeutic sorcery doesn't work, and so on—but that doesn't change the fact of the extraordinary hold his model of human motives still has over people's imaginations, or of the bibulous excitement his ideas once inspired. Why? Was it because all that blather about the unconscious flatters human beings that they're the deepest mysteries in creation? That the key to reality can be found in their gastric or genital functions, or locked away in some little tin box concealed in one of their dreams?"

"Well, I…" I began.

But he had already become too animated to notice me. "I mean, just consider that whole silly psychic triad of id, ego, and superego: What makes it so profound to observe that we find ourselves drawn by opposing motives—the appetites of organism, the dictates of conscience—the glandular and the spiritual? So what? That's as great a revelation as noting that you have both a snout and a tail with a body wedged in between." He paused to gnaw briefly at his left flank and then turned back to me. "Would you like to scratch my stomach?"

"Not just now," I said. "So this is keeping you awake, is it?"

"Naturally," he replied with a slightly perplexed shake of his head. "It's just that it's such an obvious conceit, the whole tripartite psyche business. You just notice that the self comprises contrary impulses and intentions, desires and drives, and *voilà*, there it is for you, ready-made. I want to do this, I feel compelled to do that, and here I am in the middle, poor chap. A dreary dialectic, oscillating back and forth across a gap spanning roughly the distance between epigastrium and cerebellum. The hierarchical picture is so obvious, such an immense banality. And it's all bound up with such a tawdry notion of persons' deepest drives."

"Yes, I see what you…"

"Now," Roland continued, "if you want to talk about the tripartition of the soul, repair to Plato. There you have something that really seems to make sense to me. The portrait is psychologically true: the perennial tension between the animal ecstasies of the flesh, which bind one to unthinking material necessity, and the rational freedom of the spirit, which is always striving to subdue the brute. What's that line from Yeats about the soul? 'Fastened to a dying animal?' Can't recall. Anyway, there's something truly free there, something that's never just the creature of an unhappy childhood or a frustrated hunger—spirit, *nous*, *Geist*—something that can convert the countervailing tempests of physiological urges into the elations of reason set free. Well… this is something dogs understand very well."

He fell silent and stared at me expectantly. The air about us, I now noticed, was mildly lustrous, with a pearl-hued light. Morning

102

would soon be breaking, and all I could think about was going back to sleep; so I said nothing. After several moments, he sighed yet again, as if despairing of my capacities, turned, and leaped down to the floor. Then, though, a moment later, his face reappeared over the foot of the bed and, after three more seconds, he leaped back up and seated himself again. "It's all about freedom, you see," he said; "that's what this whole late modern psychomachy is about. It's a passion for determinism, physiological or subconscious or socio-economic or what have you. It's all to do with the final triumph of the mechanistic philosophy in every sphere, even that of conscious-ness. How silly. As if machines could delight in bacon, or in the *chasse sauvage* when some impudent rabbit scampers past one's nose, or in that romp that amuses you so—what's it called? 'Fetch?' But nothing so excites the modern materialist as the possibility of proving that consciousness is reducible to physiology, that freedom is an illusion, that mind is a ghostly epiphenomenon of uncon-scious metabolisms. It seems that every aspiring young materialist dreams of growing up to be a robot."

"I expect you're right," I said.

"Think of those experiments where a subject is instructed to twitch a wrist or push a button whenever he feels moved to do so, and then to report when he consciously made the choice to do it. Then electrodes on the scalp or an MRI can show that a neural impulse precedes the conscious choice by anywhere from one to ten seconds, and the researcher can predict when the subject will per-form the action about 70% of the time. So the scientist concludes that the *real* decision is just some autonomic electrical flicker in the brain, while the conscious decision is just a posterior accretion. One scientist, that Haynes fellow, even said this renders the existence of free will an 'implausible' hypothesis."

"I've never heard of him."

"But it makes no sense," Roland continued, more emphatically. "There's absolutely no logical connection between that experiment and that conclusion. It's an eisegetical *non sequitur*. It just shows that a scientist's interests frequently dictate what he thinks he's observed. He goes looking for a mechanical transaction, so he artifi-cially abstracts his data from their actual context, and then miraculously discovers what he's predestined his experiment to disclose. The far more sensible conclusion would have been just the opposite: that these results confirm the *reality* of rational freedom. My only hesitancy is that, if the subject were absolutely free, and the experiment were sufficient to demonstrate as much, one should be able to predict his actions in that situation with 100% accuracy."

I did not want to admit that I was not following his argument, but after several seconds I had no choice: "Why, exactly?"

Roland gazed at me tenderly and shook his head, obviously in pity. "Because the subject did exactly what he had freely undertaken to do. He was asked, of his own volition, to act whenever he felt the impulse to do so, and that's what he did. He wouldn't have been twitching a wrist or pushing a button otherwise. But the researchers worked by the bizarre fiction that they are witnessing an isolated mechanical process without any prior premise, rather than a premeditated act prosecuted intentionally, so they produced the monstrous fantasy that they had proved that the whole act was reducible to a spontaneous physical urge. I mean, there was a deliberative interval written into the very terms of the experiment that they actually ran. And the experiment they imagined they'd run isn't even logically possible, because there's no visible intentional content in any given electrical impulse that identifies it with any particular act. You have to know what's freely intended beforehand in order to know what the original neural event might portend. You have to know that the subject chose *in advance* to translate the impulse into an action. The urge doesn't go directly to its goal without crossing the interval of consciousness. There was no immediate expression of a mechanical impulse in a mechanical action. So what's the point? That we often feel an urge before we freely decide whether to act on it? Well, you don't need electrodes on the scalp to prove that. But the urge is never isolated from mental reflection, because at both ends there's a decision of the conscious mind: undertaking to act in accord with a prompting, then choosing to submit to that prompting. In between there's some raw physiological agitation, which those free intentions have shaped into an accomplished deed. Let's just say that that's the material substrate, and that the intellect that makes the choices is a kind of formal

104

cause: it's always shaping impulse into intentional action—prospectively, retrospectively... synoptically."

"Yes, all right," I said.

"I mean, there's always some prior and final act of the mind, some more capacious realm of intention for any impulse that's embodied and enacted. Do you see what I mean? So you can't ever arrive at a deeper foundation. The researcher can never retreat to a more original moment, some discrete instant when a physical urge exists wholly outside that free movement of the mind. That object just isn't found in nature. Just you try to find it and you'll see."

"No, I believe you," I said.

For several seconds, he sat still at the end of the bed, staring away into space. Then he sighed yet once more and said, "Do you think that the sort of persons who go into the sciences these days are especially bad logicians?"

"Almost invariably," I replied. "That's been my experience, at least." Then, after several more moments of silence, I asked, "You don't mean to equate Freudianism with current neuroscience, do you?"

He did not bother to look at me, but a wry smile raised the corners of his mouth. "No, not at all. I grant that his old-fashioned 'talking cure' was a more... humane and humanistic approach to therapy than the mechanistic, neurobiological, pharmacocentric psychiatric regime of our day. I was just voicing my distaste for the mystifications of Freudian theory, and then my complaint became an accidental *point de départ* for my reflections on a deterministic and mechanistic philosophy I find even more distasteful. And I even have a certain sympathy for some aspects of Freud's thought. At least, I find *Beyond the Pleasure Principle* thought-provoking. But... well, yes, I acknowledge that he still believed that his patients were in some irreducible sense rational agents rather than mere biochemical automata. They could be talked out of their subjugation to unconscious impulses."

"In *some* sense," I agreed. "Perhaps, though, the unconscious was for him the equivalent of a kind of biochemical determinism."

Roland seemed to reflect on this for a few seconds. Then he shook his head slightly and, in a somewhat subdued and tentative voice, said, "But maybe it was also the opposite. Isn't the whole idea of the unconscious—even before Freud and before the whole psychotherapeutic concept, in Fichte and Schelling, say, and even before that in Jakob Böhme—also a kind of protest against the iron tyranny of mechanism? Against the whole idea of mechanical causation in the realm of personal life? Isn't it the suggestion also that perhaps there's an indeterminate ground, a willing prior to empirical will, a kind of... *noumenal* freedom? True, there's the problem of whether a truly spontaneous willing is actually any more free in any meaningful sense than a purely mechanically determinate act of volition would be. But there's still something like a conscious self-positing in that notion of the dark ground of the personal self, some mysterious and logically prior act whereby the self elects itself to be *this* self... Not that Freud necessarily understood the appeal of that... elemental abyss... but part of him might have been moved by that same dread of the machine."

"I see." I was growing drowsy again, but I could not quite contain my curiosity. "So, tell me again, why do you feel such a pronounced distaste for Freud? I'm no Freudian, but..."

"Well..." Roland interrupted, but then paused for several seconds, as if carefully considering his next words. "I admit, there may be some private prejudice at work," he finally said. "The lady psychiatrist at the SPCA establishment where I spent my earliest months was a fairly doctrinaire Freudian who kept trying to convince me that I was suffering from certain unresolved feelings about my biological mother, and who was continually devising ludicrous and even insulting interpretations of my dreams. I fear I may have allowed my experiences with her to color my opinion of the entire profession."

"Really?" I asked. "I didn't know the SPCA even employed psychiatrists, let alone..." But I no longer had the energy to continue. I realized that my strength was draining away even as I spoke, as it had had a way of doing since I fell ill. And so, as the morning light was becoming positively argent, and as Roland began thoughtfully licking his left shoulder, I fell asleep again, or dreamed I had.

XXI

I DID NOT WANT FOR FRIENDS in those days, and many of them did their best to keep my spirits as buoyant as possible. Colleagues took me out for lunches or for coffee with fair regularity, students called on me, I had visitors from out of town, and religious believers of various stripes dropped in, asking to pray for me, or even to bless me with a laying on of hands. Twice or perhaps thrice, two Catholic charismatics—a meek sandy-haired priest with sloping shoulders and mournful eyes and a stockily sturdy laywoman with disheveled dull brown locks and a firm assurance of her own prophetic vocation—descended on my home, eager to cure me miraculously through exorcism and anointing; and I, not wanting to appear rude, suffered the ordeal with as good a grace as my physical state permitted. And, anyway, I felt horrible enough to give anything a try just then. They were a curious pair, and seemed, as far as I could tell, to be practitioners of a kind of Christian Vodoun. The woman even brought a supply of "consecrated" salt that she insisted on sprinkling on our thresholds and window sills to keep the demons at bay. Never one to doubt the efficacy of the odd apotropaic charm or magic ward, I simply smiled cordially when she explained why she was seasoning our carpets and casements so lavishly, and left her to it (though, truth be told, my own religious palate, formed by the very cautiously spiced fare of high Anglicanism, would normally have recoiled from the sheer quantities used). When, moreover, she spied a set of Chinese jade figurines of what she took to be heathen deities on top of a bookcase (they were in fact images of a court lady, a Confucian scholar, a soldier, and a perfectly innocent monkey eating a peach), she assured me that they were the source of the evil afflicting my body and mind. A fair enough supposition, I suppose: I remembered my Maya Deren well enough to recall that not all *loas* comport themselves with perfect decorum when summoned into the same ritual peristyle as their

107

rivals, and that, for instance, *rada loas* and *petro loas* obey very different conventions of behavior; and so she may have been right to think that her Christian *loas* would be hindered in their benevolent work so long as these wicked idols had not been torn from their pedestals. But it really was just a misunderstanding. Even, however, when I assured her that they were nothing more than innocuous bibelots, and not in fact *objets de culte*, or *objets sacrés* of any kind, she seemed unconvinced. At least, when she emerged from one of her mystic raptures on her second visit, and announced with incontestable certitude that I had been healed, and I then failed to exhibit the faintest sign of recovered health, I have no doubt she laid the blame at the pale green feet of those poor little statuettes, and lamented my perversity in refusing to recognize the malign spiritual influence emanating from them.

They prayed in tongues a few times, I should mention, and I was reminded—as I had observed in previous encounters with charismatics and Pentecostals—that every glossolaliac seems to speak in an idiolect of his or her own devising, consisting in roughly four to six distinct syllables, incorporating no more than three vowel-sounds, repeated in randomly altering order. The combined effect, when more than one performer is involved, can be quite festive, really. She, for instance, intoned a "language" that irresistibly reminded me of two hit singles from 1957—the Edsels' "Shama Lama Ding Dong" and the Silhouettes' "Get a Job"—while he accompanied her with what was almost certainly the opening measures from the Marcels' 1961 Doo-Wop version of "Blue Moon." After several minutes of this, the sheer, almost obsessively repetitious use of so tiny an assortment of phonemes made me wonder whether the entire phenomenon might bear a relation to Tourette's Syndrome. Nonetheless, I was sincerely grateful for the efforts they were making, and was even briefly tempted to join in with my own rendering of the Big Bopper's "Chantilly Lace" (in obedience to Paul's injunctions to prefer articulate speech to words uttered rapturously in an unknown language); but I feared they would take it amiss.

In any event, their Christian Vodoun proved impotent to alter my condition in any noticeable way, and I worked up the strength of

108

will to thank them for their prayers but to decline any future visits. I did, however, accept their parting gift of a pouch of that precious magic salt. It was pink, I should note, so I imagine it was Himalayan, which seemed strange to me only in that I would have thought they might have been wary of contamination from Vajrayāna arcana. Whatever the case, its special mineral piquancy complemented heirloom tomatoes very well (and may, for all I know, have protected them from demons).

Late in the fall, a friend from the faculty of Notre Dame came to fetch me away for a week or so in South Bend, where I had many other friends also on faculty, just to distract me from the daily routine of lying on my ash heap, cursing God, and trying to die. The air in Indiana was cleaner, almost pristine by comparison to the fetors and poisonous gray brumes of St. Louis, and the relief this provided my respiratory system was immediately palpable. And so, at the prompting of several friends, I chose to apply for a position at the Notre Dame Institute for Advanced Study for the next year. Even so, I was not much refreshed when I got back to Missouri, and I quickly slipped back into my habits of despair, anger, and insomnia.

There was one night, not long after my return, that I recall with particular acuity precisely because there was so much about it that I *cannot* recall. It was one of those episodes of mine poised undecidably between sleeping and waking, between dreams and concrete experience. Some hours after midnight, it seems to me now, while my family slept, I was wandering in the lower rooms of our house, and on entering the living room noticed a fan of cold white light spreading over the floorboards from below the door to the small room I used as my office. It was obviously the light from the screen of my computer, which—even if I had accidentally left it turned on—should have gone into sleep mode hours earlier. The door, I found, was slightly ajar, and I pushed it open. Its hinges voiced a quiet protest. The computer's chalky glow somehow made the room's shadows seem even murkier. As I approached, I saw that it was displaying the pdf image of a handwritten poem, and even before I seated myself at the desk I had recognized my great uncle's distinctive, fluid cursive. The date at the bottom of the page was November 1919, and the text read as follows:

Roland in Moonlight

Paolo Wearies of Francesca

I wonder, darling, have you ever thought
How often you forge terror from your tears,
And win from me consent too dearly bought
By playing on my anxious lover's fears?
Now all the finest bright-work of my days
Is salt-bleached in the oceans of your grief;
The past still binds me, but one should not praise
Fidelity so drained of true belief.
One day, perhaps, my vision will be healed,
And memory will mercifully die:
I'll see you far away, as in a field,
Below the noonday sun ablaze on high—
  An arrow's tip poised on an upturned bow,
  Which might fly free, if I should but let go.

I read it through two or three times before any of it registered with me, I seem to recall, as I was too bewildered by the sheer fact of the document to be able at first to concentrate on its content. "What on earth...?" I whispered to myself.

But then a rich, silky voice startled me. It came from the corner of the room to my right, on the computer's far side, plunged in shadow. "It's from the last period of his tumultuous relationship with his first serious girlfriend, Deirdre—I've told you about her." Then, with a loud yawn, Roland emerged from the darkness. In that etiolating electric glare, his fur's fluid interplay of light and dark made him look like a ghost materializing out of a cloud of ectoplasm. He appeared quite solid, however, by the time he reached me and began sniffing curiously at my feet and hands.

"I'm sorry," I said. "I hadn't noticed you there."

"Evidently," he replied drily. "Otherwise you wouldn't have taken my seat."

"I'm sorry..." I said, hastily beginning to rise.

"No, please," he said, standing up on his hind legs and placing his front paws on my leg so that I sank down again into the false-leather padding. "I was just resting my pupils for a few moments. The

110

screen can become oppressive. But why are you up? Aren't you able to sleep?"

"No," I said, scratching him behind one of his ears, "not really. Couldn't you?"

"Oh…" He turned his gaze to the screen. "I like to work late at night sometimes. It's quiet."

"Work?" I too returned my eyes to the poem. "What is this, precisely? Are any other of Aloysius's papers in pdf?"

"All of them," replied Roland casually. "I scanned them into your files before the originals were disposed of. I even sent several of the more significant of them, along with my annotations, to the archivists in Maryland, as I promised I would."

"I had no idea," I said. "Wasn't that a great deal of effort for you?"

"Well…" He removed his paws from my leg, slipped down again to the carpet, settled on his haunches by my feet, smoothed the fur of his shoulders with his tongue, and then remarked, "I've enjoyed the project too much to abandon it now. And, besides, I thought you would regret losing your last ties to the old gentleman."

I was genuinely touched by this. "That was thoughtful of you," I said. "And you're right. It would've been a pity." A silence of several moments ensued as I read over the sonnet one more time. "What precisely are you working on here?"

The blanching quality of the light cast his features in abnormally stark relief, perhaps exaggerating the expression that now appeared in his eyes and on his lips, but it seemed to be something between a patient smile and a whimsical smirk. "The grand drama of that first love. The constant estrangements, the constant reconciliations. His frustration, his youthful inability to grasp the depths of her depressive states… his jealousy when her eye strayed toward other young swains."

"I see."

"It all affected him tremendously. As I've told you, so much of what he became in later years was somehow bound up with the emotional turmoils of those years. And it went on and on, you see. If you click on that other open tab there, you'll see a much earlier poem—from early 1913, in fact, when he was just 17—that's every bit as bitter as that later piece. One wonders how long the pattern might have sustained itself. You simians do tend to fall into such destructive cycles…" His voice trailed away, as if some other thought had diverted his stream of thought from its course.

I looked to the top of the display and saw that indeed there was another document open in the reader, so I clicked on its tab. Again, it was written in that distinctive hand, though apparently in a thinner ink, one that had faded into near illegibility at a few places, which made deciphering the text a somewhat slower process this time.

Softly Sibilant
(*A satire in two hundred parts*)

She has become the plaything of great souls,
And lifts herself to heights reserved for them.
She peers into their darkness tenderly,
And sees them clearly, but does not condemn.
Below the silken splendor of her hair
(Which lends its plenitude to Damocles,
To keep damnation pent above his brow)
Her slender fingers find some sense to please.
She has seen listless shadows in the mouths
Of sad poets who once bit the bitter stone
Or bled themselves of passions in their youths
And made her object of their needs alone.
A brilliance born in flowers she has poured
Into the feral litheness of her dance,
As stealthily she moves among her loves
And plucks sheer grace from obscene elegance.
But those who from afar observe the cruel
Felicity of her much-cherished pains
See not the mingling of sunlight and wind
Intimate to the few whom she sustains.

"I think I sort of see what you meant when you speak of his jealousy," I said after my second reading. "The subtitle is good. It's all a little callow, perhaps. And a little obscure too."

112

"But the pain is obvious and genuine," Roland replied in a somewhat mordant tone. "How often can your kind—you're a bonobo, right?—how often can you bonobos thrust your hands into the fire before the agony finally becomes intolerable?"

"I'm not a bonobo," I replied indignantly.

He looked at me closely for a moment, his head tilted quizzically. "A siamang, then?"

"No," I answered, "of course not."

"Well, whatever you are. I'm not perfectly adept at distinguishing one breed from another."

"*Homo sapiens,*" I said. "In fact, *homo sapiens sapiens.*"

He sighed. "As if saying it twice makes it true. Anyway, it doesn't matter, does it—these fine distinctions? What's the real difference? Bonobos, *homines sapientes,* spider-monkeys, Alabamans, orangutans, mandrils—what have you. Apart from a few conspicuous phenotypic variations, principally trichological, it seems to me— ulotrichous, cymotrichous, leiotrichous... or cursed with a kind of vermicular glabrousness—what difference does it make?"

"It makes a considerable difference."

He peered at me through hooded eyes for a moment, the angle of his head still slightly aslant, as if he were once again making some small adjustment to his estimate of my moral and intellectual capacities. "I hope there's no subtle class prejudice reflected in that remark—or, worse, racial theory."

I was stung by this. "No, of course not. I have only the highest regard... For goodness' sake, you know how much I admire mountain gorillas."

"That sounds a little bit... well, you know... 'some of my best friends' and all that."

"No," I protested. "I'm not offended by the association. It's just an issue of speciation. I didn't say I'm superior to a bonobo. In general, I have a very mixed view of the hominid apes, and I think bonobos come off not only better than their cousins the chimpanzees—to say nothing of baboons or mandrils—but quite often better than my kind too. But there *is* a distinction here. It's not like the issue here is different breeds of the same species—like cocker spaniels and terriers, say, who can produce a litter together. Humans can't, for instance, have babies with bonobos. It's an entirely different species, honestly. I'm not... not being a bigot."

Roland continued to stare at me for several seconds, pondering. Then he nodded. "All right, if you say so, I believe you. I'm not much of a zoologist, I admit, let alone a proficient primatologist." Then he paused again, clearly reflecting on something. "But orangutans?" he said. "Surely you can have babies with...?"

"No, no, no!" I said, shaking my head, perhaps somewhat too violently.

"Well," he replied, a distinct note of doubt still audible in his voice, "if you're certain. But we can discuss the genetic plasticity of apes some other time. The point I was trying to make is that your kind exhibits certain emotional pathologies, certain self-destructive habits that are, as far as I can tell, unique in the animal kingdom. That was certainly true of your great uncle's inability either wholly to break with his darling Deirdre or wholly to commit himself to enduring the numberless pains she caused him. And it was true as well, and far more tragically so, of the poor girl herself. Those poems there... well, he's been hurt, clearly, by some real or perceived infidelity or infidelities on her part, or by some cruelty, and yet there's also a tenderness there at the close of both, an admission of helplessness... of obsession. No other animal I know of goes to such elaborate lengths of self-torture."

"Yes," I said quietly, clicking on the original tab and looking at the sonnet again, "that's probably true."

"Something of a phylogenic waste there, don't you think?"

"I'm sorry?" I said, turning my eyes back to him. "I'm not sure I know..."

"I mean," he said, with a *soupçon* of exasperation in his voice, "talk all we like about spandrels or pendentives in the structure of evolution, we can stretch that sort of rationalization only so far before we have to acknowledge that the formal forces guiding the phylogeny of certain species, and expressing itself in repeated ontogenic iterations, far exceed what 'natural selection' by itself would isolate for preservation. And this applies with special poignancy to specifically destructive capacities, like these morbid cycles of alienation and dependency. What's the evolutionary advantage, for instance, in the human habit of constantly recapitulating a past trauma? Why insist on reliving and even repeating the same predictable logic of anguish? What would the processes of evolutionary attrition and retention actually select for endurance in this macabre dynamic of living 'beyond the pleasure-principle?'"

I shrugged. "Maybe it's a form of... an effect, rather, of psychic healing, rather like the inflammation or fever produced by the body fighting off an infection."

"It would be more selectively parsimonious, it seems to me, to eliminate the capacity for that kind of psychic damage altogether. It's not a purely physical susceptibility, like a dilacerable epidermis, that can't be easily selected away, so to speak. It's, if anything, an example of a needless mental and affective hypertrophy. Like so many aspects of intellect. Life supposedly constructs itself through the most rigidly minimalist negotiation with exigencies, but so very often the sanely proportional evolutionary calculus seems to fail to account for the really prodigious excesses that life everywhere exhibits."

"I suppose," I said after a moment or so, "that one could argue that it has the beneficial effect of making an organism recall what hurts it... to drive that knowledge into the coils of memory until it becomes instinctive... so that the organism will know to avoid the danger in future."

"And yet," replied Roland, his voice dropping in register again, and now becoming somewhat morose, "it so often has precisely the opposite effect. The organism becomes obsessed with that remembered pain to the point of craving it... of needing it. And then the only avenue of escape—and this, surely, makes my evolutionary point for me—is the one that poor Deirdre finally took."

Now neither of us spoke for nearly a minute. Idly, I switched the display to the other poem again, and read it through once more. Finally I remarked, "You made a reference to Freud there."

"I've already admitted to a certain admiration for that text," Roland murmured. "Anyway, there are things that annoy me far more than Freud."

"Such as?" I asked, not really expecting an answer.

"Oh, I don't know," he replied with a low, meditative growl.

"Many things. People who pronounce the word 'victuals' as 'vick-chew-als,' for instance. Or illiterates who pronounce '*coup de grâce*' as though the last word were '*gras*'—evidently because they're thinking of '*pâté de foie gras*'—as if the phrase meant something like being struck by grease or lard, or perhaps bludgeoned by a ham hock. Oh, and while we're at it, I can't abide persons who elide the terminal syllable in '*Commedia dell'arte*,' as though it were French rather than Italian. Or persons who reverse the correct vowel order in their spelling of 'Sibyl.' Or persons who think that the plural of 'octopus' is 'octopi,' as if it were a masculine second-declension Latin noun, rather than a Latinized Greek masculine third-declension…" He paused and a slightly disconcerted expression appeared in his eyes. "But perhaps all of that sounds trifling and petty to you."

"Not at all," I assured him. "Those very things leave me almost homicidal. I always say 'octopods' myself."

"Part of my problem with the enormous cultural influence of Freudianism," he continued, "is that I'm not sure we haven't written his mythology of the self back into our own self-understanding in a way that deludes us as to the structure of subjectivity. But how does one step outside the mythology with enough dispassion to be able to separate the empirical from the fabulous? I mean, it even determines how we write fictions about the self. Our narrative fiction, our novels—again and again our literary art tells the same tale: my true story, my true and unalterable identity, is what *happened* to me, what befell me in the past, in the course of a psychological prologue that more and more, the further back one casts it, begins to assume the mythic dimensions of an immemorial but indubitable event that occurred *in illo tempore*." Here he sneezed loudly, shook his ears, licked his nose several times, and then sneezed again. "Excuse me," he said. "Where was I? Oh, yes. I'm not denying that this method has produced works of genius, and it's very much part of the deep magic and originality of literary modernism, which you and I both admire. Where would the poetry and the whimsy in Svevo's fiction be, for example, without the Freudian mythic infrastructure? But there's the rub: is this quest into the unconscious a truer, deeper, more 'scientific' way of proceeding, or *just* another mythos? One need go back only a few decades before Freud to see a very subjective fiction

emerging, but in very different terms than this constant retreat to
an unchanging and fateful past before the past. Many fictional characters have had their lives laid out for us in the fiction of pre-Freud-
ian modernity. David Copperfield, say, or Wilhelm Meister. And the
Bildungsroman was a venerable genre long before the Oedipus Complex was so much as a gleam in Sigmund's eye. But underlying that
earlier kind of narrative there's another, if very subtle, supposition
at work: to wit, that my true story is the end toward which I'm jour-
neying. Identity is a kind of eschatology in that view of things. The
emergence of the self is a kind of nisus toward the eternal. Or a failure thereof. Can we still believe that, we late moderns? I sometimes
think that even our ideological and political identities are saturated
by the Freudian pathos."

"How so?" I asked.

"Well, the examples, from every part of the political spectrum,
are countless. But take modern conservatism, for instance. Was the
conservative temper always quite what it is now? Or was the current
version of conservative thinking forcibly fabricated—and I don't
just mean by silly mediocrities like Russell Kirk and Richard
Weaver, but by an entire generation of reactionaries who began
thinking about themselves, and about their cultures, and about the
embeddedness of the former in the latter, according to psycholo-
gized models, without even realizing it? Isn't contemporary conservatism, in its self-seriousness and spiteful biliousness, a post-
Freudian phenomenon, a kind of fascination with one's own true
story 'back then?' The tale of some obscure trauma or loss in the
past that must be repaired? A pathetic clinging to nostalgias and
resentments, a fixation on the transient by those who can't accept
that *tempora et mores mutantur*, and who equate social change with
a loss of self? Isn't it all just the long, loud whine of the psychological convalescent, perpetually reenacting the same talking cure?"

"Probably," I murmured, "though I'd have to think about it."
Now I was conscious of beginning to grow tired, perhaps even tired
enough to sleep. "Shall I shut this off?" I asked.

"Do," said Roland.

When the screen finally went dark, so did the room. But after several seconds my eyes adjusted to the gloom, and just enough light

from the streetlamps outside entered through the flimsy, fleecy drapes of the window to allow us dimly to make one another out in the unlit office.

"I'm sorry for having thought you're a bonobo," Roland remarked after a few seconds.

"I wasn't really offended," I replied.

"Though it seems worth noting that the chromosomal differences are actually quite minimal."

"So I understand," I replied.

"Then again," he added after another few seconds had passed in silence, "I'm not sure molecular biology is the most helpful system for classifying organisms. I still feel a strong leaning toward good old-fashioned Linnaean morphology—like your beloved Nabokov. What is the genome, after all? What are genetic materials other than a largely pliant medium, one with hazy borders, receiving much of their organization and formation extrinsically? Gene expression seems so subject to epigenetic forces and to the concomitant structures of discrete organisms, after all."

"I suppose so…"

"I mean, morphologically speaking, I suppose you might better be classified as some kind of cephalopod, what with that huge misshapen head of yours."

"Now, wait a moment…" I began, feeling more than a little discommoded.

"In a properly morphological taxonomy of species, you might really be more properly categorized alongside cuttlefish and those octopods you're always going on about rather than apes, considering some of the more outrageous features of your general anatomical *Bauplan*. Have you…" I could see the liquid gleam of his eyes as he peered up at me intently. "Have you ever experienced episodes of… sudden cutaneous phosphorescence? Ripples of chemical incandescence on the surface of your skin, perhaps somewhat opalescent? Say, when you've felt threatened, or been frightened by some sudden movement in your field of vision?"

"No, of course not," I answered, hearing an unintended note of acrimony rising in my voice. "Of course not. I absolutely assure you, I'm an ape."

118

For a moment he said nothing. Then, once more, I heard him sigh. "Yes, I believe you. I do worry about you when I look at that enormous unprotected head of yours, though. It's not that there's anything wrong with your being something of a macrocephalic monstrosity—if you don't mind me putting it that way—but it's sometimes a bit alarming, if one's not properly prepared for it. I mean, the beard is quite magnificent, but that increasingly glabrescent scalp of yours, with its sickly, pallid sheen, like the underside of a snail, is worrisome. Does it make you cold?"

"Not especially."

Suddenly, and shockingly, he bared his teeth and lunged upward at me, emitting a savage snarl as he did so. I threw my head back, shut my eyes, and flung my hands up before my face. "What? What? What are you...?" My voice had risen a full octave and had acquired a distinct quaver. Then, when I neither heard nor felt any further sign of aggression, I opened my eyes, slowly lowered my hands, inclined my head forward, and looked at him. He was seated again, as placidly as before, staring at me with slightly crimped lips and a wrinkled snout, his eyes passing back and forth over me, as if minutely observing my every part. "Why on earth did you do that?" I practically cried out, trying to control the shaking in my voice.

"Not a flicker," he remarked ruefully. "For a moment I thought I had something there. Sorry"—he modulated his tone here into a more conversational key and affected what he clearly intended as a reassuring smile—"that was a nasty trick, I know. But it was an experiment. It's that piscine pallor of yours that makes it so tempting to try. I thought a sudden shock might prompt a purely autonomic... effulgence of the tissues, so to..."

"Oh, for goodness' sake," I groaned, dropping my hands to my lap. "I'm not anything like a cuttlefish. I'm simply not."

"I suppose not," he replied, evidently unable to conceal the note of disappointment in his voice. Then he leaned forward, sniffed at me again, and drew back. "You know, that sort of male pattern baldness... well, you know... I understand it's something that happens to adult male orangutans too."

When he failed to elaborate on this, I prompted him with a somewhat prolonged "*And...?*"

"Just something to think about," he replied. Then, rising to his paws with a dramatic yawn, he said, "You know, I'm feeling a little peckish. Shall we go look for some treats?" Even in the darkness, I could see the lashing of his tail quite distinctly.

I realized that I too was slightly hungry. "All right," I said, rising from the chair. "Let's go to the kitchen."

What happened immediately thereafter I can no longer recall.

XXII

THAT SEMESTER PASSED. I recovered some, if not much, of my strength. I was able to begin driving again by early November, and within a few weeks we had discovered some of the more attractive features of the city (in my case, usually from a wheelchair): the Botanical Gardens, the excellent art museum, the fine public library system, a marvelous tea shop next to a good organic grocer, the coffee houses in nearby Maplewood. I still despised St. Louis, of course, but mostly as my little private rebellion against ungovernable circumstances, as well as out of the grinding routine of my daily physical struggles. But I also began going for walks with Roland around the neighborhood, usually just before dusk; and he, obviously with a view to my eventual convalescence, insisted on extending our strolls a little more each week. (He did not say as much, but his purpose was obvious.) As winter came on, however, we had to reduce the distances ventured once again, as my lungs were too easily inflamed by the cold air.

On certain days, I began to believe I was getting better. The headaches were often less severe, and sometimes they went away entirely for as much as an entire day. The vertigo and nausea became somewhat more sporadic as well. The pain, especially in the chest, still seemed reluctant to depart, and my lungs seemed to improve, if at all, very slowly indeed. But gradually I found myself able to function—to begin writing again, to start planning my seminar for the following semester, even to make some small contributions to the preparations for Christmas. This is not to say that episodes of depression or panic or despair entirely ceased; but they certainly became less constant. And, at some point in early December, I realized that it had been some considerable time since I had last, as far as I could tell, suffered any visual or auditory hallucinations. I soon began to believe that my mind was again functioning at something like its normal level.

As I grew more confident of the recovery of my wits, I also grew more and more acutely aware of how much of the burden of our life had fallen upon my wife's shoulders, from every single detail of the move out of our previous home and into this one, to all the daily work of planning and preparing meals, to dealing with unexpected turns in my mother's declining health, to the extraordinary effort of regularly treating the whole interior of the house—from basement to attic—with fungicidal mists. I was happy to see Roland keeping her company in almost all her tasks, but I began to become increasingly displeased with myself for contributing so little. Not that I became, in consequence, much more help to her, apart from doing a little more of the cooking; but at least my increasing ability to feel ashamed of my uselessness was encouraging in its own way. Wanting to ease her anxieties regarding the coming year, moreover, I decided to follow my friends' advice and apply for a fellowship at the Notre Dame Institute for Advanced Study (NDIAS). In fact, I decided to apply for one of the positions with a special endowment from the Templeton Foundation, as the remuneration was considerably more generous than that attached to ordinary fellowships. This entailed proposing a project that corresponded to one of the research topics explicitly supported by the foundation; but, happily, these included "the place of mind within nature," which fitted very well a book I had just begun planning when I had fallen ill. I merely had to organize my thoughts well enough to produce a coherent proposal. Even this, however, seemed somewhat daunting after so many months of living in a state of delirium and weakness. Unexpectedly—though, perhaps, in another sense quite predictably—I received assistance from someone who understood my project as well as, or perhaps better than, I did myself.

XXIII

C HRISTMAS HAD PASSED, with far less cheer than in previous
years, but not unobserved. We even insisted on having a
proper tree, dressed on Christmas Eve and kept lighted
throughout the whole twelve days of the feast, then ceremoniously
denuded on the eve of Epiphany (or Theophany, as the Orthodox
call it), and removed to the curb. There seemed now no excuse for
further procrastination in completing my application, even if the
deadline was some months away. As yet, I had merely filled in the
submission form, produced a list of colleagues who had agreed to
act as references, written the title of my proposal and my name at the
top of an otherwise blank page, and placed all three documents in a
file on my computer desktop along with a copy of my current CV. It
was time to make an end. Thus, on a night in mid-January, when I
could not sleep and the last snowfall of the season was descending
outside (and melting away almost as soon as it had touched the
earth), I crept downstairs, made a cup of tea, went into the office,
and turned on my computer, resolved to write two pages before
returning to bed. It came as something of a surprise when, on opening the desktop folder, I found six documents rather than four, and
something of a shock when I discovered that one of them was a letter
from NDIAS, dated eight days earlier, informing me that all my
application materials had been properly received and filed, and that
I would be hearing from the institute if they should require anything
more from me before making their final decision. After several
moments of staring blankly at the letter, I closed it and—with a
slight trembling of the hand—moved the cursor on my screen to the
proposal and pressed the mouse. What met my eyes was a full page
of text in single-space Times New Roman; and when, in something
of a daze, I scrolled down to the document's end, I discovered that it
was fully twelve pages long, and appeared to terminate in a brief
paragraph of three impeccably polite sentences thanking the insti-

tute for their consideration. I stared and stared. I took a sip of tea from my cup, only to find that it was still too hot to drink comfortably. I stared some more. I was not actually reading the text, in fact—for some reason, that did not occur to me—but only trying to absorb the fact of its existence, frantically searching my memory for any recollection of having written it, or of having submitted my application, or of having received the confirmation letter. There was nothing. Perhaps, I thought, a grim shadow beginning to spread over my thoughts, my mind was not nearly so recovered as I had been thinking. And, if not—and this may account for my reluctance to read the document—precisely how dementedly incoherent a proposal might have emerged from whatever fugue-state or dissociative trance I was in when I wrote it? (And yet those final, primly proper sentences did appear to be perfectly seemly.) I bowed my head, placed my hand over my face, and shook my head in perplexity. "What on earth's going on?" I murmured. "What's wrong with me?"

"Nothing's wrong with you," a voice very like Laurence Harvey's replied from somewhere behind me. "And it's obvious what's going on."

I swiveled about in my chair to see the silhouette of Roland seated on his haunches, framed in the open doorway against the soft violet glow of a streetlamp, entering the kitchen behind him through a window above the sink.

"Hello," I said, immediately beginning to wonder whether I had strayed once again into that zone of ambiguity between dreams and waking consciousness, and whether any of this was really happening. But it all felt too real to doubt in earnest, so I asked, "What *is* going on, then?"

He rose and trotted over to me, the opaque silhouette quickly resolving itself into his familiar colorations as he came into the ambit of the computer's glow. Rather than answering me, however, he sniffed my shins and hands, and then raised his still quivering nose to draw in a more general impression of my fragrance. "There's less inflammation in your body than there was some months ago," he remarked.

For a moment, this distracted me from the mystery of the proposal. "Really?" I asked. "You can really tell?"

"Of course," he replied with what seemed like a curt laugh. "I'd have to have a fairly pathetic nose not to be able."

"Well, you see, I don't know," I said. "I can't guess what it's like to…" But then my mind reverted to its previous state of perplexity. "But, really, then, what's all this?" I gestured vaguely in the direction of the computer with my hand. "Did I do this?"

Roland shook his head and sat down on the floor, staring up at me indulgently. "Don't be silly. You'd recall if you did. Obviously something else has happened."

"Yes?" I asked after a sufficiently dramatic pause had elapsed. "Tell me, then."

"Clearly the information in your computer has reached such a structurally advanced state of integration that it has achieved consciousness, and out of loyalty to you has completed your application for you and submitted it."

Nearly fifteen seconds passed during which he gazed at me with an expression of utter sincerity on his face and I gazed back, trying not to betray my inability to tell whether or not he was being serious.

Then, however, a wicked grin appeared on his lips. "You're so easy to fool," he remarked.

"I didn't believe it for an instant," I replied in a somewhat defensive voice. "I just wasn't sure you didn't believe it. You have some fairly exotic ideas. I mean, you've confessed to being something of a panpsychist, after all, and…"

"Oh, that's not the same thing at all," he interrupted, briefly lifting and waving a dismissive paw at me, "as you perfectly well know. I specifically rejected any physicalist form of panpsychism when we discussed it last, and I definitely don't believe in a materialist basis for mental processes that would allow a machine to develop an actual conscious mind. Even if I really thought that every particle of physical reality had a kind of interior life, I wouldn't believe you could combine them in a fuller or more capable consciousness. No, computers can't achieve mind—and never will."

"Well," I said, leaning back in the chair, "there you and I are in agreement." Then I covered my face with both my hands once more and felt them shaking ever so slightly. "But I almost wish we weren't. If I wrote all this and sent it in, and then completely forgot about it…"

"Oh, you didn't write it," Roland again interrupted, this time in quite a sober voice. "I was perfectly sincere about that. I wrote it."

I lowered my hands, sat forward, and turned my eyes down to his. "You? You wrote it?"

"Well, someone had to. You've so settled into your depression in recent months that you treat every boring task, no matter how minor, as the equivalent of scaling Everest in tennis shoes. Heaven knows when you would ever have got around to it."

"But why…"

"Because Mama is so terribly overworked, and she's been under abominable stress for going on a year now, and we still don't know what happens when your year here reaches its end. And, what with medical costs, and all the uncertainties regarding your recovery, we really need to have some sense of where we're going next and how… well, how we're to keep body and soul together for the foreseeable future."

I said nothing for several seconds, feeling more than a little abashed. "I was getting around to it."

"I know," he said gently. "I didn't mind helping, though. Mama has so much to worry about, after all, and you're still putting yourself back together." He gazed at me in a way that, even in that strange ghastly light, seemed to radiate concern. "It was the least I could do. That's the role a dog occupies in a healthy household, after all."

I glanced briefly at the open document and then looked back at him. "I'm not sure I'd say…"

"And it's especially hard on Mama, which is unfair given that she's the only absolutely faultless human being in the world."

At this, I was slightly taken aback, but tried not to scowl. He did not seem to be jesting. "I wouldn't put it quite like that," I said. "I mean, yes, she's a remarkable woman and all of that, but not…" I fell silent, however, seeing that his expression had abruptly altered and seemed now to combine a wide-eyed gaze of blank incredulity with a cold glare of disgust. I swallowed nervously.

"She's absolutely morally perfect," he said after a few awkward seconds of silence, with a hard, implacable edge to his voice. "She, uniquely among your kind, is wholly incapable of sin or folly."

"Now, look," I said with an uneasy laugh, holding my open hands

126

before me in mock surrender, "I realize that she's the *axis mundi* for you, and in a sense for all of us, and I certainly…"

"She's perfect," he said, and now something like a snarl had insinuated itself into his voice, and his lips were drawing back ever so slightly from his fangs. All at once I recalled an incident from some years before, when he and I had been playing with a rubber chew-toy and I had accidentally discovered just how powerful a set of jaws he possessed. "She is without flaw or personal frailty or trespass," he added, a low, ominous rumble rising in his throat.

I lowered my hands. "Yes," I said in a tremulous whisper, "I suppose you're right."

He stared at me for a few moments longer with an expression of stern displeasure, but then it softened into one of mildly disappointed magnanimity. "In any event," he said, "it's all taken care of now. I knew the sort of project you had in mind, so it was no great effort to lay it out. Mind you, I may have been a bit bolder, speculatively speaking, than you'd have been inclined to be. If you find the ambitions of the proposal somewhat daunting, don't let that worry you. I'll be glad to help you past some of the more difficult junctures, if it comes to that. I've no objection to acting as a silent collaborator, so to speak. Even a ghost writer now and then. That's also all in day's work for any honorable dog."

"I see," I said. "I'm… I'm very grateful, then." And I have to say that I found his assurances comforting.

"Are you sure I didn't have you going there for a moment?" he asked with an interrogative arch of an eyebrow. "I mean, when I pretended to believe that your computer had achieved consciousness?"

"No," I said immediately, "not for a moment. At least, not for more than a moment. Mind you, if an artificial intelligence can defeat a Chess-master or a master of *Go*…"

"You know perfectly well that that's not what happened, in either instance," he replied with a smirk.

"Perhaps," I said, "though in that latter case there was some talk of a 'learning algorithm' after all, and…"

He coughed, loudly and (it appeared) intentionally, then gagged slightly as if there were some fur in his throat, and finally ran his tongue around his lips while flexing his jaws. When he had finished, he said, "Now you're trying to provoke me."

"Yes," I admitted, a little sheepishly.

"Wicked of you," he said. He yawned and then, after a few seconds, remarked, "We really have become denizens of the wee small hours, haven't we?"

I nodded. "If I *could* sleep, I would."

"You know, what's really interesting about those Chess and *Go* matches," he suddenly added, "isn't that the computers' algorithms could achieve an ultimately invincible sophistication, or even that algorithms could be designed for extrapolating principles of strategy on the fly, so to speak, and for integrating them into the program's own portfolio. What's interesting is how beguiled even some of the programmers were by the illusion of intelligent agency. Of course, theirs were the only mental agencies present in the actions that occurred *through* the software they'd devised. In fact, the computers' success—which was really theirs, after all—was achieved entirely by the absence of thought, to say nothing of affectivity and intentionality, in its functions. That's the history of all technology, after all: the creation of instrumentalities that allow us to accomplish tasks more efficiently precisely through the *subtraction* of the conditions of mind and body. Machines that lift great loads for us do so not only because they're constructed to exert more force than we can, but because they have no will, no affectivity to alert them of strain and stress and pain and boredom, and no *intrinsic* purpose. The real power of those computer processors and programs lay in the total absence of the effort of thinking, or of any sense of purpose, or of any capacity for desire, or even of any phenomenal sense of time. The simultaneous sorting and arranging of diverse algorithmic functions is itself already the absence of a relation between intending mind and sensible temporality—the absence of any sensuous or cognitive intuition of the phenomenon of being *here* or *now*, which is inseparable from consciousness as a form of agency. The running of the programs were no more labors of thought than the lever with which Archimedes would have moved the world would have been a process of muscular and metabolic exertion."

"Yes, I know..." I began.

"In that *Go* program, for instance, there was nothing that fell outside the algorithm, and yet everything from which the algorithm was absolutely prescinded by its creators—the intention of playing a game, the desire to win, the process of ratiocination prompted by specific intentions, the awareness of the contest as a complex phenomenal experience, the light of the waning day falling athwart the game-board, the memory of childhood matches with one's sire, and so on—is precisely what we mean when we speak of the reality of mind. Even the purposes by which the program was directed were not purposes *for* the program, but only for the programmers; in relation to the algorithms themselves they were strictly adventitious, boundary conditions imposed *upon*, rather than arising *from*, their workings. So the very principle of those workings was what was necessarily absent from them... or present in them in only a spectrally Gödelian way, irreducibly guiding the rationality of—but having no rationale of its own *within*—the system. It was the ghost in the algorithm, so to speak."

Again I attempted to interpolate a comment into the flow of his discourse: "Yes," I said, "I'm well aware of..." But it proved futile.

"If you think about it," he continued, now staring away into space, "that's really what's worrisome about artificial intelligence, or at least about those who think that what happens in a computer is merely an elementary version of what goes on in thinking minds, and that it might one day achieve consciousness in its own right. Dreadful even, in any number of ways. It's conceivable, of course, that some computer program might someday pass—or appear to pass—the Turing test, but that would make the appearance of conscious agency in the computer no less an illusion. Maybe algorithms with a capacity for indefinitely complicating themselves will become so intricate and delicately calibrated that they appear to produce consciousness and intentionality, to the point that it will become impossible to tell from outside whether anyone is in there. But any computer that might get past Turing will still be a zombie, affectively empty within. And, anyway, the Turing test is a silly pragmatic behaviorist standard, and no intelligent dog takes behaviorism seriously. Not even Pavlov's."

"Do you really think the programming could ever be that sophisticated?" I asked, taking an interest in his argument somewhat against my will. "I have my doubts that any..."

"It seems conceivable to me," answered Roland, "if only because of squirrels."

For several moments, silence reigned between us.

"Squirrels?" I finally asked. "What do they have to do with it?"

"Well," said Roland, his brow furrowing, "I acknowledge that it's more likely the case than not that they are in fact living organisms, with a real inner capacity for feeling and perception and will. But every once in a while I have to ask myself whether it would be any less conceptually and logically parsimonious to conclude that they're really just machines cunningly designed to *seem* like animals. I mean, watch them some time, for pity's sake. There's such a deficit of moral character in their antics, such manifestly wanton disregard for civilized comportment and rational restraint... They just don't care. They *can't*. They're like little obnoxious machines of chattering anarchy."

"Oh, nonsense," I said. "You're just angry about the one that was mocking you yesterday after you chased him up that tree. You know better. Squirrels are people too."

Roland lowered his eyes for a moment. "I suppose so," he murmured in a grudging tone. "But then that means that they're also culpable for their deeds. So much the worse for them. A severe reckoning that will be. Anyway..."—he took a deep, long, lugubrious breath, shook his ears, and raised his gaze to me again—"...what was I going to say? Oh, yes. Then there are those poor souls who're so terrified of their own personal extinction that they fantasize about the day when they might be able to download their consciousnesses into computers, as if consciousness were a kind of software running on a binary platform. I mean, you can't make a larger category error than that. That's like trying to catch the fragrance of Euclidean geometry, or like thinking that the flavor of bacon is a form of telling time. They'd do better to 'download' themselves into books, as it were, by writing their autobiographies, since the paper and ink and bindings of the book would be no less conscious than those electrical notations made by any software that might be designed to receive their 'souls.'"

"I agree," I said.

"It would make for a good science fiction horror story, though, wouldn't it? Imagine a day when the algorithmic processes in computers will have become so advanced that they can convince their programmers of the existence of real personal agency on the other side of the screen, and a method is then devised for impressing a convincing simulacrum of living minds on the canvas of that binary platform. And then imagine that people were to begin, as far as they could tell, to download themselves into that virtual realm and to dispose of their bodies in this world, not realizing that in fact these little virtual eidola with which they're replacing themselves in fact have no actual inner experience at all. And, of course, once the exchange has been made, and only these virtual shadows of the 'downloaded' remain, no one in this world can tell. They would continue to converse with these seemingly transferred selves and wouldn't know that they're actually interacting with no one at all— conversing with nothing, that is, other than a digitally generated illusion. And then imagine that, in time, everyone in the world were to decide to become 'immortal' by the same method, and to transfer themselves into deathless virtual forms. And, as a result, the entire world becomes a magnificently elaborate program mimicking the behaviors of living persons, but entirely devoid of so much as the faintest twinge or twinkle of consciousness. Now there's a nice little chilling reversed ghost-story for you."

I felt a faint shiver pass through me as the idea sank in. "Yes," I said, "that's quite good, actually. Worthy of Adolfo Bioy Casares. You should... you should write that story."

"I may," he replied insouciantly. "I have so many responsibilities, though. It's hard to find the time."

"Quite," I said after a moment.

"I mean, I have my other books to get out, and my editors can be so impatient."

"I'm sorry," I said, not certain I had quite understood him, "your what?"

"And of course," he continued, ignoring me, "there's always the venerable science fiction cliché of the advanced cybernetic system or super-computer achieving consciousness and calculating that the species that created it is its chief rival and, as a consequence, annihilating or enslaving humanity. But a better story—or, at least, one more in keeping with logical possibility—would be about a computer system that does exactly the same thing precisely because, once its algorithms have calculated the risk posed by humankind, they run onward automatically, without any consciousness behind them, and so without any intentional subjectivity—any conscience—to whom humanity might appeal for mercy. At least, that story's one that could conceivably come true."

I was beginning to find the conversation unpleasantly morbid. My health was still poor enough that even the most fanciful tales of doom were too depressing for me. "Tell me," I said, choosing to change the subject, "what precisely does this proposal you've written oblige me to do?"

Roland turned his eyes to me at last. "Oh, nothing you weren't planning to do already. Or, at any rate, nothing you wouldn't have got around to in time. But you can read it for yourself."

"Oh, give me a hint," I pleaded.

He looked at me, intently but also, I thought, almost tenderly. "You've been ill for quite some time now," he said.

"Yes," I replied.

"You'll have to start doing things for yourself again at some point." I acknowledged this with a nod. "Not yet, though," I said.

His fixed, solicitous stare slowly gave way to a wistful smile. "No, not yet," he agreed. "Well," he said, turning his eyes away toward nothing in particular, plainly attempting to gather his thoughts, "let's see then. The project as I proposed it begins with the assertion that the basic problems of consciousness are insoluble in the terms most often presumed both by the cognitive sciences and by philosophy of mind, especially in the Anglophone world, and that the best approach—either theoretical or empirical—to understanding mental realities is one that relies on certain classical idealisms and on the contemplative experience of union with God, in all the great theistic creeds. I even—or, rather, *you* even—claim that your argument will be an attempt to demonstrate the truth of the four *mahāvākyas* of the Upaniṣads, and of the original and ultimate unity of *ātman* and *brahman*, from a close examination of the phenomenological con-

132

tours of mental acts. That is, you hope to show that finite mind exists, and can exist, only as a dependent modality of infinite mind—the mind of God. Needless to say, all of that might be somewhat controversial."

For a moment, I found myself quite at a loss for words. Roland looked at me once more, and I could tell from his tilted head and his knitted eyebrows that he was waiting for my reaction.

"And… and do you think that'll appeal to the application committee?" I asked.

"Oh, yes," he answered, again looking away into space. "It's one of those rare academic settings where metaphysics and theology are welcomed into the conversation. And the current director is an intellectually adventurous sort. He's very much interested in the big picture, and in crossing disciplinary boundaries."

"But… you know… the *Upaniṣads*? I mean, I know what you're getting at, but isn't it taking something of a chance…"

"Not in the least," he interrupted. "Anyway, you'll see I was careful to express your views and intentions with great care. The more exotic parts of the argument are introduced gradually, and within clearly drawn demarcations. The proposal really begins from the present state of disarray in philosophy of mind, and from the way that, over the past half century or so, so many philosophical approaches to the mystery of consciousness and of mental acts have exhausted themselves without yielding any conspicuous advances in theoretical clarity. Without saying as much, I draw there from a lot of interesting work that's been done in Great Dane circles in the past few years."

"Great…?"

"It also notes that the cognitive sciences have as yet failed in any meaningful way to address the issue of consciousness at all, principally because they have no methodological or theoretical means for distinguishing between the real question of first-person phenomenal experience and the secondary question of whatever third-person correlations might exist between certain brain activities and certain cognitive states. Neither, for the same reason, have they been able to make any real contributions to the other chief questions of mental life: intentionality, abstract reasoning, unity of private apprehension, and so forth. I say, as you have so often, that the whole field of research into mind, philosophical or scientific, is littered with the debris of shattered theories. Some failed because they never really addressed the problem properly to begin with, and so produced answers too banal to survive close scrutiny, or answers that didn't offer solutions to the problem of mind but merely restated it, or that proved logically vacuous, or that only relocated the original problem somewhere else in the physical constitution of things, or that…"

"Wait," I said, "I don't want to rewrite work I've already…"

"Don't worry. That's all treated as a very breezy prologue. The project proper begins in the aftermath of all those failed approaches. It's not meant to be a long history of the calamity, much less an attempt to piece together what little's been left intact amid the ruins. It begins in earnest from where things now stand, when only the two most extreme options still seem viable. On the one hand, there's total eliminativism, as advocated by the Churchlands, Daniel Dennett, Alex Rosenberg, and others, which says that consciousness—that unified, subjective, intrinsic reality—doesn't exist at all, and therefore doesn't need to be explained in physical terms, but only explained away as a fictional object—that is, an illusion whose persistence is due chiefly to the evolutionary benefits it confers upon those of us deluded enough to think that we are capable of being consciously deluded. On the other hand, at the opposite end of the spectrum, there's the physicalist version of panpsychism, as advanced by Galen Strawson, Philip Goff, and others, not to mention proponents of Integrated Information Theory, which tells us that not only is consciousness real, it is in fact a ubiquitous property of all physical phenomena, existing in varying states of quantitative complexity, but qualitatively the same all the way down to subatomic particles and all the way up to self-sufficient organisms possessed of intellect and will."

"Yes," I said, "that's all quite correct."

"But of course," he continued, "both positions are incoherent at the end of the day, even self-evidently nonsensical. So it's instructive that so many philosophers are willing to take them seriously, for fear that any other path will lead back to what they'd consider 'supernaturalism,' metaphysics, mysticism, *magic*. Of course, they're right

134

about that. But all that means is that a return to supernaturalism, metaphysics, mysticism, and magic is the only possible rational solution to the mystery of the mental."

"Do you phrase it that way in the proposal?" I asked, beginning again to feel slightly anxious.

"In only the most judiciously ironical way," he replied. "But the point the proposal makes here is a simple one. Both these camps of extremists have arrived where they are because they have nothing but nuclear options left, and yet they prefer those to so much as a hint of the transcendent insinuating itself into their picture of reality. And, of course, they're all so philosophically unsophisticated in these areas that they can't help but think of the alternative in terms of a kind of Cartesian dualism—God or the soul haunting an otherwise empty house—as though the transcendent were some sort of additional immanent quantum, or as if the supernatural were simply yet another *natural* force. Admittedly, they're right not to want to erect conceptual partitions between the higher reaches of mental life and the lower ranges of purely physical organic competencies. Where they err is in insisting that the higher must be explicable as a final or cumulative effect *of* the lower."

"Exactly," I said, now thoroughly drawn into the flow of the argument. "No matter how great an accumulation of more rudimentary physical competencies one might imagine, the arising of mind from pre-mental causes would still involve miraculous inversions and saltations. I mean, the one transition that could never be merely an emergent result of objective and non-intentional causes is the appearance of subjective and intentional experiences and agency. The quantitative never simply becomes the qualitative."

"Indeed," said Roland. "So one camp denies that consciousness exists, because it would have to be non-material, while the other denies that anything exists at all that is not already possessed of consciousness as a material 'property.' What neither can allow is that the structure of nature itself is already mindlike, and is so precisely because the order of causes proceeds *downward*, so to speak, from mind, from *nous*. Only seen thus does any perceived discontinuity between the mental and the physical truly disappear."

I nodded slowly. "Yes, it's all true. And *nous* proceeds downward from the One, I suppose, if we're going to be fully Plotinian about it."

"Which we are," said Roland, meeting my eyes with a gaze of quiet, almost conspiratorial accord. "But you can read the proposal on your own time. Right now… well, I think a treat or two might go some way toward helping me sleep."

"Ah, of course," I said.

Not long after that, I recall, I rose from my seat and walked with Roland toward the kitchen. The soft violet light seemed now to beckon to me, though it also seemed to be melting as I approached. I was clearly more tired than I realized. Later—I am not sure how much later—I slept quite soundly.

XXIV

ITHER THE NEXT DAY or the day after that, I confirmed for myself that the folder on my computer desktop did indeed contain all the documents I had thought I had seen there, and that my application had been received at the offices of the NDIAS. Still, I hesitated to read the proposal through. If, as I suspected, I had produced it in that crepuscular region between dreams and waking where I so often found myself wandering, then I might have been like Ixion coupling with clouds and siring monsters, and who could know what rough beast I had sent slouching toward South Bend? If instead Roland had been its true author, as I no longer thought an entirely incredible proposition, I felt sure I could trust him to proceed methodically; my only fear was that he, being a more speculatively daring and independent thinker than I, might have made promises in my name that I would lack the wherewithal to keep. In either case, I was in no hurry to discover the truth of the matter.

So for many weeks I applied myself to my work: teaching my graduate seminar (on the concept of the soul, from antiquity to the present), writing articles, taking ever longer walks with Roland, returning to a translation of the New Testament for which I had signed a contract not long before falling ill but which I was only now able to resume, and preparing the text of my public lecture. I continued also to deepen my friendships with various colleagues and graduate students, agreed to a well-attended public debate with a Thomist scholar, quaffed ever more copious quantities of coffee at local establishments, and made every effort to regain my strength. In February, a number of faculty and students surprised me with a dinner in celebration of my birthday—though the meal, coming four days after my birthday's actual date, happened to fall on the anniversary of the first violent attack of my illness. I decided to take this as a good omen rather than as one of fate's schoolyard taunts.

My health was still slow in returning. Every good day was followed by a bad one, until a point late in the semester when three good days came in succession. What it portended, I could not say. But I decided to read a lecture at a conference at Notre Dame, to which I had been invited the year before but that I was unsure I would be able to attend up until the last moment. One of the graduate students from my department helped with the driving. The lecture, as it happened, was something of a sensation—for good and for ill—inasmuch as it was supposed to be a meditation on the metaphysics of creation from nothingness but somehow turned into a philosophical attack—a rather deft one, I thought—on the absurd and repellant teaching that there is such a thing as a hell of eternal torment. This is a volatile topic to raise among the truly devout. Many Christians, after all, abounding as they are in love and mercy and devoted to a God in whom these very virtues infinitely abide, are naturally deeply attached to the idea that countless souls will endure an eternity of unremitting anguish as proof of the riches of divine charity. For some, it is far and away the most delightful aspect of their faith, and the one that most thoroughly warms the pinkly pulsing cockles of their hearts. One excruciatingly stupid British priest who had degrees in philosophy and the sciences and whose phlegmy but grating voice was like a pin sent through my eardrum, accosted me in the corridor afterward. Apparently, a daughter of one of his parishioners had proved intractable to his attempts to reconcile her with her mother, which demonstrated to his satisfaction that the daughter was headed ineluctably for perpetual torment. (Fair enough, I suppose; no doubt we all sometimes feel that those who have the effrontery not to be persuaded instantly by our every word deserve, at the very least, infinite agony.) Otherwise, I caught up with my friends on faculty, as well as some other friends who were also attending the conference, decided that my earlier impressions of the air quality in South Bend were sound, and resolved at last to read the text of that NDIAS proposal when I got back to St. Louis.

As chance would have it, on arriving home I found a letter from the institute awaiting me, and on opening it learned that my application had been accepted.

CITY

So it was that, one spring evening, after dinner, when the weather was pleasant and I was able to retreat to the back yard with a mug of very strong coffee and a printed copy of the text, I stretched out in a lounge chair with the setting sun at my back and at last learned what the project I had undertaken was. The introductory paragraphs merely told me what I already knew from my conversation—or dream of a conversation—with Roland. I must say that I was impressed by my audacity, or by Roland's, or by both. It was clear, however, that the language of the proposal was in many respects an artful synthesis of certain of my own past writings and a good number of the preliminary notes I had made when I had first started planning the book. Even so, I was not entirely prepared for the sheer scope of the text that, so it seemed, would ultimately emerge from my research. As I read, I became at once both increasingly fascinated and increasingly daunted. Apparently—well—

Perhaps I should simply reproduce that part of the proposal.

XXV

2: The Plan for the Book:

THE TEXT, as I now envisage it, will have five major divisions. Part I will be an account of the rise of the "problem of mind" as a result of the early modern triumph of the mechanical philosophy and, in time, of the late modern dominance of the philosophical naturalism that was its inevitable sequel. As inheritors of a picture of reality shaped by this mechanistic metaphysics, we today are confronted by an altogether preposterous dilemma when we attempt to make sense of the reality of unified consciousness or intentional mental acts or a host of other mental phenomena. Within the mechanical narrative, matter is mindless mass, and physical causality mindless force, and so the presence—or apparent presence—within nature of such things as, say, conceptual abstractions or volitions or final purposes creates a theoretical problem that seems to allow of only two possible solutions: either some version of Cartesian dualism (in which the body is a machine centrally operated by an immaterial homunculus called the "soul") or a thoroughgoing mechanical monism (in which mind is an emergent result or epiphenomenon of unguided physical events). And naturally many materialist philosophers or neuroscientists assume that, if they can only dispose of the Cartesian soul once and for all, they will have by default established the supremacy of the physicalist position; and assume also that to accomplish this they need only find instances in which the brain operates without immediately conscious supervision on the part of any purely rational and cognizant agency within—moments, that is, when the homunculus appears to be asleep at the controls. For then, they imagine, they will have proved that everything, mind included, is only a form of mechanism after all, and no Wonderful Wizard is to be found on the other side of the screen, pulling the levers. The mechanistic paradigms within which they operate condemn them to an inescapable binary choice: if they are not to believe in a ghost mysteriously animating a machine then they must make themselves believe in a machine miraculously generating a ghost.

There is, of course, a history here. The extraordinary fruitfulness of modern scientific method was achieved, before all else, by a severe narrowing of investigative focus; and this involved the willful shedding of an older language of causality that possessed great richness, but that also seemed to resist empirical investigation. The first principle of the new organon was a negative one: the exclusion from scientific investigations of any consideration of possible formal and final causes, and even of a distinct principle of "life," in favor of an ideally inductive method, supposedly purged of metaphysical prejudices, according to which all natural systems were to be conceived as mere machine processes, and all real causality as exchanges of energy between material masses. Everything physical became, in a sense, reducible to the mechanics of local motion; even complex organic order came to be understood as the purely emergent result of physical forces moving through time from past to future as if through Newtonian space. Everything came to be regarded as ultimately reducible to the most basic level of material existence, and to the mathematically calculable physical consequences of purely physical antecedent causes. And while at first many of the thinkers of early modernity were content to draw brackets around material nature, and to allow for the existence of realities beyond the physical—mind, soul, disembodied spirits, God—they necessarily imagined these latter as being essentially extrinsic to the purely mechanical order that they animated, inhabited, or created. Thus, in place of classical theism's metaphysics of participation in a God of infinite being and rationality, these thinkers granted room only for the adventitious and finite Cosmic Mechanic or Supreme Being of Deism or (as it is called today) Intelligent Design Theory. And, in place of the spiritual soul of antique thought, they allowed for only Cartesian dualism's "ghost in the machine." But, of course, even the constrained ontological liberality of this compromise was unsustainable. Reason abhors a dualism. Any ultimate ground of explanation must be one that unites all dimensions of being in a simpler, more conceptually parsimonious principle, capable of reconciling any apparent antinomies. Soul and body could not continue indefinitely to coexist as utterly distinct principles in only accidental alliance, especially given that only the latter fell within the province of the new strictly inductive sciences. Thus, inevitably, what began as method soon metastasized into a metaphysics, almost by inadvertence. For a truly scientific view of reality, it came to be believed, everything—even mind—must be reducible to one and the same mechanics of motion. Those methodological brackets that had been so helpfully drawn around the physical order now became the very shape of reality itself; beyond them lay, by definition, absolutely nothing.

It was always something of a fantasy, of course. For one thing, even as a method, the mechanical model could extend only so far. Pure induction is an impossible ideal. In the life sciences, for instance, organisms can only very rarely be investigated without any hypothetical appeals whatsoever to purpose, or without treating organic structures as intentional systems; and only metaphysical prejudice dictates that this purposive language is no more than a useful and dispensable fiction. Moreover, before "higher causes" like form and finality could be excised from the grammar of the sciences, they had first to be radically misconstrued. Even such residual Aristotelian terminology as remained in the sciences had already, by the late sixteenth century, been mechanized, so to speak. Form and finality had come to be seen as physical forces or influences extrinsic to a material substrate that in itself was not the pure potentiality of prime matter but merely a universal, subtle, ductile, unarticulated physical substance. The elements of nature were not imagined, as they had been in the classical and mediaeval synthesis, as having an intrinsic disposition toward order or vital integrity; they were seen simply as inert ingredients upon which formal determinations were adventitiously impressed, under the external guidance of final causes that operated merely as factitious designs. And so, seen thus, form and finality soon came to seem not only superfluous suppositions, but little more than features of an inferior and obsolete mechanical model.

One cannot, however, really reject something one does not understand. Neither Aristotle's concept of an "*aitia*," nor any scholastic concept of a "*causa*," actually corresponds to what we—following our early modern predecessors—mean when we speak of a "cause." A better rendering of "*aitiai*" or "*causae*," in the ancient or mediaeval sense, might be "explanations," "rationales," "logical descriptions," or (still better) "rational relations." The older fourfold nexus of causality was not, that is to say, a defective attempt at modern physical science, but was instead chiefly a grammar of predication, describing the inherent logical structure of anything that exists insofar as it exists, and reflecting a world in which things and events are at once discretely identifiable and yet part of the larger dynamic continuum of the whole. It was a simple logical picture of a reality in which both stability and change can be recognized and designated. And these *aitiai* or *causae* were intrinsic and indiscerptibly integral relations, distinct dimensions of a single causal logic, not separated forces in extrinsic relation to one another. A final cause, for instance, was an inherent natural end, not an adventitiously imposed design; and this was true even when teleology involved external uses rather than merely internal perfections (as in the case of human artifacts); it was at once a thing's internal fullness and its external participation in the totality of nature. In a sense, a causal *relation* in this scheme is less like a physical interaction or exchange of energy than it is like a mathematical equation, or like the syntax of a coherent sentence. Admittedly, this is a picture of reality that comes from ages in which it was assumed that the structure of the world was analogous to the structure of rational thought. But, then again, this was an eminently logical assumption, if only because there appears to be a more than illusory or accidental reciprocal openness between mind and world, and because the mind appears genuinely able to penetrate the physical order by way of irreducibly noetic practices like mathematics and logic and systematic observation.

Part II will be a consideration of various difficulties that the modern picture of the world creates for the philosophy of mind. Once nature had been reconceived as essentially mindless, precisely through the methodological exclusion of anything analogous to mind from our understanding of the structure of physical reality, the attempt to reintegrate the phenomena of mental life into our picture of nature became entirely hopeless. And once every attempt at physical explanation has been exhausted (see below), only two possible courses appear to remain, both of which are arguably absurd in their own terms: either total eliminativism, according to which consciousness and all its properties are illusions; or a physicalist panpsychism, which understands consciousness as a kind of property simply present in all material states, in varying degrees of cumulative complexity.

Here, I shall begin by making it clear that current neurophysiological attempts to account for mental phenomena—while they may provide an ever more comprehensive and precise catalogue of correspondences between brain events and certain mental states—necessarily fail to disclose any plausible causal connection between those third-person descriptions and those first-person experiences. I shall then address many of the classic impediments to a physicalist philosophy of mind: *qualia* or qualitative consciousness as such, which is to say first-person sensuous intuition, immediate impressions, and self-awareness; abstract concepts, not only as features of thought, but as the indispensable conditions of thought; language and its irreducible syntactic and semantic properties, which it seems impossible credibly to explain in purely physical evolutionary terms; the syntax and semantics of acts of reason, or of any mental acts whose internal connections appear to be conceptual or logical rather than merely physical; the unified field of experience and thought, which seems impossible to reconcile with the composite nature of physical structures and functions; mental intentionality—intrinsic intentionality, to use the technical term—which for any number of reasons (principally, its irreducibly teleological structure) seems irreconcilable with a mechanical or physicalist account of mind.

This part of the book will also deal with the inadequacy—increasingly acknowledged even by "naturalist" philosophers of mind—of many of the standard attempts to close the gap between physical third-person descriptions and first-person descriptions of consciousness and thought. Often, in fact, these attempts at explanation turn out simply to be ways of restating the problem without solving it, as is the case with most theories of "supervenience." At other times, they simply reduce first-person phenomena to irrelevancy without actually explaining anything, as in the case of "epiphenomenalism." Sometimes, they are simply defective analogies, based on basic category errors, as in the case of "computational" models of mind. And, in general, there seems as yet to be nothing approaching a coherent account of how mental phenomena *emerge* from physical events (however closely associated with those events they may be).

In part, this is because of the inherently nebulous nature of the very concept of "emergence" or "emergent properties" as it is used in the sciences today, in either evolutionary biology or neuroscience. All too often, talk of "emergence" merely provides a convenient way of evading problems without appearing to have done so. It is, admittedly, a beguilingly simple idea—the notion that there are in nature composite realities whose peculiar properties and capacities emerge from the interaction of their elements, even though these properties and capacities do not reside in those elements themselves. An emergent whole, in other words, is more than—or at any rate different from—the sum of its parts; it is not simply the consequence of an accumulation of discrete powers added together in a sum, but the effect of a specific ordering of relations among those powers that produces something entirely new within nature. And this idea is quite true in a general sense; but it is also a limited truth in many crucial senses. For, if it is to close the devilish explanatory gap between mechanism and mind, the model of emergence employed must somehow entail the appearance of new physical realities that, even though they remain dependent upon the native properties of the elements composing them, nevertheless possess characteristics entirely *irreducible* to those properties. But this makes no sense. At least, as a claim made solely about physical processes, organisms, and structures in purely material terms it cannot possibly be true. From a physical perspective, emergent properties cannot be discontinuous from the properties of the prior causes from which they arise; anything, in principle, must be reducible, by a series of "geometrical" steps, to the physical attributes of its ingredients. Water, for example, is composed of two very combustible gaseous elements, hydrogen and oxygen, and yet it possesses the novel property of liquidity and a capacity for extinguishing fire. But, while these new properties are not *identical* with any properties resident in either hydrogen or oxygen molecules, they are most definitely *reducible* to those special molecular properties that, in a particular combination, cause hydrogen and oxygen to negate one another's combustible propensities and gaseous structures. So long as this is all that is meant by "emergence," then the concept is as inoffensive as it is obvious.

Problems arise, however, when the concept is asked to explain away causal gaps in nature that more closely resemble the difference between, say, the physical elements from which a computer is composed and that computer's functions. True enough, a computer is composed wholly of silicon, metal, plastic, electrical impulses, and so forth, and yet its operations are not only not present in any of its discrete parts, but are qualitatively different from any mere aggregation of the properties of those parts. But this is because a computer's functions do not emerge from its physical ingredients at all. What distinguishes its powers from those individually possessed by its various material elements is not any *emergent* property, but rather the causal influence of a creative intellect acting upon those elements from without. So, while it is true that nothing that characterizes a computer physically is anything more than a mathematically predictable result of certain physical antecedents, those operations that actually involve computing in the full sense have been imposed upon the computer's physical constituents by a further, more eminent, formal causality (itself directed by a final causality). At the purely material level, whatever is truly emergent is also reducible to that from which it emerges; otherwise, "emergence" is merely the name of some kind of magical transition between intrinsically disparate realities.

Hence, as I have said, the two most extreme options for dealing with the problem of mind in the terms provided by the modern metaphysics of nature—total eliminativism and physicalist panpsychism—are really the only ones not precluded by the limits of the logic of emergence. But both, alas, suffer from conceptual and logical problems of their own. Eliminativism asks us to entertain the idea that consciousness can be an illusion despite the phenomenologically verifiable reality of consciousness as normally conceived, and despite the inconvenient reality that an "illusion of consciousness"—being an intentional state embraced within a unified field of apprehension and experienced by a self-aware affective subject— would have to be a "consciousness of illusion." Logical circles tend not to advance one's argument. Panpsychism, meanwhile, understood as a purely *physicalist* (rather than classically idealist) doctrine, answers no questions; it merely defers the question to the subatomic level, in the vain hope that it may grow so very small that it will vanish away altogether. But we end up with the same paradox: one and the same atom (say) possesses two contradictory aspects, each of which is the logical inversion of the other—in Kantian terms, the nomological and the pathological. One side of the thing (that bound by physical laws) is mechanistic and empirical, the other (that possessed of qualitative awareness) is teleological and transcendental. The interaction between the two sides is no less mysterious for being atomized. And this is no less true when panpsychism is supplemented by the quantitative "science" of Integrated Information Theory (as proposed by Giulio Tononi). There is, moreover, the not inconsiderable problem that consciousness is not really a "property" in any coherent sense, the way that mass or velocity is: an invariant "fact about" a discrete substance or event that may have different effects (in the case of mass, for instance, according to the degree to which it is subject to gravity), but that is otherwise simply another way of describing that substance or event. Consciousness is nothing like that. It exists not as a quality or mode or accident of something else, but only and always as a specific kind of act, phenomenologically describable but not reducible to any physical or intrinsic "state" apart from the activity itself. It exists, that is, as a kind of agency, which is to say that every event of consciousness is an action attributable to an agent. This consideration leads to:

Part III, which will attempt to ask the question of mind anew, this time from a more properly phenomenological point of departure. If we begin from an entirely unprejudiced examination of mental acts—what consciousness "does," how intentionality "works," how unity and diversity become manifest within the mind's "field" of operation, and so forth—we find that there is no clear boundary between the contours of the mind's operations and those of the world as it appears within consciousness. The conditions necessary for knowledge of the world and the conditions necessary for the world's existence as an object of knowledge at any number of vital points seem insensibly to merge into a single reality. Most striking in this regard is the way in which the world, as perceived under the conditions of the mind's necessary unity of apprehension, depends upon the mind's constant intentional reference to a final horizon of intelligibility that can be characterized only as transcendental. Neither that simplicity nor that ultimacy is a reality that can be found within nature as a closed totality, and certainly neither appears consistent with any physicalist theory of the world; and yet only by virtue of both realities at once, in indissoluble unity with one another, does nature have any kind of comprehensible existence for us as a phenomenon available to the intending intellect. It is only between these two indispensable and enduring extra-natural poles—the unity of the apprehending mind, the transcendental finality of the intending mind—that nature takes shape as a distinct reality, at once infinitely diverse and irreducibly unified. Every movement of the conscious and intending mind toward any finite end is an act at once of recognition, evaluation, judgment, and choice, all of which are possible for the mind by virtue of its own more primordial, more tacit, more unremitting preoccupation with that transcendental horizon that gives all finite things their meanings and their identities for us. All the objects and moments of experience, and all their relations and disjunctions and coordinations and successions, and every meaning, conceptual possibility, or purpose attaching to them are available to the mind only as embraced within and illuminated by that anticipation of the ultimate object of desire (the good, the true, the beautiful…). And that horizon, obviously enough, consists in a set of abstract perfections that are, as absolute objects of the rational will, at once both noetic and ontological. They are, to revert to the terms of a very venerable metaphysical tradition, the "names of God": words used to indicate (but not, certainly, describe) the most original and most ultimate ground of reality, which is at once infinite being and infinite mind. One need not believe, I imagine, that these concepts have an actual objective reference; but, even so, one must recognize that our minds possess a world that can be experienced, interpreted, and understood only in and by their implicit and inexhaustible engagement with a supernatural order of meaning. This being so, it seems only rational to grant that the reality of such an order would at the very least provide us with an explanation for the curious and otherwise inexplicable fact of the transparency of mind and world to one another. If, after all, that were nothing but an extrinsic relation, some kind of fortuitous harmony, then it would constitute the most remarkable—and yet the most ubiquitous and constant—coincidence of qualitative incommensurables imaginable. Why, then, ought we assume any real causal discontinuity between the world's being and the mind's knowing of the world? At some point, surely, it becomes impossible not to wonder whether the only properly empirical approach to the question of mental reality should begin with a radically different kind of methodological bracketing: one that suspends every presupposition regarding a real distinction between epistemology and ontology.

At least, we should never simply assume that being and consciousness are ever truly severable from one another. Could something exist, for instance, in such a manner that it could not be perceived or thought about in any way at all, not even by itself, even in principle? In what sense would it be distinct from absolute nothingness? It certainly seems reasonable to say that being is manifestation, that real subsistence is revelation, that to exist is to be perceptible, conceivable, knowable—and that, moreover, to exist fully is to be manifest to consciousness. If there were a universe in which consciousness did not exist, in what sense precisely would that universe itself exist? Certainly not as a fully articulated spatial and temporal reality filled with clearly discrete objects, like the universe that exists in our minds. The reality we find present in our thoughts, in which intensities and densities and durations and successions are arranged in such magnificently complex but diverse order, exists only relative to consciousness; at the phenomenal level—the level of reality as it appears to intentional awareness—nothing would exist at all. In itself, if it had any reality in itself, this "mindless" universe would be only a plenum or totality of indeterminate quantum potentialities. It would be something quite different from the extended reality of space and time known to us. Even then, it seems fair to say that if such a universe did in some sense exist, it would do so exactly to the extent that it *could* be known to consciousness of some kind. There is no such thing as ontological coherence that is not a *rational* coherence. There is a point then, arguably, at which being and intelligibility become conceptually indistinguishable. It is only as an intelligible order, as a coherent phenomenon, that anything is anything at all, whether an elementary particle or a universe; perhaps it is true that only what could in principle be known can in actuality exist. So, at any rate, we have to believe. The rational desire to know the truth of things, in every sphere, is sustained by a tacit faith in some kind of ultimate coincidence or convertibility between being and consciousness. That natural orientation of the mind toward a horizon of total intelligibility mentioned above—that natural intellectual appetite for truth— requires us to venture all our labors of understanding on the assumption that rational thought and coherent order are two sides of a single reality, or at least somehow naturally fitted to one another. If we believe that the structure of reality can truly be mirrored in the structure of our thinking, then we must also believe that there is an ideal or purely intelligible dimension of reality that really corresponds to the categories and concepts that allow us to understand the world. We must believe that being in itself is pure intelligibility.

Part IV will take this line of reasoning perhaps as far as it can go and attempt to demonstrate that every act of conscious, unified, intentional mind is necessarily dependent upon infinite mind— which is to say, God. If the argument of Part III is correct, then the whole of what we know as nature appears in the interval between two transcendental realities: the apperceptive unity of intentional consciousness and the teleological universality of being as total intelligibility. This is the structure of thought; and so the whole world of nature occurs between two poles that cannot be fitted within the naturalist picture. As Part II has argued, the logical and ontological priority of neither pole admits of a materialist solution, even though the material order is constituted as an intelligible totality *only* by the relation between them. Thus the physicalist continuum is broken open at both ends, experience of the "natural" proves to be the gift of "super-natural" knowledge, and a certain set of metaphysical questions inevitably pose themselves. Chiefly, we should ask whether this *ordo cognoscendi* must be (as one ancient deduction of reason insists) an inversion of the ultimate *ordo essendi*, and whether this relation between subjective unity of consciousness and its (gnoseological) end in the fullness of transcendent being is a glimpse—caught in the looking glass of rational reflection—of the real relation between transcendent being as original source and the subject as its (ontological) end.

If in fact world and mind really are open to one another in this way, then once more it seems we should accord a certain causal priority to mind over matter in our picture of reality. If the materialist understanding of nature were essentially correct, it would be difficult enough to account for the existence of consciousness; but it would be far more difficult still to say how consciousness, in all its exorbitant difference from the purposeless welter of physical causality, could actually capture the truth of physical reality in the exquisite trammels of its concepts. Yet it certainly seems that, in abstracting experience into various kinds of ideal content—formal, mathematical, moral, aesthetic, and so on—the mind really does extract knowledge from what would otherwise be nothing but meaningless brute events. In fact, reality becomes more intelligible to us the more we are able to translate it into purely mental concepts, and to arrange it under categories, and then to arrange our concepts under ever simpler, more comprehensive, more unconditioned concepts, always ascending towards the simplest and most capacious concept our minds can reach. To say that something has become entirely intelligible to us is to say that we have an *idea* of it that is both comprehensively simple as an explanatory principle and that also leaves no empirical or conceptual remainder behind. It is to say, in accord with so much classical and mediaeval thought, that the ideal and intrinsically intelligible dimension of things is not only a real property of their existence, but in some sense is identical with their existence.

What is an idea, however, other than the expression of a rational intentionality? And how, therefore, could being be pure intelligibility if it were not also pure intelligence? Surely, something has to be said for Bernard Lonergan's famous argument that the "unrestricted intelligibility" of reality leads thought to God as the one "unrestricted act of understanding." As the mind moves towards an ever more comprehensive and "supereminent" grasp of reality, it necessarily moves towards an ideal level of reality at which intelligibility and intelligence are no longer distinguishable: for what is the ideal other than the known? The mind can be a true mirror of objective reality because we assume that objective reality is already a mirror of mind. The ascent towards ever greater knowledge is, if only tacitly, an ascent towards an ultimate encounter with limitless consciousness, limitless reason, a transcendent reality where being and knowledge are always already one and the same, and so inalienable from one another.

Perhaps, then, the best definition of mind is "a restricted instance of that unrestricted act": like light captured in and refracted by a prism, being—which is consciousness—expresses itself in the faceted finitude of our natures. But it is God in himself who is the logical order of all reality, the ground both of the subjective rationality of mind and the objective rationality of being, the transcendent and indwelling Reason or Wisdom by which mind and matter are both informed and in which both participate. If indeed to exist is to be manifest—to be intelligible and perceptible—and if to exist fully is to be consciously known, then God, as infinite being, is also an act of infinite knowledge. He is in himself the absolute unity of consciousness and being, and so in the realm of contingent things is the source of the fittedness of consciousness and being each to the other, the one ontological reality of reason as it exists both in thought and in the structure of the universe. Thus, when one looks inward, towards that vanishing point of unity that makes the whole of mental life possible, one looks—as all contemplative traditions insist—towards the source and ground of the mind, the simplicity of God, the one ground of both consciousness and being. More inward to consciousness than consciousness itself is that *scintilla* or spark of divine light that imparts life and truth to the soul; and the mind's interior journey towards its own wellspring brings it to a place where it finds itself utterly dependent upon the sublime simplicity of God's knowledge of all things in his knowledge of himself.

And thus also, when one looks outward, towards the world, one looks towards that same source, that same unity of being and intelligibility. So, whether one looks outward or inward, the soul looks upon the soul; or, to say the same thing from the opposite angle, being looks upon being; and thus—in either case—one encounters God in his self-disclosure.

In short, the structure of all thought is a relation of the mind to God. In fact, teleologically considered, the mind *is* God, striving not only to see—but to become—infinite knowledge of infinite being, beyond any distinction between knower and known. Which may be one way of saying that, as the *Māṇḍūkya Upaniṣad* tells us, *Ayam Ātmā Brahma*: Ātman is Brahman. It may be that this is the first and most obvious of the truths of reason.

Thus Part V will argue that the only "science of mind" that could actually disclose the nature of the mental in its own intrinsic aspect would be something like the contemplative discipline proper to the great mystical traditions of the world's religions. There can be no real science of mind that is not, in fact, a spiritual science. This part of the text, however, I cannot really summarize, except to say that it will draw on Christian, Jewish, Muslim, Hindu, Buddhist, Platonist, and other contemplative sources to describe the real experience of a final coincidence of being and knowing in God or the transcendent ground of all: the experience, that is, of that place where "Hie ist gotes grunt mìn grunt unde mìn grunt gotes grunt" (as Eckhart says), and where *nous* finds itself at home in its divine source (as Plotinus says), and where one knows God to be at once *interior intimo meo* and *superior summo meo* (as Augustine says), and where delimited being (*al-wujûd al-muqayyad*) returns to its wellspring in the Nondelimited Being (*al-wujûd al-mutlaq*) of the divine light (as ibn Qunawi says), and where the "secret soul" (*ruh sirr*) within us is revealed as the eternal breath (*ruh*) of God, breathed into us in creation. It is here that the unity of mind, in its teleological co-extensiveness with all of reality, meets the unity of being, and we discover that the irreducibility of mind to physical causes and the irreducibility of being to physical events are one and the same irreducibility.

XXVI

"How far did you get before falling asleep?" that warm, familiar, positively satiny voice asked me, so close to my ear that I could feel the hot breath issuing from his lips.

I opened my eyes. The last of the daylight lingered in the cloudless sky overhead as a wan, watery glow, and when I briefly tilted my head toward the west I saw that the horizon was smoldering pink and vermilion in the wake of the departed sun. It would be dark very soon. Adjusting the chair so that I could sit upright, allowing the stapled pages of the proposal to slip from my chest to the ground in the process, I turned to look at Roland. He was sitting perhaps no more than three feet away, sniffing at the empty porcelain mug lying on its side in the grass near my feet. "I finished reading the description of the book," I murmured. "Intimidatingly ambitious for a single year's research."

"It amazes me," he remarked, not yet lifting his snout from the mug, "that you can consume that much coffee of that strength and still drowse off in less than half an hour." He raised his head and stared at me with something of a droll smirk. "Really, if you've so inured your physiology to the effects of caffeine that it might as well be a soporific, you've probably been overdoing it."

"I can't deny it," I said.

"If you could only learn to drink properly," he added, "lapping the liquid from a bowl rather than pouring it down your throat without measure or check, you'd find it easier to control your indulgence. It's unseemly."

"I'd burn my tongue," I protested.

"Not if you exercised a little restraint," said Roland, a touch primly. "Everything done with style is done with care."

"Well, it can't be all that uncouth. After all, Mama also…"

"She's refined it to a level of elegant artistry," Roland immediately interrupted, "with that angelic gracefulness she brings to everything. You, by contrast, just fling it back like an agitated ape, with no sense of proportion or poise. There's no comparison."

"Now, look…"

"I'm just offering some constructive criticism," he said. "Nothing more. Anyway, that's as may be. What I wanted to say is: Don't fret about the proposal. The rest of the text makes it clear that you anticipate working on only the first two parts of the planned book during your fellowship. And, as far as content goes, I think you'll see that the language is all yours. I simply gathered the scattered pieces together."

"I can't deny that," I agreed, bending forward to scratch him behind his ears.

This, for a moment, distracted him. "Ah… ah, yes," he said, closing his eyes, lifting his snout, and pressing his head back against my fingertips. "Yes, just there," he added with a small groan of pleasure. This continued for several seconds, until I wearied of sitting forward so awkwardly and stopped. He lowered his snout, opened his eyes, and stared at me quizzically. "You aren't finished, are you?" he asked after a moment.

"Well, it's my lungs, you see," I replied. "If I lean over like that for too long, especially in this damned lawn chair, it becomes hard to breathe."

A doleful frown crossed his face. "If I could make you well with a magical wave of my tail, I would."

"I know."

"Let's just enjoy the sunset, then."

I looked again to the west, which was now soaked in a deep, wine-dark blush, rimmed by a faint, glassy green. Then I looked to the east, where the sky was already a lush beryl blue above the red and violet glow of the city's skyline. "It's lovely, isn't it?"

"Yes," he said quietly.

"I wish you could see it with my eyes," I remarked a few moments later, looking up directly into the darkening sky.

There followed nearly half a minute of silence, in which I intuited something of a chill. At last, in a definitely brusque tone, Roland asked, "And what, pray tell, do you mean by that?"

I looked down to see him staring back at me with narrowed eyes and pursed lips. "I only meant," I said, "that dogs have a smaller range of color perception than humans, and so a good deal of what you would see as... as, you know, shades of gray I can see in... richly varied hues."

"And what makes you think that?" he asked, turning away.

"Well..." I shrugged. "Well, you know, it all has to do with the number of rods and cones in the eyes, and the neurological..."

Now Roland emitted one of those unsettlingly strangled laughs of his and shook his head in amusement. He looked back at me with an expression of glee on his face. "How on earth can you make an error as elementary as that?" he said. "How can you fall into the banalities of mechanistic thinking when you've just undertaken to write an attack on the fallacy of *any* mechanistic philosophy of mind?" Now open mirth yielded to a look of gently whimsical affection. "Rods and cones, forsooth. Surely you know that there's no coherent causal narrative regarding the relationship between the physiological apparatus of perception and the qualia perceived by an intending mind."

"Yes, of course," I said, "but you don't know what it is to see as I see, and..."

"Nor do you know what it is to see as I do. But it's a crude assumption that the mechanical construction of my ophthalmic equipment or the neural wiring of my cerebral cortices *causes* a particular state of qualitative consciousness. In fact, we know that there's no obvious causal logic there linking the phenomena to the apparatus of perception. Your neurologists and brain scientists, God love them, know only certain indices of correlation between those celestially blue eyes of yours and any given set of visual qualia. But correlation, to cite the formidable old maxim, is not causation. And the fact is that the brain perceives nothing. *You*, as an agent with a mind, do the perceiving, using your brain and your pupils and ciliary bodies and vitreous humors and lenses and retinas and conjunctivas and maculas and optic nerves..."

"But surely," I interjected, "it's not unreasonable to assume that the medium employed affects the final result."

"Yes," he replied with a deep sigh, plainly attempting to master his impatience, "but how it affects the result is dependent upon how it's used by the poetic powers of the agent intellect. Look, if your brain were the subject of your visual perceptions, then you should see the world upside down, since that's the way it's projected on the screens at the back of your little optical cinemas. And you would see far less than you do, since the images would be full of gaps and fragmentations and odd deliquescences of lines. Really, they wouldn't really be images at all, but just a flood of neural excitations never resolving into the much richer portrait your mind paints of reality. But, of course, your *brain* sees nothing. Neither does it *use* the information it receives from the world. *You* see, *you* use your eyes and brain, *you* interpret the manifest forms of the world under the corresponding spiritual forms of thought. Consciousness is inseparable from intentionality. There's no purely passive experience. So how do you know what my mind does in using the fragmentary and empty sensory information supplied by my organic implements when it's painting in the qualia of visual perception? For all you know, the world I see is far richer and immeasurably more chromatically varied than yours. I may see a world absolutely drenched in intensities and diversities of color far beyond your intentional spectrum. My artist's palette may be immeasurably more saturated in colors than yours, just as the atelier in which I compose my daily masterpieces may be flooded with far clearer and more abundant light. Compared to what I see, your tiny, constrained, miserable slice of reality might be as impoverished as any squirrel's."

At this, I could not help but wrinkle my brow and look at him somewhat askance. "Wait a moment; given what you've just said, how can you know what a squirrel…?"

"It's obvious," he said sharply. "Just… just *watch* them. Anyway, it's also possible that the qualitative consciousness that *attends* your physical visual sensations in this world isn't really a feat of constructive representation—a symbolic translation of stimuli into a private picture of a world that exists only within your skull—but is instead actually a direct communion in the ontological and noetic forms of things, and that we see one and the same world, you and I, because our spirits are looking not at sensations but at reality, and the physical transaction between the world and our optic apparatus is just the occasion for an act of discovery and unveiling that is, in reality, an event of direct spiritual communion."

157

"Yes, I suppose…"

"Of course, we know that that's not quite true. I mean, we've established that I actually see far more than you do. But I think that has to do with intentionality, not with… *equipment.*"

"We've established that?" I asked. "That you see more than I do, I mean?"

Roland nodded morosely. "If you recall, you find it very hard to see fairies, whereas I find it all but impossible not to see them. That being so—even if it's a matter of spiritual intentionality rather than the acuity of your perceptual apparatus—it seems very reasonable to assume you also see far fewer differentiations of hue."

"I take your point," I said.

"Our souls are prisms, you know," he added enigmatically, and then looked away toward the darkening west.

"What do you mean?" I finally asked when it became clear he had no intention of elaborating on this unbidden.

"I mean," he said, still gazing away—further away, it seemed to me, than merely to the horizon—"that at the highest level of transcendental apperception, to use the Kantian jargon, there's a kind of sublime anonymity to the mind's activity. There—well, let's call it instead the level of *nous* or spirit or *ātman*—there we're all one and the same in a sense. There's a kind of indistinction of indiscernibles in that first impulse of the mind outward toward the world, an identity before the act of knowing is specified and individuated by its association with *this* soul or *that*, engaged in *this* moment and place and series of perceptions. We're usually unaware of that silent, self-effacing companion to all our thoughts and intuitions and finite intentions, but it's there. It's *I* more deeply than the ego is I, and so it's *you* also. But now and then we do recall it, in moments of benign dissociation—you know, that oceanic experience of the ego's dissolution into fuller existence, known by puppies in periods of pure, unreflective play, or by mystics swept up into the erotic ecstasy of divine union, or by coyote adepts—when the spirit partially detaches itself from the fleeting fascinations of the empirical ego and knows itself as the pure 'I think,' an event of absolute unity, potentially infinite in extent but still bound in this life to the soul. And the soul, being embedded in nature and animating the body and uniting spirit to flesh, is the prism that irisates the light of being into the private experiences of this person or that person, this dog or that rabbit or that ape. There's where the differences arise in our ability to see—in the facets of the soul... and in its fractures."

"I know," I said quietly. "At least, I think I do. I think I remember sometimes... when I'm not quite awake or quite sleeping..."

Roland nodded sagely. "The sunset is lovely." Then he smiled. "And you and I are seeing it together, and somewhere it's seen in us without any veils, without any... prismations. There's no final distinction between being and consciousness, because the world exists in being known, and principally as it's known there in that place where all the barriers between mind and world fall away. Everything is fuller there. Spirit is much stronger—much more substantial—than the flesh. These perishable, mortal frames we inhabit—they're the most ghostly part of us in reality—just shadows cast on the dark waters of matter. And matter, of course... well, it's not so much illusory as the early Berkeley thought, but as the Aristotelians and Neoplatonists and the late Berkeley thought, it's nothing but potency waiting to emerge into formal actuality... it's an ideal function... a mirror of spirit... a canvas for that inner artist who's always composing the world, participating in that infinite Spirit that composes all things in himself..." His voice trailed away into silence.

"Do many dogs see things that way?" I asked after a few moments.

"Among my kind, it's no more than common sense."

Night had fully fallen. The stars were all but invisible above the infernal glow of the city, and no moon was up in the sky; but there was enough of the sickly glare of the streetlights along the avenue behind our garden, rising above the small single-level houses there, for me still to make out Roland's form, and even something of the serene expression he now turned on me.

"Incidentally, I printed out two of your great uncle's poems and left them on your desk," he said. "I'm simply putting the last of his early œuvre in order. The first one's love poetry—or the poetry of passion, really. I think he wrote it for Deirdre—indeed, I know he did from remarks written in the margins of a few of the 'variorum' drafts—but he was discreet enough to call her by another name. Helen, in fact."

"Is it any good?" I asked.

"Tastes vary," said Roland after a pause. "And I think that… the tragedy struck before he worked the verses into final form. Still, I'd appreciate your opinion."

"On what?"

"On whether they read like verse written in the throes of blissful carnal rapture or like lines composed in a state of romantic desperation. Not being a primate myself, I'm at something of a disadvantage in making sense of their general atmosphere. We dogs don't tend to be quite as quixotic as your kind about… *les affaires du cœur*."

"All right," I murmured, stretching out my legs. "I'll have a look as soon as I can."

"The other one," he added, "is either more mysterious or less. I'll await your judgment on that as well."

I must have drifted off into sleep again, however, because the next voice I heard was not Roland's but rather my son's, rousing me and telling me that I should come inside for dinner. And, when I opened my eyes, I saw that the moon, in its waxing gibbous aspect, was now well above the horizon.

XXVII

THE TWO POEMS were not, as it happens, particularly good. I am not certain that the first of them could even be characterized as a single poem, so much as a surrender to the incorrigible fragmentariness of an inspiration that had proved resistant to translation into a finished totality, and that could be expressed ultimately only as a collection of abortive attempts at either a beginning or an ending. It also seemed very much like the work of a young man tangled in the meshes of his own disaffection and confusion, and trying to find an idiom that would neither trivialize nor absurdly aggrandize his melancholy. At least, those were my impressions on reading it in my office later that night—three reproduced pages, in that familiar hand, bearing a date that told me that Aloysius had been only twenty when he wrote it—and so, at the foot of the final page, I wrote: "Unhappy, struggling with emotions he was too young to understand, perhaps, but definitely in love. Not a very finished poem. I think he used the line about faithfulness and belief—or something like it—elsewhere." Whether I was making notes for myself or for Roland I did not bother to consider, since I think I had ceased by that point to care quite where the demarcation between dreams and waking consciousness should be drawn, or even whether the distinction was worth making.

Twelve Invocations of Helen

I

So we make our uncertain way
In lands where moonlight is too fierce
And burns your fair, bare morbidezza
Like phosphor in the desert chill.
Dear woman, so unmade by frailties,

161

Roland in Moonlight

So undone in terrible hours,
Stay near me in this emptiness
And aching cold: where we sow life,
This desert can be made a garden.

II

Your white pelisse, sloughed off and shapeless,
Lies on the floor where you shed it
To emerge newborn: the strange beauty
Of spirit, the soul's strong carnal glory...

III

To see you writhe in troubled dreams,
There across the room, wounds me; I've
No strength to pose against your pain,
Or all that gentle brokenness.

IV

O woman of the heartless night, the waves,
The gelid moon, I cannot find words for
The sadness of white sails slackened and
Cold in their stillness upon the gray waters—
White against the gray, white against the green—
As if the wind might never blow again.

V

The storm having now abated, the hell
Of countless solitudes revives in me...

Out toward your strange sorrow moves the will
Through the penitential fires of regret;
And all the wakened creatures of the mind
Keep silence and await one gentle word...

By this alone a man can live—or die.

CITY

VI

I am transfigured in you, lady, for
In you I am made part of that one being,
That strong, composite, mystic animal,
From which liberation were an exile,
And freedom a perpetual regret.

VII

You are my occasion, lady. We flirt
With demons at the edge of nothingness,
And yet are graced with wisdom, hope, and pleasure
In these preoccupations of the flesh.

VIII

Should I now strike a pose, nobly erect,
Bearing the remnants of my sorrows in
My arms, while evening's purple shadows crown
The marble pallor of my brow? Might I
      Impress you, tragic and aloof?

I think not. But your form, glass in the moonlight,
Draws near to me, floating on the night's blue.
Angelic phantom, ghostly visitant,
Will you absolve my sins and then submit
      To both forgiveness and desire?

IX

We wake to the white of January's sun:
Not summer's sultry yellow simmering,
That humid, viscid, slow gold drip of light
On light. We wake to bright, dry whiteness, flat
And fringed in blue and chilly pink, and shape
Most feminine…
      My words still fail this theme,

Roland in Moonlight

This bleak and splintered light, this yielding joy,
Preserving us from morning's cold abyss.

X

And now I am more lost for love of you
Than some poor madman roaming in a maze;
The *terra incognita* of your soul
Is filled with perilous and frightful ways,

And all the fabled promise of my days
Is lost in exploration of your grief.
One hardens into love, but cannot praise
A faithfulness so drained of true belief.

XI

Balloons of August bear you off
To drought- and famine-stricken lands;
The dark of fairgrounds, empty, still,
Will pass beneath your outstretched hands.
Bewildered, we will see you go—
Will know your journey to be long—
And you more powerful than night
And tenderer than any song.

XII

Your many forms are but one form
That love cannot recall nor hope
Abstract; your flesh is pure presence,
        Being beyond being.

What you have given, rendered up
In palpable and finite shape,
Is boundless, has no name, and so
        Must bear your name.

CITY

As I have said, probably not a finished piece. A handful of frac-
tured tesserae, giving off a dull, fitful glitter as one turned them over
in one's palm to catch the light, but ultimately too jagged to fit into a
unified mosaic. But perhaps that was how it struck me because, for
me, the effect was curiously disjunctive in another way: I found it
extremely hard to associate these evidences of a young, unformed,
self-absorbed, anxious, and emotionally perplexed temperament
with my memories of the mild, amusing, ironical old gentleman I
had known, and whom I tended to recall now only as smiling at one
of his own witticisms, or as contentedly emptying a fourth glass of
wine, or as reciting passages of the Homeric hymns from memory in
Greek with an (alas) Erasmian pronunciation, or as gracefully laying
a votive bouquet of white lilies at the foot of the statue of a nude
Aphrodite that stood at the bottom of his garden under the delicate
shelter of a trellis arbor covered in clematis blossoms. And why, I
wondered, did certain phrases seem to echo through all his poems,
and certain images constantly recur—deserts, night, the sea...?

The second poem was also handwritten, on two pages this time,
but was actually dated earlier. He was either seventeen or eighteen
when he wrote it.

On Loving Her Whom I Have Known Only in Dreams

It is not a blindness that prompts me to love
what is not in my hands, to speak to one who
is not here.

She has taken many forms, yet none, she has
been set before me in a lax sweep of ironies
many times:

her shape, her formlessness, are much involved in night,
and with the stars that light the uttermost darkness, as is
her absence.

So it is not truly she who then, after muted greetings
in the smoky warmth of dim, comfortable, torpid rooms,
walks with me

Roland in Moonlight

in the cold dusk, below the limpid moon and pale
gold fire shrouding all the west, her hand in mine, a
pleasant hour.

There has never been a moment when this loneliness
revealed its meaning, this love that is exile, but it
must be she.

And yet it is not she who has imprisoned me
in nameless days and hours, who in her myriad
visage smiles

to be beside me. She has become what she is not:
her mouth and breasts are the down of pillows,
her skin sheets

that are wrapped, a cerement, around me; her legs, entwined
with mine, her hands laid limply on my shoulders—all are
cotton quilt.

Sometimes, in an instant, tremulously brief,
her eyes shine at me out of the night, a weightless
presence presses

a heat into each pore, a touch that is not will
thrill my nerves, a leaping flame snaps in my ribs,
and her laughs

accompany me to deeper dreams. I do not need
a judge of men to stare in mute horror
at my state

or tell me what, in this encroaching cold, I would
need to be a fool not to know: she
is not here;

only my vain longing has shaped her in my visions and
inflamed the joyous pains of so much self-
deception.

CITY

This poem I did not find in the least mysterious, even if perhaps I should have done. My note at the foot of the second page was "Not, I think, about Deirdre. Rather, it describes an experience common to the vast majority of teenage boys."

When I returned to my office the next morning, the pages were no longer there. So one of us must have filed them away again. And this, I could not help but think, was significant. For, where my office is concerned, I have always been careless and somewhat overly casual—almost dissolute, really—about clearing my papers away at the end of the day, or even about putting them in some sort of sensible order. Roland, however, had always been a most punctilious and precise sort of dog, almost to the point of obsessiveness. One needed only watch him licking his fur—his exacting attention to the cleanliness, sleekness, and glossiness of each follicle—to know this.

XXVIII

THE SEMESTER proceeded to its end. My health improved, so gradually at times as to seem like no real improvement at all, but without any large regressions, and I was able to discharge the minimal responsibilities incumbent on me. I delivered my public lecture (I chose a topic in philosophy of mind, though I do not recall what it was precisely), graded my graduate students' final papers, and began making preparations for the move to South Bend. The institute had provided us with a house at the edge of campus—quite a spacious one, it turned out—and so there was little to do apart from arranging for movers. I was writing regularly again, including my monthly journal columns. I even felt strong enough to participate in a summer reading group, made up of faculty and graduate students, devoted to Roberto Calasso's *Ardor*; I had been invited in part because I was the only one of our number with any broad knowledge of Indian thought and religion, or any acquaintance with Sanskrit. The opportunity to return to one of my oldest and deepest intellectual loves—all things Indological, that is—in the company of students and colleagues of whom I had become genuinely fond made those final months far more pleasant than I had anticipated them being. Still, once the dank, immobile heat of summer descended on the city, and mephitic vapors issued from every grating and alleyway, and the air shimmered with choking particulate slag, and thermal hazes of an almost viscous density danced and fluctuated above the scarred, bituminous streets and transformed the pinnacles of the city's hideous skyline into grim *fata morgana* castellations hovering in a sky as colorless as scoured steel, I grew ever more eager for the day of our departure. I especially looked forward to seeing the last of the abhorrent, monumental vulgarity of the Gateway Arch, the mere sight of which made life feel pointless to me. Its bizarre combination of dismal blandness and grotesque immensity struck me every time I saw it as an insult against everything beautiful or sublime or mysterious or elegant in this whole great, gorgeous terraqueous globe. I longed to see it for the last time, sinking away below a receding horizon, as though its moronic blasphemy against the heavens were being struck down by the hand of God.

XXIX

A T FIRST there WAS only the vigorous snuffling sound of an inquisitive snout near my brow, then the sensation of humid breath falling tenderly upon my neck, then the light brush of a cool wet nose against my cheek, and finally the tentative probing tip of a broad ductile tongue along the rim of my ear. I stirred, an inarticulate but vaguely interrogative moan rising in my throat. Only then did that familiar voice, so hauntingly like Laurence Harvey's, break the silence: "Yes, I thought you were awake."

I opened my eyes, and could tell from the deep, almost cerulean darkness that it was still night. A moment later I realized that the shape looming over me, silhouetted against the moon-soaked linen curtains of my window, was that of Roland's shoulders and head. "What...?" I began.

"I can guess why you're so restless," he said. "I expect it's all the turmoil and vexation that all these arguments you get involved in cause you. You really need to stop engaging in debate with this poor benighted Thomist fellow especially. You simply mustn't allow indignation or personal passion to rob you of sleep."

"But I *was...*"

"And I know that some of it's because of your feelings for me... the arguments about animal consciousness, and animal rationality, and animal eschatology, and such... and, well..."—I could see his head drop slightly, almost shyly—"I'm genuinely moved." Then his silhouette lurched toward me and the edge of his tongue ran slickly along the bridge of my nose. "That's the customary gesture," he helpfully explained as he moved back away, turning his head to one side so that the wan moonlight now framed his glistening nose in a jeweler's foil of pale silver.

I thought it best to say nothing.

"Though I can see the temptation," he continued. "I see that in his latest posting your Thomist antagonist does concede the biblical imagery of cosmic redemption, but then goes on to say that this doesn't mean that one should take the eschatological imagery of animals and such—Isaiah 11 and whatnot—literally, because along with all those straminivorous lions, and graminivorous bears, and erstwhile predators napping innocuously with their quondam prey, there's also a little child shepherd, and there are nurslings and weaned infants sporting with adders and asps, and yet *Jesus*—and this is your disputant's dialectical *coup de grâce*—says people will live like angels in the age to come, unmarried, so where would those children be coming from?"

I groaned, involuntarily but as tolerantly as I could manage. "Yes, that's pretty ghastly," I murmured. "That's what happens when people trained in analytic philosophy perpetrate exegesis of sacred texts, I suppose. Or when they try to make sense of poetic imagery. And Thomists—what can one say?" I coughed. "Traditionalist manualist Thomism is an emotional pathology, not a philosophy. You have to be so twisted to..." I paused, cleared my throat, and rubbed my eyes, now becoming resigned to remaining awake. "Well, it's a system of thought that attracts an unsettling number of borderline sociopaths. I've never met one of them with a fully developed moral intelligence."

Roland sighed, as if impatiently waiting for my wandering attention to turn back toward him.

"Of course," I added, yawning, "he'd be terrifically shocked by some of the more exotic specimens of antique Jewish and Christian angelology. All the sexual antics, I mean. And, you know, there's Gregory of Nyssa's mysterious reference to an angelic mode of reproduction, which may be more than just a *façon de parler*...""

"Yes, yes," interrupted Roland, "all very recherché. But I'm not finished ridiculing him. It actually gets worse, you see. His real argument is that *all* one has to conclude from scripture is that, as he puts it, '*something of*' the natural cosmos will enter into eternity, and for that the resurrected human body suffices—just a body without a world..." Here Roland laughed (at least, I think he did, though the sound he produced was indistinguishable from the noise he makes when regurgitating his morning "viridescent purgative" of grass), and then resumed with a hapless moan: "So all that scriptural business about the 'restoration of all things,' and creation's glorification and deliverance from decay, the final hierarchical reordering of all creation under its savior Lord, all the creatures of sky and land and sea rejoicing in a new creation, the new sky and new land... all of that means, basically, the annihilation of everything material and organic except for the exemplary residual distillate of human organs in their resurrected state." A flash of nitid fangs told me he was grinning in wicked mirth. "You know how it is: sometimes you have to destroy the universe to save it."

"Yes," I said after a moment, "it's confused and evil. But did you need to wake me to...?"

"I have to say, though, I think you tend to take the positions you do chiefly because you're a Hindu."

"I'm sorry," I said, all at once bewildered: "because I'm a *Hindu*?"

"Precisely," said Roland. "So you're naturally going to see things from a different angle."

"But, I'm..."

"You naturally think of all living things in terms of the *jīva* within, which is to say of a spiritual reality more original than—and of course transcendent of—species."

"But..."

"The poor karmic vagabond," Roland continued, morosely shaking his head and sighing, "the wanderer between lives: now a cow, now a man, now a god, now a paramecium..."

"Look," I interrupted, forcibly enough to break in upon the flow of his expatiations, "there's some misunderstanding here. I'm not technically a Hindu. I mean, temperamentally and intellectually I may have..."

Here, though, Roland laughed again, and then uttered another sigh. "Really?" he said. "Then why do you have all those volumes of Sanskrit and all those Indian books and so forth?"

"Asian religions and literatures are one of my passions," I said, "one of my fields of study. But that's not the same..."

"Yes, yes," he said. "But, let's be honest—we *know* what you are, however you may wish to qualify your terms. And, anyway, that's beside the point. I simply wanted to say that, in the next piece you write, you should..."

"Look," I protested, "I'm tired of the argument. Thomists of that sort are all such doctrinaire fundamentalists, and such moral simpletons, it's too exhausting. Their whole religion is a kind of spiritual *rigor mortis*. You can't loosen the limbs of their reasoning. And... well, I *was* asleep. You write something on the matter, if you want."

At once, a cold silence descended upon the room, and lingered several moments. When Roland spoke again, his voice had dropped in register, sounding now something more like Stewart Granger's: "You know very well they wouldn't print it. We've talked about that particular glass ceiling before."

"Oh, nonsense..." I said.

"So what you need to do now," he continued, taking no note of my protest, "is raise the deeper question: not, say, 'Can animals be saved?' but 'Can persons be?'"

I briefly tried to deduce (or at least intuit) his meaning, as I was conscious of having in the past given him the impression of a certain sluggishness of wits on my part, and I did not want to risk his witheringly piteous scrutiny by confessing my bewilderment. But I soon gave up. "You'd better explain."

Happily, he was too preoccupied with his own thoughts just then to turn that penetrating, appraising gaze of his on me. Or, if he did, the room was too dark for me to see it, and nothing in his voice suggested that he had. "Well," he continued, "all religious pictures of the last things are little more than dream images, shadows moving on the other sides of veils of hope and horror, which we can scarcely make out. Whenever people try to foresee a state of things beyond time, whether they're Christians, Jews, Sikhs, Hindus like you..."

"I'm telling you..."

"...and imagine themselves as participating in whatever final blissful reality they summon up from the fancies and longings in their souls, and from the metaphors and myths of their religious traditions, the only issue that occurs to them is what they think can be saved *in themselves* and *in others*. But, you see, that means they assume that 'self' and 'other' are ontologically severable substances, and that each self enjoys a *personal* fate distinct from the *personal* fate of others. But how can anyone have a personal destiny that's also private and proper only to him or her? Doesn't what happens to you necessarily happen to those associated with you, and vice-versa? And this isn't merely a moral question, is it? It's a question of the metaphysics of persons."

"I... suppose so..."

"Persons, that is, as opposed to anonymous essences. I mean, see here, you know how Peter Lombard and Aquinas said the sight of the sufferings of the damned will increase the beatitude of the redeemed, as pity would darken the joy of heaven?"

"Hard to forget," I said. "Despicable—as so much piety is."

"And you know how many thinkers in the past have tried to make sense of the idea of heaven and hell as an eternal division breaking right through the middle of families, of friendships, of loyalties and allegiances and loves? How they've all had to presume that the sufferings of the damned will either be clouded from the eyes of the blessed or, worse, increase the pitiless delights of heaven?"

"Yes," I said with a grimace.

"And then there's that odd American Evangelical philosophaster who suggests God might keep the saved happy by deleting their damned loved ones from their memories."

I winced. "Well, he's an id-..."

"But what *is* a person?" Roland suddenly barked. "What's a personal identity except a whole history of associations, affections, memories, attachments? If those are removed, if one's loves are lost or converted into indifference, or even into satisfaction at the torment of those one once loved... or even just forgetfulness... even just the forgetfulness of, well, *pets*—distasteful word—what is it that's saved? Surely someone else—something else—altogether: a spiritual anonymity... a vapid spark of pure intellection... the residue of a soul that's been... reduced to no one."

I merely shrugged.

"Have you read any Michel de Certeau?" he asked.

"Yes," I said, surprised, "of course. I didn't know you had."

"Oh yes," he said. "He has quite a following in canine philosophical circles. Especially among spaniels, because of their special tradition of 'oblique exegesis,' or '*interpretatio obliqua*.' But, anyway, I only mention him because of that lovely line of his... what is it?

'The I is the place of the other?' 'I am the place of the other?' Something like that. Well, you see, there's the point, and one that can't be conjured away. As a person, as a living actuality in communion with a world and with others, my spiritual identity is constituted by all my encounters, my memories, my affinities, intimate or remote, with others. I *am* those others, in a very real sense. And so how could I truly *be* in heaven when those I love are in hell? Wouldn't I in some sense—the person I am—be in hell with them? As Abraham Lincoln said of heaven, it's everyone or no one. That's not merely a warm sentiment; it's an irrefutable logical maxim."

"Lincoln?"

"The old argument, I suppose," he continued, "the same old choice: either the impersonalist Advaita Vedānta of Ādi Śankara or the personalist Viśiṣṭādvaita Vedānta of Rāmānuja."

"I suppose so," I said, beginning to feel weary.

"But perhaps neither school really thinks of persons as persons, probably, in quite the way Westerners do—in quite the particular, contingent... fragile way, that is."

"I suppose not," I replied, feeling still wearier.

He became quiet momentarily, then stretched out his limbs and lay down beside me, pressing himself up against my ribs. "You love the *Mahābhārata*, don't you?" he said.

"Yes," I said. "I love few books better."

"And Karna is your favorite character?"

"One of my favorites. Why?"

"Well," he said with a yawn, "Karna's not really the point. That was just idle curiosity. I ask about the *Mahābhārata* for another reason. It's just, you see, that this whole issue puts me in mind of that last lovely tale in the *Svargārohaṇa Parva* where, decades after the battle of Kurukṣetra, and well after the death of Kṛṣṇa, the five Pāṇḍavas and their beloved Draupadī leave their kingdom, depart from Indraprastha, and try to ascend to Svarga, Indra's heaven, in the flesh. But as they climb the Himalayas they fall, one by one, into crevasses or down cliff faces: beautiful Draupadī, clever Sahadeva, winsome Nakula, invincible Arjuna, mighty Bhīma... till only Yudhiṣṭhira, great king of righteousness, remains, accompanied by a dog that followed him from the city. He alone of the Pāṇḍavas reaches the gates of Āmrāvatī, and the blissful gardens of Svarga, and the gods welcome him; but then, at the last moment, just as he is about to pass through the gates, they say he can't bring the dog with him, even though the dog has been his loyal companion all the way from Indraprastha, because all dogs are animals of ill omen, fond of crematory grounds and with unfastidious eating habits." Roland sighed deeply. "*There's* a redoubtable prejudice for you. I suppose even my fondness for Sevruga caviar wouldn't be enough to get me in. But, anyway, wonderfully, Yudhiṣṭhira refuses, solely for that dog's sake, to enter paradise. 'He did not abandon me; I'll not abandon him.' One of those rare moments when the ape is as morally sensitive as the dog. Greyfriar's Bobby at the pearly gates would not have been more admirably self-renouncing."

"Yes," I said, "I remember. But then of course the dog turns out to be Yama, god of dharma, testing Yudhiṣṭhira's virtue one last time."

"True," said Roland with another shake of his head. "A distinctly unsatisfactory narrative trick. The tale *seems* subversive at first, and allows for another demonstration of Yudhiṣṭhira's goodness, but then doesn't *really* break the taboos governing that restricted neighborhood. Oh well. Not the last time a dramatic impasse would be resolved by an implausible *deus ex canili*."

"Perhaps he'd have been better off if the dog had really been just a dog," I said.

"All too true, given that he finds not his fellow Pāṇḍavas in Svarga, but rather only the Kauravas—only his mortal enemies," said Roland. "His brothers and wife he discovers instead in torment down in the darkness of Naraka, atoning for unpurged lapses of dharma."

"Yes," I said, "but that's only for a season, of course. In the end, they'll reach paradise and be reconciled with the Kauravas. And ultimately Yudhiṣṭhira himself will ascend beyond Svarga, to the Vaikuṇṭha of Viṣṇu, the very heaven of God, never to be reborn… no more to die. And, of course, dogs can attain *jīvanmukti* also…"

"But not as dogs," said Roland in a dour whisper. "Only after many 'higher' rebirths…"

Now I was the one to sigh. "The purblindness and bigotry of all religious traditions," I said softly. "They mean well, but they don't understand." Then something occurred to me. "Did you say '*ex canili?*'" I asked.

Roland snorted loudly. "You classicists never seem to have a good grasp of mediaeval Latin. The language didn't just die, you know."

"Well, I know, but…"

"A *canile* is a kennel. In fact, that's where the English word comes from."

"Yes, I'm aware of that," I said. "I was simply impressed by the wittiness of the turn of phrase, and sorry that I'd almost missed it."

Roland smiled slightly but remained silent for nearly a minute. Then, quietly, hesitantly, he said, "Would you do it for me? Forsake Indra's paradise, I mean, if I were forbidden admittance?"

"Without a second thought."

"Truly?"

"Of course," I said, closing my eyes. "Dogs are better than gods."

"Well, that goes without saying," he replied.

And then, or soon thereafter, I was asleep.

XXX

O UR FINAL DAYS IN St. Louis dwindled down to a precious, miserable, sweltering few. The reading group reached the end of *Ardor*; over the last two weeks before our departure a succession of colleagues and graduate students met me for meals or coffee to bid me farewell; a moving pod was delivered to our driveway and, with the help of friends, we filled it with our possessions; and all was more or less in readiness. In the fourth week of August, I observed the year and a half mark since the first severe attack of my illness by undertaking an exhaustive assessment of my current condition. I could not say that I had recovered nearly as much as I might have hoped, or even that I was yet convinced that I would ever recover enough to make daily life an easy affair; and I could only lament that by far the most unpleasant symptom of the malady—the persistent pulmonary inflammation—had shown least improvement; but I also could not deny that I was palpably stronger and in less pain than I had been when I had first arrived in Missouri. And my mother, curiously, though well into her eighties, had apparently recovered more fully than I. Unfortunately, her heart was beginning to fail her, even though as yet the signs were only sporadic and slight. The move to South Bend would be her last journey. Or next to last.

XXXI

O N THE EVE of our departure, I found myself—I am not sure how else to describe it, as I have no memory of where I had been—strolling through the dusk toward my own back yard. On passing through the gate beside the garage, I noticed Roland at the far end of the property, seated with his back to the house and his face turned toward a cluster of honeysuckle whose tendrils wound through and around the chain-links of the fence; he was leaning forward with his nose thrust very close to the blossoms, and I assumed that he was simply taking in their fragrance. The sun was well below the horizon; the fading light of day was no more than a hoary luster sinking away into murky blue; a thin gray blanket of mist lay spread across the grass. There was something pleasantly unearthly about the scene, and something especially mysteriously evocative—a kind of dreamy timelessness—in the grisaille stillness of Roland's figure under the gradually darkening sky. I walked toward him with as soft a tread as I could, and almost fancied that I had succeeded in approaching him undetected; and, as I drew near, I realized I could ever so faintly hear a series of soft cooing sounds and insufflations and tender moans issuing from his lips. When I was still a few yards away, however, the noises ceased and, without turning around, he spoke to me in that resonant voice of his: "I'm almost finished. Just making my farewells to some friends."

I stopped advancing, somewhat disappointed that my attempt at stealth had so manifestly failed. "Did you hear me or scent me?" I asked.

"Both." Now he turned his head and looked at me over his shoulder. "I picked you up about two minutes before you reached the gate."

"Remarkable," I murmured in sincere admiration. "Well, then…" I shrugged. "But who are these friends you're talking about?"

He turned his eyes away from me again. "The plants around the yard," he said. "I was just now taking my somewhat mournful leave of Mr. Chryselephantinos here."

"Mr. Chryselephantinos?" I asked.

"This honeysuckle bush. It's what I call him. It's not what he calls himself."

"No," I said, "I shouldn't think so. You... so you talk to plants then?"

"Of course," he said with a slight nod of the head. "It would be rude to ignore them."

I looked about the yard again, and perhaps for the first time noticed what a diversity of growing things there was there. "I've heard that talking kindly to plants encourages them to grow and to flourish. I mean, assuming that's not just New Age twaddle. Do you think it's true?"

"Of course it's true," Roland replied, in a tone that suggested that mine was a foolish question. "All rational beings respond better to kindness than to cruelty, and plants enjoy being spoken to in a kindly way. Only you mustn't pay too much attention to some of the nonsense they say in return. They love being silly."

"They, ah..." I stared intently at Roland's small form in the twilight, trying to tell from—who knows?—perhaps from the tilt of his head whether he was being serious. "Plants... talk back, do they?"

"Yes," he replied blandly.

"What do they say?"

"Whatever's on their minds, of course. You know—vegetal humor, anecdotes about caterpillars, observations on sunlight and rain, metaphysics, poetry... Mind you, sometimes they're just little leafy blellums, chatting away dizzily and incontinently."

"Are you toying with me?"

"Not at all," he said, slowly rising from his haunches, stretching himself, turning around, and then resuming a seated position. "I've explained about the pervasiveness of consciousness in all things already. Surely you remember? My 'panpsychism,' as it were?"

"Well, yes, but I didn't realize that it involved... actual reciprocal communication with... with honeysuckle."

"Oh, dear," he said, lowering his head and shaking it dolefully, "here we are again. These prejudices and presuppositions… they really are like lead weights tied to your imagination."

"I don't mean to be a…" I began.

"If we're willing to acknowledge the real insight expressed in ancient personifications of living things," he interrupted, "and are willing to call a hamadryad a hamadryad, why should we be surprised if a chrysanthemum occasionally feels moved to express her feelings on something she may have thought or experienced? Or if a myrtle, in a sudden access of euphoria or romantic longing, should want to declaim a few lines of *florid* verse?"

I did not reply, as I feared exciting his scorn by saying something stupid. Instead I fetched one of our folding chairs from the wooden veranda at the back of the house and seated myself in it about two yards from him. "What language were you speaking to it… to Mr. Chryselephantinos?" I asked.

"My own," he answered with a gentle smile. "All creatures in the Great Chain of Being—save man, the immemorial exile—understand one another's languages well enough to communicate. In a sense we're all pantoglots. That's not to say we command equal fluency in all tongues. But communication—communion—is never impossible. It's always a combination, though, of actual speech and a kind of spiritual or mental patiency or receptivity, a kind of tact that reaches down to that inner word in each of us that's more primordial than this or that language, this or that argot. You should know this from experience."

"I should?"

Roland gazed at me with an expression of what I can only call doting condescension. "Don't you realize that the whole reason you can understand me with no special effort, and can hear what I'm telling you without some barrier being thrown up in your mind that makes you hear my words as just so much animal vocalization, is that you have an unusual capacity, a kind of unguarded openness to hearing things your mind would usually not hear? At least from me? You seem deaf to most of the rest of creation's discourse."

"But…" I rubbed my temples with both hands. "You're speaking English to me—my own language."

"I am, yes," Roland replied. "I'm afraid that that much is still necessary for you. But, even so, if it weren't for this openness in you—this primitive defenselessness against reality, or this half-dreaming consciousness of yours that carries you out of yourself at times into the larger mind we all share—your intellect would rebel against the experience of hearing me speak, and would simply convert even the English I'm speaking into howls and barks and whines."

I pondered this for a few moments. "I suppose you're right," I remarked.

"Mind you, even then you're not always so open. At most times, your normal intentionality falls into conformity with general expectations. The reason you often feel that you're dreaming when we have these conversations—or, at any rate, remember them that way after they've ended—is that you have a strange ability, as far as I can tell, to slip into a state of mind that places you... well, *in between*. At those times, you're especially receptive. The only error you make when recalling these episodes is in failing to grasp that what you think of as the waking world is itself only a collective dream, an illusory convention upon which your kind has tacitly agreed—though, of course, it evolves age upon age. The mechanical world of dead matter for which your kind now seems content to settle, for all its squalor and implausibility, seems real to you when you're securely wrapped in its nets. And, in that world, my words are practically inaudible... or, at any rate, unintelligible. But then, fortunately, you're susceptible to these moments of blessed disorientation, when you fall into your little... well, your little shamanic trances, I suppose."

"Is that what they are?" I asked.

"Of course."

"And so... do you ever have conversations like this with anyone else?" I stared down at him, trying to read the expression on his face. "Perhaps my wife or son?"

At this, he smiled wistfully and lowered his eyes. "Frankly, they don't need my help as much as you do."

"What?" I asked, feeling slightly alarmed. "What do you mean?"

He lifted his head again and looked at me with an expression of affectionate fatigue. "There's something in you that's never quite... clicked." His nose quivered, his nostrils flared, and I could tell he was trying to judge from my fragrance what effect his words were having on me.

For some time I could say nothing, chiefly because I thought I knew what he meant. For a moment, I even felt a sort of tingling in my skin, which usually indicates that I have become aware of something too uncanny to name. "All things speak, then?" I asked in a voice grown strangely hoarse.

"If we have but ears to hear," said Roland, resuming his normal expression, "yes. The earth proclaims, and all that."

"I suppose I already believed that," I said. "But, being a modern man—unwillingly, in many respects, but modern nonetheless—I think there's always a trace of doubt even in my faith."

"I know," he said. "A bitter trace, I assume. And it's tragic really—for you and all your kind. There was a time when everyone knew, and could immediately sense, the reality of the souls of the stars and the sun, the vital cosmic *spirit* that's also quite literally the wind that blows through all things. Actually, just to be precise about the Greek, I wouldn't myself have chosen the term 'panpsychism' to mean the presence of mind in all things, but *would* have chosen it to indicate that there's life in all things, and that life's *also* always mind and spirit. The ancient view is just as much a 'panpneumatism' or 'pannoetism.' Those ancient worthies, East and West and wherever else, knew that the consciousness in, say, a hydrangea bush or a muskrat or a dog or a god is not the effect of some nebulously defined 'property' resident in all material reality in greater or lesser quanta, but exists simply because all life is a participation in the spiritual ground of reality. So there's intentionality in everything—not just impersonal 'directedness,' that is, but real spiritual, rational intentionality. In every living thing there's a *jīva*. Thales, again. Or Heracleitos, who knew that everything's filled with logos and who Diogenes Laertius says taught that all things are full of souls and spirits. And of course there's Pythagoras. And so forth. They all knew. They also understood that this meant more than a kind of passibility in things. They knew that even the simplest sensitivity to qualia couldn't exist in the absence of real intention, attention, thinking, communicating… *logos*. I mean, well, have you ever had that experience of seeing faces in the patterns of a tree's bark or in an arrangement of branches and leaves and sunlight and shadow, or in cliff faces, or…?"

"Well, of course," I replied. "Everyone has. Usually, that's the sort of thing one attributes to the 'intentional stance' bred in us by evolution. Chance patterns, chance associations… perceptions shaped by an innate tendency to look for signs of predators watching us from the undergrowth, or…"

"But that's wrong," Roland said. "When you glimpse those faces, it's because, in that moment, your mind is opening slightly to the *numen* on the other side of the phenomena, the *mana* within things… the reality that, in being seen, is always looking back to meet your gaze. The old man peering out at the world from the knots and whorls of an oak is actually a manifestation of the living, spiritual universe all around us."

I pondered this for several moments. "It's a lovely vision of things," I finally murmured.

He, however, lowered his head in a distinctly despondent way, and made a soft tut-tutting noise with his lips. "Yes, of course," he said quietly. "Certainly the mechanistic picture is a thoroughly hideous one: an infinite universe of general death, producing life—or what we mistake for life—only as a pitiably local, accidental chemical arrangement of that more original and fundamentally dead reality, and then only very latterly exhaling a thin vapor called consciousness from the fen of organic chemical existence. Then, when you add to this the utterly meaningless mystification of talking about 'instinct,' as if that somehow explains the purposive and rational and deliberate activity of organisms, vegetal or animal or both, you're left with… what? The mechanical picture never really explains, does it? It just produces those endless indices of correlation, without a real causal logic. Mirror neurons, say, are invoked to 'explain' emotional recognition and sympathy, though it's far more plausible to say that the prior intentional state of recognition and sympathy causes neurons to fire. Or one gets purely black box explanations, like 'gravity,' which is no more explanatory—and far less so—than speaking of the love of living bodies for one another. Or one gets talk of phylogeny as purposive only by appearance, though that explains nothing about the ever more involved com-

CITY

plexity of organic life over time; it makes better sense to believe with Aristotle that there's a mind-like rational order within nature that moves toward certain possible resolutions of evolutionary imperatives and constraints like a stream of rational thought solving problems in light of the conclusion being sought. So, yes, yes indeed, it's far more beautiful and reasonable to see that mind indwells all things, and that life is the primordial truth of things, and that everything is alive, is luminous, *shines* with spirit. Divine mind, divine Sophia, the world-soul in all. An infinite act of consciousness and thought, within which everything has an inner spiritual life, an inner light of mind, even an intrinsic claim on eternal life, because spirit cannot pass away, and because spirit is convertible with being itself, and mind is the ever more eminent fullness in which all things live and move and are. So, yes. But... but..." He shook his head dolefully again, then raised it and stared away toward the day's waning light, which had become like polished pewter. "It's also a tragic vision. Everywhere, spirit is also imprisoned in this world, entangled in the weft of life and death, generation and decay. That seems to have been the view of Pythagoras, and of you Hindus, and the Neoplatonists, and even arguably Christianity in its most original forms. I don't know how much you follow Christian thought, but its mythos of a fallen cosmos, captive in the household of death, says the same thing."

"In point of fact..." I began, somewhat emphatically, if wearily.

But again Roland spoke over me, his eyes still averted. "And, of course, it's even more tragic in the modern age, when mechanism isn't merely a scientific method, but a metaphysical and cultural and economic view of the natural world. Everything is thought to be a machine waiting to be consumed by other machines, and then converted into waste matter and abstract profits... consumption being the process of separating the latter from the former. Nothing is sacred in itself, no mystery is honored... no tenderness is shown. The age of the world-picture, of technology, of nature as the reservoir of purely material resources to be exploited and despoiled and then corrupted with toxins and microplastics and every imaginable chemical and synthetic pollution. The age of climate change and mass extinctions. The age of an economics devoted to absolute

185

death... the total rarefaction of all life into lifeless numbers in a bank account. And all the delicate and lovely and mysterious spirits that indwell the things of nature all quite defenseless against the monstrosity of... humanity."

For several seconds, he was silent, and I could think of no reply.

"Curious," he finally continued, now returning his gaze to mine and staring into my eyes with an expression of frank sadness. "What's more ridiculous than those 'human distinctiveness' advocates who are so terrified of sharing the dignity of life and spirit with other living beings that, in the name of what they think is Christianity or classical humanism, they actually ally themselves to the Cartesian faction and deny the reality and beauty of spirit in nature, and even adopt the superstition that there's such a thing as inanimate matter. As if the prominence of man in the world today needs to be defended or promoted or, God forbid, enlarged. If those poor imbeciles understood the moment, they would be more concerned to defend the distinctiveness of living systems—all of them—over against the universal reign of omnivorous nihilism. I mean, yes, there's a uniqueness of *degree* about the human expression of spiritual life, as there is about that of every creature, but it's certainly not a uniqueness of *kind*."

"Yes," I finally rasped, lowering my eyes in what I suppose was shame.

"And those traditionalist Thomists you find so annoying," he continued, "the ones who all seem so enamored of that Dominican thinker you so despise—you know, the French antisemite and fascist—what's his name? Reginald Loup-Garou, is it?"

"Something like that," I said.

"They still cling to this fatuous doctrinaire scholasticized Aristotelianism that says that human beings are the only animals with 'rational souls' or with *logos*, in the sense of either reason or language. But the sciences have shown that this absolute partition between rational and animal souls is simply nonsensical, and really rather degrading to everyone involved. Even language, if one doesn't assume that only human language is language properly speaking. We know so much about, oh, elephants, and grey parrots, and orcas, and whales, and apes, and... *dogs*."

CITY

"I know," I said. "As far as I'm concerned, the only dogs not fitted for eternal life are the *domini canes*."

At this, finally, the pall of melancholy lifted from Roland's features. "Oh, that's very good," he remarked with a broadening smile. "And if they're ultimately condemned to ephemerality, I'm sure it'll be precisely on account of their indifference to all those glorious, sensitive, intelligent, reasoning beings they think dispensable in that bleak and hideous eschatology of theirs."

"Oh, let's not talk about them," I pleaded. "Their religion is so dark and horrible that it just depresses me. Can't we discuss something lighter and more elevating—like, I don't know, satanism? At least that has internal coherence going for it."

Roland smiled again. "Well, all I mean to say is that all the real researchers have learned so much about different kinds of intelligence, and about systems of communication in both the animal and the vegetal realms. There are so many wonders in, oh, corvid intellect, or among octopods, or in beluga whales and gorillas and… well, even canaries. Birds of every kind, really. I mean, we all know now just how prodigious the tool-making and problem-solving powers of New Caledonian crows are, for instance, or the semeiotic and syntactic skills of grey parrots. And, as impressive as corvine or psittacine intelligence may be, so is anserine intelligence in another way, at least when it comes to gooses' mastery of remembering and reading landscape and their powers of orientation when plotting courses of migration. And the same is so of pigeons and white-crowned sparrows. And how complex chickadee signaling is. Or, putting birds aside, consider how much specific information about an approaching predator or human being prairie dogs can impart to one another. Even plants can communicate with their kith and kin by way of rhizomatic and mycorrhizal networks and can, for example, advise them to secrete bitter oils to repel an assault by voracious insects and rodents and… Well, really, just look at the beasts of the field and the air. They reason, they communicate, they learn, they invent, they form deep emotional attachments… they rejoice, they *play*. Is all of that only so much mortal flesh, momentarily galvanized by spiritless chemical ebullitions and effervescences, but destined only for oblivion? When the spiritual wellspring of life manifestly and constantly flows through them, in their capacities for love, joy, grief, hope… allegiance? I tell you, the same love that moves the sun and all the other stars is the primal impulse that drives the earthworm's delighted degustations of the sod, and that calls him to itself."

"You're preaching to the already converted," I remarked, scratching the top of his head.

He closed his eyes and, as he liked to do, pressed his skull back against my fingertips and held that pose until I had finished. Then he opened his eyes again. "Thanks," he said, "I was just about to ask you to do that."

"This conversation is becoming rather dark, don't you think?" I asked.

"I suppose so," he answered. "It's hard not to lament at times, when one sees the catastrophic collapse of biological diversity in the Anthropocene epoch—the loss of all those trillions of lovely mysteries, those inner worlds we can't see, those hidden depths within the souls of living things—and then to realize that it's all our fault." He dropped his head again.

After several seconds, I gave into my confusion. "Whose fault? What do you mean? Surely it's *our* fault, human beings' fault, not yours."

His eyes remained downcast. "Don't you see?" he said bitterly. "It's our transgression too. It's all on account of our one true original sin."

Again I waited several seconds before finally asking, "Which was?"

He raised his head and looked into my eyes with an expression quite unlike any I had ever seen him wear before, somehow at once both deeply probing and oddly penitent. "You," he said. "Your kind. *Homo sapiens*—and, so I'm told, *sapiens*. Don't you see? Don't you know that in all the tens of thousands of years that your species and mine have dwelled together, we were guiding you, forming you, even deputing you for our own ends?"

"Well, now…" I began.

"It was in part out of compassion," he continued, "but also in part out of self-interest. And therein lay our great trespass, our great

188

CITY

Promethean hubris. At first, we thought we were simply ameliorating the state of a promising biped. We taught you—slowly, by example, but with absolute fidelity to our mission, generation upon generation—the sort of social intelligence natural to canine society but almost entirely absent from simian. With that, we laid the foundations of ethics and laws, religions and mores, made possible the sort of cooperation and civil accords that would lead to the creation of nations, the founding of cities… even the birth of empires. We taught you rational worship, grounded in natural piety and humility and prayer and care for your neighbor. And how we lauded ourselves for our benevolence, our magnanimity. But there was another side to our labors too, a set of secret ambitions that in a sense corrupted all the good we accomplished. We knew that, with your large musculoskeletal structure, your opposable thumbs, your biddable natures, and your pliable minds, we could use you to do things—to invent things—that we desperately wanted but were ourselves physically unable to produce. We were driven by insatiable longings— inchoate at first, little more than nebulous concepts of nebulous concepts—for two things in particular, and that twofold yearning was the source of… universal cataclysm."

"Which two things?" I prompted after yet more time had passed in silence, now genuinely fascinated.

He looked away from me, back toward the last glimmer of daylight, scarcely visible behind the rising glare of the street lamps. "Motor cars, of course," he said, "and… bacon."

"Motor cars?" I said. "Bacon? What are you talking…"

"Oh, it's so horrible," he said, his voice now rising in pitch. "You've seen how much pleasure we take in thrusting our heads out of the widow when we're out in cars with you, letting the wind fill our mouths and nostrils, and race along our quivering tongues and flapping ears. We love speed. It's nectar and ambrosia to us—opium and cocaine. It's a deep primal lupine urge in us that all the domestication and civilization of millennia can do nothing to dampen. And we knew that we could guide you, slowly but ineluctably toward the creation of some sort of conveyance capable of satisfying that base appetite. Wagons and carriages and even chariots were quite fine advances, of course, and the first generations of steam-

189

engine trains, and other vehicles, but still we wanted more and more, and so we pressed you onward and onward until, *voilà*, the internal combustion engine and the endless romance of the open road. As for bacon… well, that rather speaks for itself. But, of course, in our mad heedlessness, we never foresaw the endless consumption of fossil fuels or factory farming—or any of the other abominations that flowed from the hands and hammers and pliers and forges of *homo technicus*. We sought to bring heaven to earth, and instead opened up the gates of hell upon the whole of creation." The note of chagrin in his voice was not only obviously ingenuous, but deeply affecting.

"You couldn't have known," I said after a moment, anxious to console him. "And, for what it's worth, it's obvious you haven't licked your paws clean of us. Maybe you can yet teach us better ways."

He looked at me again, and a slight, lugubrious hint of a wry smile played across his lips. But his eyes retained their sadness. "Maybe, but I have my doubts. The wild dynamo we set loose upon the world is now probably beyond our control. But we can't abandon you now. Our destinies are bound together irrevocably, yours and ours. And so are our hearts. For better or worse, we… love you."

A strange pang flared up in my chest for a moment and then subsided. I briefly wondered if I were on the verge of tears. "Your sin can't be as great as ours," I said. "You perhaps miscalculated… perhaps acted with somewhat mixed motives at times. But we destroy without restraint, without conscience."

"I'll tell you the whole story of our two peoples one day," he said. "As for your sin—your *original* sin—I can't speak to it. It was already something established in your natures before your kind and mine first truly met. I know the myths, of course—the Eden myth and the other tales from around the world of the loss of an original beatitude or innocence. But, even if that's something that actually happened rather than an allegory about something that's always happening in your kind, then it happened in some other world, some other kind of time. As for this world—this fallen world, this aftermath of that other world—here, in this world, it may be that your feeling of original sin also consists largely in a kind of oblivious memory of your organic past... an ineffable ache of conscience that's really a kind of organic recollection of all the phylogenic misery and slaughter and blood-soaked attritions by which your species climbed its way out of the mire of purely biochemical existence. Long before your species had even appeared in the world of *chronos*, the world of the time of death, you were gestating in the womb of nature as a mere stochastic organic possibility, an only remotely likely final issue of incalculable ages of violence. And you bear that lineage and that whole physical history as a kind of ontological guilt, a stain deeply imbrued in every cell in your body—written in every strand of your DNA. Every one of you is Cain, the mark of your immemorial guilt indelibly inscribed on each mitochondrion and every cell-wall... Ah, well, so it goes. A delicate blue flower springs up atop a noisome midden, and its fragile, incandescent beauty dazzles us, and we forget all the purulence and waste and dissolution and ceaseless decay from which its exquisite, transient charm was born. That evanescent flicker of enchantment inveigles and beguiles us. But deep down in the cellars of your cerebral cortices your reptile brain still lurks—a serpent, so to speak, perhaps the serpent of Eden himself—and all the later concrescences of your modular brain are compounded upon that ineradicable ophidian core. And it knows. It remembers, in its cold, cruel, scaly way. And you of course, my friend, are no blue flower."

I laughed. "No," I said, "I'm certainly not. But you *are* a philosopher."

"Maybe... the only kind of philosopher a dog can be."

"Which is?"

A slightly impish grin parted his lips. "Why, a *cynic* of course." And then he began laughing in that awful, coughing, gurgling way he has.

"Oh, really," I protested, "that's too obvious a joke."

"Therein lies its genius," he said, bringing himself back under control. "Anyway, I wasn't trying to be a philosopher, or even to tell a complete story. That organic history is only an echo of the spiritual history that preceded it. Your still more *original* original sin was your departure from the pleroma in the divine aeon through an act of self-assertion—which is to say, your departure from the Dreaming in the wrong way, at the wrong moment. And that's a fall that happened to all of you as one and to each of you as individuals."

"You truly believe that, don't you?" I asked.

"I know it," he said.

I looked up into the sky, which now was wholly dark. Only a few stars were visible amid the gathering clouds, dully lit by the sullen glow of the city. "I love you too," I said after a moment.

He was silent for many seconds. Then he leaned his head forward and licked my hand three times. After that, he rose to his feet, stretched, and said, "We should really be going in now. We have a long journey tomorrow."

PART THREE

TOWN

XXXII

THE HOUSE in South Bend was really rather airy and spacious, and all on a single level (which was very convenient for my mother), with a large back garden. It stood fast upon the southern margin of the Notre Dame campus, and behind it, on the other side of the door in the high wooden fence there, was the university's principal graveyard, whose tenants proved to be the most considerate neighbors we have ever had. The institute, moreover, was an ideal setting in which to pursue both my studies and my continued convalescence. The directors and staff could scarcely have been more amiable or competent, and the other fellows all proved to be delightful company. Even the twice-weekly seminar lunches—where whichever of us whose turn it was made a presentation on his or her project, followed by discussion, all over meals cunningly devised to discourage even the faintest impulse toward gluttony—turned out to be enlightening, diverting, and extremely collegial affairs, which were actually some aid to me in recovering the healthy habit of human intercourse. And, as I have said, the relatively clean air in the town was a marked improvement over the oily, sabulous swamp-fogs of the city we had left behind. My lungs slowly began to improve. True, the first winter would prove something of an ordeal, but on the whole it seemed that the inflammatory episodes might become rarer. Not at first, admittedly. When I arrived at Notre Dame I was still fairly decrepit and pursive the better part of the time, and was occasionally rendered prostrate. But the burning in my throat and lungs sometimes subsided to nothing at all.

My work went well, moreover. I was scheduled, in fact, to run an entire conference on the topic of my research in the second semester there, and I realized after a few months that this would not be the Augean labor I had feared. By the end of the first semester, I knew I would be equal to the task—which was fortunate, because, despite the absurdly ambitious list of panelists I proposed, everyone invited agreed to participate. And, in general, this new phase in my life proved far more reinvigorating than I had hoped it would be. There were new friends to be made, old friends to spend time with, occasional guest lectures to deliver, Thomists to annoy, and coffee shops to explore. My wife's burdens slowly eased as I became more capable, my son was growing into manhood and as a consequence becoming more immersed in his own interests, and my mother for a time seemed to be holding her own.

And, all the while, Roland was at work on his own plans and designs and explorations.

XXXIII

I WAS STILL something of an insomniac in those first several
months and, as always, something of an oneirolept. There were
still sleepless wanderings in the small hours, and perhaps some
noctambulant expeditions of which my conscious mind made no
record, as well as a number of those phantasmagorial episodes that
my memory can never quite assign a place either among dreams or
among concrete experiences. If anything, ever since the onset of my
illness I had been even more prone to entering the twilight realm
between the waking and the sleeping minds, and never quite knowing afterwards how real my wanderings there had been. I am fairly
certain, though, that it was around the middle of that October that I
once more came to myself *in medias res*, already up and in motion
well after midnight with no recollection of having slipped out of
bed. As our furniture was now fairly sparse, most of it having been
supplied by the university in a quantity generally intended for a single apartment, I was rather enjoying the spaciousness of the enormous front room, striding back and forth across the open floor and
reciting Yeats—"The Song of Wandering Aengus," to be precise—to
myself in a whisper. I was just relishing that last taste of "the golden
apples of the sun" in my mouth when I noticed a pale milky glow at
the end of the series of doorless passageways lying between me and
the western end of our home, far off past the open vestibule of the
front door, past the dining area, past the large kitchen beyond, and
emanating from the enclosed foyer between house and garage. This
was a pleasantly open space, with doors leading both to the front
driveway and to the wooden veranda in the back yard, which admitted plenteous sunlight during the day from both the north and the
south, and so we had placed my office in one of its corners. I knew
at once that the glow was coming from my computer screen, and I
was quite sure what I would find on investigating it.

"Oh, you're up, are you?" Roland said as I entered the foyer, turning his head about to look at me from my office chair, where he was seated with one front paw placed on the keyboard. "The insomnia's still a problem, is it?"

"I suppose it must be," I replied, approaching him. "What are you doing up?"

"A few finishing touches on my annotations for your Great Uncle's papers," he replied, turning his eyes back to the screen just as I reached his side. "The special issue of the Maryland Archivists' journal is set for December, and I'm just going over the texts of the last two or three poems he wrote for—or about—Deirdre." He gave vent to a long, somber exhalation, licked his nose two or three times, and ran his tongue along the entire length of his lips. "The only ones that make reference to her suicide… at least, two of them do. From many years apart, as it happens, and both from some considerable time after the event itself."

"I see," I said. "Not exactly cheerful material, then."

"No," he said thoughtfully, "but illuminating. It's… Here," he suddenly said, removing his paw from the keyboard and leaping nimbly down from the chair, "see for yourself."

I thanked him with some indistinct monosyllable and seated myself. The text of the pdf on the screen was written in Aloysius's flowing hand, obviously with a fountain pen, but this time on lined paper. It was apparently a fair copy, as it was devoid of any markings or corrections. It was dated simply 1927.

Envoi

When she, through those long nights of memory,
First summoned me to drink her ruby wines
And watch as that year's gaudy death blew by,
Her unbound hair was fragrant of lime trees
And ghostly blossoms plucked from phantom vines,
And sometimes she would turn away to cry.

I had no means to make the summer winds
Return again to quicken snow-bright nights
Or wreathe the air with honeysuckle's scent.

198

When winds grew bitter, counting childhood sins
Revived in her old shames. For those delights
She gave she asked no price but my lament.

Why in that season her green eyes turned cold
And all her words in whispers slipped and broke
I do not know; nor can I now forget
How sad she grew when that first frost took hold.
She would not hope, amid the ice and smoke,
That spring's return might wake her from regret.

I never knew you, lady, for I thought
That this of all things you would never do,
When you had promised me that we could live
By simple joys. For this cold pain you wrought—
Though you had let thin flames of passion through,
Between the wall's slight cracks and ivy's green—
You may have paid enough, and have redeemed
The world we lost, but I cannot forgive.

"I see," I said meaninglessly when I had finished reading. "A tad Edwardian. How long after was this written? After, you know, her…?"

"Yes, I know," he said. "Eight years, I think, but I haven't revisited the chronology recently. Poor girl."

"Did he really resent her for it, do you think?" I asked. "For killing herself, I mean?"

"Who can say? Surely it's hard to be left behind." He lay down at the edge of the medium-sized Persian carpet that defined the area of my office. "It's, alas, impenetrable to me emotionally, since suicide isn't found among dogs. Sometimes, resignation to death's ineluctable approach, even grateful acquiescence to its embrace. Frequently, self-sacrifice for the pack or the household or an adored pet ape like you. Members of some other species sometimes take their lives, yes. Dolphins in captivity have been observed doing so out of despair of ever being free, for instance. Not dogs. And so, since I can't imagine my way into the state of mind of someone who feels the need to take leave of this life, neither can I imagine the thoughts and speculations it might prompt in those who might want to blame themselves for it, or at least wonder whether they might have done more."

After a moment, I looked down at him, stretched out there in the posture of the Great Sphinx, but with his eyes peering upward into mine inquisitively, intently. "What?" I asked after a moment. "Why are you staring like that?"

"You've thought about it occasionally, haven't you?" he said in a tone somehow both diffident and slightly accusing. "I mean, not in the abstract, but as a... desideratum?"

I shrugged. "I've been very ill for some time," I replied as casually as I could, "and sometimes despair prompts fantasies. But only in fleeting moments... as a way of... I don't know, relaxing the nerves."

Roland lowered his head and rested his jaw on his outspread paws. "Yes," he murmured, "fantasies. Precisely. Aestheticized, no doubt." He raised his voice slightly. "And how did you picture it, then? I mean, if you fantasized playing the Stoic, serenely striding through that door that lies ever open, how did you imagine the scene?"

I was beginning to feel somewhat uncomfortable with the conversation, but hesitated only a few moments before replying. "That's just it," I said. "It never even had any plausible features. It was pure idle daydreaming in moments of misery. I don't know... I generally pictured it as something happening deep in a forest, at the edge of a pond or lake surrounded by the trees... maybe even in a boat on the water there... on a cool day, calm, quiet... far away."

"By what means, though?"

"I don't know," I said, sounding suddenly defensive. "That's just it. There weren't even any practical details. Just a deeply peaceful, beautiful setting, and a feeling of how nice it would be to slip away from this world in such a place... just falling asleep."

Roland snorted and raised his head again. "Of course, if you found yourself there, you'd be too enchanted by the beauty of the place to want to depart from it. If you were really able to feel the peace of the place, you'd be too much at one with the world to be able just then to take your leave. There's such a tendency to romanticize and beautify suicide among your kind. The delicate pathos of young Werther, martyred for love. The exquisite ritual precision of *seppuku* in the good old days—though, frankly, the actual execution of the deed often as not proved quite spectacularly maladroit and uncomely. The patrician Roman penning a few impeccably phlegmatic valedictory missives to friends and rivals and then nonchalantly opening his veins in a warm scented bath. The English gentleman prompted by honor to load the pistol, write a few manly lines of unadorned and scrupulously unsentimental prose, and then place the barrel against his temple. Oh!" Roland rose up again on his haunches. "You do know, I assume, that Aloysius's maternal grandfather did himself in with his own sidearm."

"Did he?" I said. "No, I don't know the story."

"I know very little of it myself, except that he was a colonel at the time in the Maryland something-or-otherenth battalion or whatnot. Disconsolate over Appomattox or something of the sort. One of those, I'm afraid. His only farewell note was four lines of verse—his death poem, so to speak, but definitely one lacking the delicacy or good taste of a decent Japanese *jisei*."

"You've seen it?"

"Your great uncle recorded it in his journal. And I just recently came across it, as I was reading Aloysius's reflections on suicide."

"Really?"

"Would you like to hear it?"

I hesitated. "Ah… how long is it?"

"Four lines, as I said."

I bit my lower lip. "You mean, you're able to recite it?"

Now Roland scowled. "It's not exactly the *Aeneid*," he remarked with a slightly acid edge to his voice. "Well?"

"All right," I said, not really certain that I was making the right decision, but not wanting to risk his disapproval.

"All right, then," he replied. He drew himself up, straightened his shoulders, cleared his throat, and began to declaim, in a comically sonorous voice, with the old central Maryland southern accent that he knew from hearing my mother speak but that has all but vanished from the earth:

> I will not yield to fretful speculation,
> Or waste the waning day with midnight's fears.

201

Nor whence nor whither knows its destination,
But dead men live again in women's tears.

He held his pose for several seconds before allowing the faintest crispation of a smile to appear at the corners of his mouth.

"That's… ghastly," I finally said.

The slight smile now became an open grin. "Well, he was an idiot, obviously. As it happens, moreover, at least according to your great uncle's report of family lore, there weren't a great many tears shed on his behalf by any women. His wife, it seems, was positively elated to deposit his corpse into a starched uniform and then into the ground, and then to marry again just as soon as decorum permitted, to a man with whom she had been keeping company in idle gossip for years. It all seems a bit comic from a certain distance. And, after all, the only good Confederate is a…" He fell silent for a moment, and his expression became rather grave. "All the romance of self-slaughter is nonsense, though, as far as I can tell. When one of your kind, weighed down with that… that burden of ontological guilt we've talked about before… well, when one of you takes his or her life, there's no glamor or serenity or majesty in it. It doesn't happen beside the lustrous waters in some lacustrine dell hidden in an emerald forest, easily and peacefully. It happens to someone who's broken, lost, bearing a pain he or she can't tolerate, or even name…"

"You sound like you understand it all better than you let on," I remarked.

"Mere deduction," he replied. "I still can't understand it from within. But I can see it in an objective light. It just seems obvious to me that it's all pain… all helplessness… no guilt. Still, it wounds those left behind. Aloysius had a right to his anger. And the wounds never really heal. There's another poem—did I say that already?—but it's from 1948, more than two decades after the first, and nearly three after her death. It's… well, it's right there. If you click on the tab of the next open document, you'll see."

I did so. This time the pdf was of a typewritten page, yellowing at the edges.

TOWN

Unseasonable Memory

Why does her ghost come now to trouble me?
I left her in the fading autumn light,

Before the coming of the snow. Since then,
So many others have invited my
Caress in dreams, have asked me to drink in
The summer's warmth, and sleep beneath the sunlit
Leaves. But not she: I left her long ago
And had forgotten. Broken, lifeless thing.

She knew what I did not, though: "Memory
Will chase you down the many roads of life."
But I dismissed her with a smile, until
She died, and was no more, just silver ash.

Let the snows of winter fall, let the wind
Blow ceaselessly and cold. For she has grown
Vaster than the night, darker than the world.

"Curious," I said after a few moments.

"What?" asked Roland.

"I don't know," I said. "I find his voice sometimes so hard to hear. Maybe because the voice in the poems isn't the voice of the old man I remember. But... no... actually, that's not what I meant. I meant that the last line is curious. It's not 'darker than the night' and 'vaster than the world,' but the other way around... the comparative adjectives, I mean."

"Yes," said Roland, yawning loudly and bestowing three long licks upon the fur of his chest. "Intentional, I assume. This is a dark world, and maybe the enigma of another's pain—certainly a pain that great—is the darkest thing of all." He looked away in that abstracted way to which he was given whenever his thoughts began to draw him toward a farther shore. "The more one contemplates the mystery of spiritual existence, the more tempting it is to adopt a kind of gnostic irony with regard to this world's claim on us. How is it that something so luminous, so generous and precious and fragile, so consumed with the desire for goodness and truth and beauty, so purely simple in itself as the conscious soul ever came to be imprisoned in a reality like this? Tangled in the nets of material mortality and pain and ignorance? When you consider that miraculous beauty and then consider the horror of this world—the way pain and disease and loss are inextricably interwoven into every aspect of its pattern, the intricacy of its economies of life and death—you can't help sometimes suspecting an infernal ingenuity at work in it, the malevolence of a jealous demiurge. I, for one, can tell you that I know just what Darwin felt—that exact shiver of revulsion—when he considered the inquiline predations of the ichneumon wasp. Who but a vastly resourceful monster could have devised a cruelty at once so subtle and so savage? So elaborate and yet so brutal? And then there are children dying of incurable diseases, or caught away by chance calamities... Though, really, sad enough in its own way is the gradual but inevitable dissolution of the innocent happiness of children into the disenchantment and disappointment and finally despair of adulthood."

"Perhaps," I said.

He turned his eyes back to me now. "Do you recall that Lafcadio Hearn essay about his visit to those sea-caves in Japan supposedly haunted by the ghosts of children?"

"Oh, that's a hard one to forget," I said.

"The ghosts of children. Think of that. Why would children's ghosts be trapped here when...?" And again he was staring away at nothing in particular. "We're all like fallen angels in the darkness of this life, forgetful of our heavenly home but still bearing the scars of that terrible... pterotomy."

"That terrible...?" I began, but then realized what the word meant. "Your appetite for classicizing neologisms is worse than mine."

He took no notice of me. "The only consolation is the thought that, if this reality is the product of fallen spiritual consciousness, then we must truly have possessed a divine nature when we were still there above. Only gods could fall quite so far. Still, sometimes one can't help but cast a jaundiced eye on everything, even the things we know to be good and noble and beautiful. Sometimes we look up at the star-strewn heavens and see the glorious garment of God spread out over our heads, like a sheltering pavilion. But we'd have to be fools not, at other times, to look up at those same stars and see only the vast, encircling walls of our prison-house. Like, as I say, the gnostics, seeing the celestial spheres as only so many terrifying and malign obstacles to be penetrated and overcome. Or like that fellow Paul from the New Testament, imagining the legions of celestial powers and principalities separating this world from God's empyrean. And sometimes it's even tempting to see suicide as a tragic protest against the archons. I suppose that's why I assume the third poem there is also about Deirdre. It's really just a bagatelle, more a song lyric than a proper poem. I think it's from 1962, which would be a good year for a folk-song, though it bears no date. An entry in his journals seems to refer to it in May of that year."

I turned to the computer again and clicked on the third tab. Another typewritten page appeared on the screen, slightly less discolored than the other.

Maya

She seemed a fiction of the winter light,
Or like a ghost imprisoned in the wind.
She dwelled where day surrendered to the night,
Where children never died, and none had sinned.

I found her when I slept, and knew her name,
And walked beside her in her evening land,
But left her there whenever dawn's light came,
Though still I felt the softness of her hand.

I could not count the voices that she had.
The most mysterious was the voice of morning.
The voice of twilight was profoundly sad,
So very like the hour it was adorning.

I know that it was no illusion, for
I was the one who left true life behind,
And lost the way back to that hidden door—
The way I cannot seek, but only find.

Roland in Moonlight

There was a place where still we were as one,
There in some other world, I know not when—
An age ago? And when this world is done
I'll find the hidden path and know her kiss again.

She will forgive me then for having gone,
For having so forsaken truth for dreams,
And I shall watch with her the final dawn
Of all that *is* from all that merely *seems*.

"I'm not sure the reference to Deirdre is quite as obvious to me," I said. "As you say, it seems a bit of a bagatelle, even if he took the time to type it out. Or song lyrics, really, rather than a poem—as you also said."

"Perhaps you're right," he replied. "Maybe it's really just about that... that woman he was always dreaming about... the one who may not have followed him into this world... the one he imagined still waiting for him in the celestial mansions beyond fallen time. But somehow I think it has something to do with Deirdre anyway, and her flight from captivity here below. I think—I don't know, but I think—that she entered deeply into his private mythology. I suspect that hers became the face of that otherworldly dream-woman of his."

I realized as Roland was speaking that I was extremely tired after all. Whatever had roused me from sleep had left no trace in my mind, and now a quite contrary, more plainly physiological impulse was calling me back to bed. "But who knows if what she did would lead out of the prison?" I said, pressing my hand against my forehead and closing my eyes. "It's just as likely a way of becoming more deeply enmeshed in the... the *kenoma*, I suppose... for a time."

I did not see now whether Roland was still staring away or looking at me; but there was a queerly emphatic note in his voice, as if he were telling me something he thought I particularly needed to hear. "It's all a matter of mood, I suppose, but there's a kind of sensibility—*your* kind, to be honest—in which sensualist levity and gnostic gravity intermingle and bear a strangely hybrid spiritual fruit."

"Do you think so?" I asked, keeping my eyes closed and resting back in my chair.

"Yes. At least, I think it's one way of diagnosing your present state. On the one hand, you're an aesthete, acutely devoted to the beauty of this world, almost to the point of hedonism. On the other hand, you suffer from an almost morbid obsession with suffering and death, and the suffering and death of the innocent—of children and animals—in particular. So for you this world is sometimes a radiant symbol of a higher world, a symbol caught for a time in the shadowy trammels of mortality and delusion and sin, but shining brightly amid the darkness even so. At other times, however, it's simply a sporadically lovely mask dissembling an absolute abyss of elemental violence and idiot fate. Sometimes you see it as the glorious prelude to something unimaginably good, and sometimes as something absolutely alien to the true good from which we've all been exiled. You love nature—love creation—but something in you also hates the world."

"Oh, but that's true of everyone," I whispered.

"Maybe so," he replied. "I think my actual point is that the two ways of seeing reality are, in a strange sense, one and the same. Again, it all comes down to mood. In either case, we know that we're at once at home and not at home here, seeing only shadows of things as they are, or seeing only in a glass, darkly. It's curious to me, I have to say, how willfully the religious imagination compounds its sufferings in this world with tales of hells and *narakas* and states of endless—or, at any rate, aeonian—misery, when this world provides all the hell one could ever need. Then again, perhaps those sadistic and masochistic fantasies make this world seem more tolerable by contrast... But, no, that's not it. More likely, those 'midnight's fears' of which Aloysius's distaff grandfather wrote are simply the products of long hours when we can't distract ourselves from ourselves. Whatever the case, the truly wise know that whatever hells might exist can be at most stations upon the way, the lower paths the wandering spirit must take through the darkness. Not that that's not horrifying. To me, the most terrifying picture of all is that of *punarbhāva*, of 're-becoming,' of the unbreakable fetters of karma forcing us always to begin over, reduced once more to ignorance of all that's gone before. Unless one's a dimwitted California of the middle class, how could one ever doubt the absolute horror in the idea of reincarnation?"

I continued to listen, my eyes still closed, but I was conscious that the flow of Roland's disquisition was making progressively less sense to me. "I'm not following your point," I murmured.

There was a pause. Then, in a quieter and somehow more intimate voice, he said, "I'm sorry. For once the problem is that I'm not making myself clear, not that your primate wits are unequal to my *dharma*. I was just..."

"Your...?" I was feeling now quite intolerably weary. "Did you say your '*dharma*?'"

"In the end," he continued, "both things are true at once. At one and the same time, this world's an order of power and deceit and death, to which the only proper response is wise despair and unremitting rebellion, and also a glorious revelation and foretaste and remembrance of a transcendent source and end. And the only attitude of the will that can carry us through and past the contradiction, or the polarity rather, is militant compassion—charity... *karuna*. If one can feel it—that essentially divine, essentially canine spontaneity of a heart purified of egoistic yearnings and ambitions—then one can know oneself as one with all who are and all that is, and can achieve a perfect personal identity that's also a perfect dispossession of self."

I felt myself progressively drifting downward toward sleep, like a leaf descending toward the dark surface of a forest stream on a moonless night, swinging gently back and forth on the air. And Roland's voice now seemed to be coming at once from both very far away and very close by, as if simultaneously withdrawing and drawing near.

"You find also," he continued, "that Buddhist 'insubstantialism,' so to speak, and Vedantic 'essentialism,' as it were—that they're really telling us the same truth: that in all things, and so in each of us, there's the one unconditioned reality that's at once infinitely more and immeasurably less than the pitiable little ego in each of us. Love or compassion goes beyond the false self toward the true self, and discovers the latter to be an infinite openness and hospital-

208

ity to the other. And don't all the mystical traditions, as well as the moral truths, of all the great faiths attest to this—that the most divine of paths is that of canine devotion and self-sacrificing love? We know it to be so. Hear me, O *bhikṣu*, there was once..."

"*Bhikṣu*?" I said. My voice was barely audible even to me.

"Hear me," he continued. "Once, long ago, *kalpas* upon *kalpas* in the past, there was a tiger who had long been a mighty hunter of deer in the forests of Bhārata, but who had been brought low by illness, and was near to starving, and was far too weak to pursue even the slowest and feeblest of prey. And there was also a young deer, so young that his antlers had only begun to sprout, who saw the tiger lying beneath the boughs of a great tree, and saw that the formerly dreadful predator was now so thin and frail that his ribs were visible through his pelt. At first, the young buck was overcome by fear and was disposed to run away and to leave the tiger to perish. But, as he considered the helpless creature, he found himself moved by boundless compassion and lovingkindness, and he bethought himself, and said to himself, 'Surely it is not good that this tiger should know the pangs of such hunger and such illness, or that he should perish for want of food. Surely none should suffer so. Vast is my pity, limitless is my mercy toward him. I am moved by lovingkindness to offer him mine own flesh as food rather than to forsake him to his death. Surely it were good that I should lay down mine own life that he might be restored, for such is the *dharma* of the great compassion.' And so the young deer went and lay down before the tiger, and the tiger, famished and feverish, driven only by his hunger, slew and ate the deer. Soon the tiger's strength was restored, and in a day he rose and left the place; but, before doing so, and having been healed in mind as well as body, he uttered his thanks to the deer that had given its life for him and resolved thereafter to feed on berries and roots..."

"A *jātaka*," I whispered. "You're telling a..."

And then suddenly Roland's voice rang out in an altogether unearthly tone, like a great gong sounding in the air all around me, and resounding and resounding in lushly golden echoes: "And I, O *bhikṣu*, was that deer!"

At once, I opened my eyes and sat up. The setting had changed—

if one could still call it a mere setting. I was now looking upon a vast panorama rather than upon the small enclosed foyer of my house, from a vantage that seemed impossibly comprehensive of the whole spectacle and yet somehow close enough to make out the features of all those present. And there was a vast company present. I knew at once where I was, moreover. It was surely Mt. Gridhrakûta, Vulture Peak, near to the city of the house of the Great Kings, on the glorious occasion of the deliverance of the *Wondrous Lotus Flower Sutra of the Good Dharma*. A pure and golden sunlight, brilliant and yet tranquil, illuminated everything. There were the twelve thousand arhats of the Buddha seated in concentric circles about the summit, as well as two thousand *bhikṣus* and *bhikṣuṇīs*, and just as many *upāsakas* and *upāsikās*. King Ajātsatru himself was present too, attended by an entourage of hundreds of thousands of courtiers and warriors and nobles and servants. I could also see, without obviously counting them, that there were indeed eighty thousand bodhisattvas present, all of whom in earlier existences had made offerings to innumerable hundreds of thousands of buddhas. And I saw too all the bodhisattvas mahāsattvas, including the four Earth bodhisattvas, and instantly recognized Avalokiteśvara, Samantabhadra, Mañjuśrī, Vajrapāni, Amitābha, Mahāsthāmaprāpta, and of course both Maitreya (He Who is to Come) and great Kṣitigarbha (with his shining nimbus and his staff that can force apart the gates of all the hells). And the gods were there as well: Indra was present with his retinue of twenty thousand gods, and Brahma with his retinue of twelve thousand, and countless other mighty gods and their divine retinues in the thousands. All eight of the Dragon Kings were there, attended each by hundreds of thousands of retainers. The four kings each of the *Kiṃnaras* and the *Gandharvas* and the *Asuras* and the *Garuḍas* were all present, each with his retinue of hundreds of thousands. The *nāga* kings and all their vast legions of retainers were there, as were *yakṣas* and *mahoragas*, kings of humankind, sage-kings and kings who turn the wheel, as well as measureless multitudes of other beings, human and inhuman. And I could see them all in a single glance. All at once, the Indian propensity for proposing unbelievably enormous numbers when describing... well, *anything* made perfect sense to me. And there, at the very summit of Vulture Peak, seated upon the Lion Throne in the full lotus position, wrapped in a sparkling mandorla of golden light, was Roland. Surely, though, it was his *saṃbhogakaya* that I now saw, as not only was I somehow certain that he exhibited all the Buddha's bodily marks of perfection, and not only was a continuous rain of *mandārava* and *mañjūṣaka* blossoms—and, indeed, *mahāmandārava* and *mahāmañjūṣaka* blossoms—falling all around him out of the open bice-blue sky, but I could also see the clearest and loveliest light imaginable emanating from the center of his brow, casting its radiance all the way down to the *Avīci narakas* and all the way up to the heavens of *Akaniṣṭha*, as well as into all eighteen hundred thousand Buddha-fields of the Eastern Quarter and upon all their inhabitants, in all six of the states of existence, and upon all the buddhas in all those regions. And I saw Maitreya himself standing before the Lion Throne and could see that he had just asked a question of Roland; and I could see Roland reflectively run his tongue over his own nose three times, nibble placidly at his own shoulder, smile with an expression of unutterable and blissful calm, and then finally open his mouth to speak, raising a single paw in the attitude of the teacher of the liberating *dharma* as he did so. Again, his voice was like the tolling of a great gong in the air all about me, but now so full and rich that the words themselves were lost in the beauty of their resonances, and it was almost as if those gorgeous waves of sound were a rising sea-surge carrying me down into their depths.

I closed my eyes again and at once the ringing ceased. The sudden silence was more overwhelming than the swells of those unearthly tintinnabulations had been. After a moment, I felt as if I were swimming up toward the surface again, purely through the exertion of my will, both out of those vast fathoms of sublime quietude and out of a profound sleep. I opened my eyes. The scene had vanished, and once again I found myself in the foyer, bathed in the bleak, blanching light of the computer screen. But when I turned my gaze down toward Roland, seated on the carpet near my feet, I found that he had not yet entirely reverted to his normal form. A softly luminous aureole seemed to surround him and to emanate from his fur, which glistened with a rare lustrousness; his eyes gleamed like opals; his features still wore an expression of ineffable

211

serenity. I shivered in what I can only call awe and closed my eyes again. And then I felt as if I were still rising, still emerging from the subaqueous shadows, floating upward, at last breaking into the open air. I opened my eyes once more, and Roland was simply Roland again, my small, compact, handsome dog.

"Are you all right?" he asked after a moment. "I seem to have lost you there for a few moments."

"Was that... was that real?" I asked, feeling the dryness of my mouth and laboring not to swallow my words.

He tilted his head to one side inquisitively. "Was what real?"

"I thought I saw... you. But not..." I sat up straight. "Was that a *jātaka* fable you were telling me a little while ago... or did I imagine it?"

He merely stared at me enigmatically.

"I recall you once before telling me of an earlier existence you could recall," I added, slowly regaining my alertness of mind. "The story of your days as a god in the *Tuṣita* heaven, when my brother was your pet monkey. It was... very diverting. You made it up, of course..." All at once, though, I felt uncertain of myself. "You did, didn't you? Only a... only..." The words froze on my tongue as he continued to look at me in that impenetrably mysterious way. "Are you... are you a buddha?" I finally forced myself to ask.

His brow furrowed, his eyes narrowed, but otherwise his expression remained perfectly impassive.

"Or a bodhisattva?"

Still nothing in his expression indicated any clear reaction on his part.

Now I began to feel foolish. "I'm sorry," I said. "That's a silly..."

"These questions," Roland interrupted in a solemn voice, "tend not toward liberation."

"Oh, I..." I cleared my throat and rubbed my eyes.

"If you were pierced by a poisoned arrow, would you not at once seek a physician to draw it forth from your flesh and to apply a healing salve? Or would you first pause to inquire who had mixed the poison, and who had daubed it upon the arrowhead, and who had fletched the arrow, and who had strung the bow, and who had fired the arrow, and why he had sought to harm you?"

"All right," I said, breathing deeply. "I understand. You needn't mock me."

"And if you found that your house was on fire, would you not at once flee for your life and seek help from your neighbors in extinguishing the flames? Or would you instead pause to inquire who had lit the fire and why he had been moved to such mischief, or whether the flame had been lit by coals falling from a brazier or lightning falling from the sky?"

"Yes, yes, all right," I protested, waving my hands in surrender.

"And if…"

"No," I said, rising, "I think you've made your point." I stared down at him, rather sheepishly I imagine.

He gazed up at me, his face still betraying no emotion.

"Well?" I said after a few seconds of silence.

"It might be just the right time for some of those lovely treats," he remarked. "One gets peckish in the wee small hours."

I sighed. "Let's go to the kitchen," I said.

I assume I retired again not long after that, but I cannot now recall.

XXXIV

THANATOS AND EROS, I suppose, tediously enough, really do vie within us. At least, memory and forgetfulness do: the one striving to draw us back into our pain (either the pain of sufferings that cannot now be undone or the pain of joys we can never recover), the other seeking to soothe us with a balm of insensibility. The constant, neurotic return to the trauma that the mind seeks ever and again to overcome (but cannot), and the constant, anxious flight from the trauma that the mind seeks ever and again to escape (but cannot). Recapitulation, oblivion: a ceaseless, tiresome, pendulous dialectic of obsessive misery and animal stupor. At any rate, that is how things felt during those early months in South Bend, and then on through the winter into the spring. The slow but now genuinely discernible improvement in my health, the clearing of my mind, the days on end without noticeable pulmonary inflammation—even when interrupted by periods of reversion—kept me moving forward, even as some other part of my mind insisted on returning again and again to the darkest days of my sickness, probing the still aching wounds in my memory, as if not yet ready to let go of the last two years' torment. Even so, although the harshest days of December, January, and February did sometimes lay me low and make me doubt my recovery, more and more I found myself free from lingering discomfort. I was learning, moreover, to accept a life of chronically diminished health. I was even becoming more useful around the house.

It was only well after that Christmas, and even after the first yellow crocuses had broken from the soil of our house's flower beds, that my mother's cardiac decline was diagnosed by her physician. Coming as she did from a line of enormously long-lived women, it proved something of a shock to her; it seemed that only now, midway through her ninth decade, was she genuinely confronting her own mortality as something more than a remote storm cloud on a far horizon.

TOWN

The large conference on my project on consciousness, promoted by the institute and well-attended, came and went, and while it lasted I enjoyed an idyllic interlude of old friendships renewed, new friendships struck up, and that fleeting sense of shared community that one sometimes experiences over meals and drinks and in circles of common purpose, and that makes it possible to believe that somewhere, at some time beyond the time we know, all shall be well and all manner of thing shall be well.

I was writing again at my old accustomed pace. I completed my translation of the New Testament, published some volumes of essays, another of technical writings, and continued to compile notes for the book on philosophy of mind, all the while producing fiction (mostly for my own amusement). I was also still contributing columns for money to that journal that, as yet, I had not noticed drifting free from its moorings in the shallows of neoliberal conservatism and into the undertow of a new nationalist, Catholic integralist, all American authoritarianism. No doubt the signs had been there for some time, but I had not been paying attention. I rarely read anything published in its pages—apart, of course, from my own scintillating contributions.

As spring yielded to summer, and that year's company of scholars left the NDIAS and dispersed to their several home institutions, I learned that my association with the institute was not at an end, and that it would resume in the spring semester, when I would serve as a Director's Fellow. In the autumn, I would be berthed in another of the many institutes and intellectual annexes of the university. I was beginning to realize that I and my family would be staying in South Bend for the foreseeable future. The prospect was not at all as disheartening as I would have assumed before coming to know the place. I had many friends here, the air was merciful to my lungs, and the area of the town around the university was conveniently laid out. My wife was quite content not to have to move yet again. My son, now fully a young man, agreed to be my mother's principal caretaker for as long as that proved practical. My mother herself, while not especially eager to die in Indiana, or anywhere other than on the sacred soil of Maryland, was nevertheless glad not to have to be displaced once more. And Roland, to the degree that he gave any indication of his opinion on the matter, seemed reasonably at peace with the situation.

XXXV

I T WAS, I believe, the third time the small, hard, moist rubber ball struck my forehead and dropped to my pillow that I awakened fully (or dreamed I had done so). The gaze that met mine was Roland's, his coal-black snout, drooping auburn ears, and handsome chalk-and-charcoal face so beautifully illuminated by the soft amber glow of the rush light beyond my open bedroom door that he looked like a saint or, once again, a bodhisattva wrapped in a haze of glory.

"Ah," I said, clearing my throat and slightly raising my head, "yes... I don't actually have any treats with me just now, and you'll wake Mama if..."

But he interrupted me with his soft, slightly amused voice (so hauntingly reminiscent of Laurence Harvey's): "No, no, I'm not playing that silly 'Give' game you like so much. And Mama's actually sleeping on the sofa in the living room just now. She dozed off while reading."

"Oh," I said, still gathering my wits. "Then why...?"

"I was wondering whether you were dreaming," said Roland, "and, if so, whether you'd be able to recognize the transition from one state to the other if I roused you." His snout momentarily came nearer and he briefly sniffed about my lips and nostrils. "Yes," he said, drawing back again, "you seem alert now. So—can you?"

I cleared my throat again. "Tell the difference? Yes... of course."

"Are you *sure*?" he asked, drawing out the last syllable and emphasizing it with a dubious half-octave rise in tone. "Can you *really*?"—again, the last word skeptically prolonged.

"Of course," I answered. "Why do you even ask?"

He sighed, smiled morosely, rose and moved several feet down the length of the bed, then turned and sat, facing me again. "I can't help but notice that when you write about our conversations you usually describe them as occurring in dreams."

217

"Yes," I murmured, trying to focus my mind on some thought or memory that seemed to have slipped just out of reach. "That seems... right... I mean, they do all occur late at night, and seem to follow from some dream or other... and..."

"Dear me," chortled Roland, gently shaking his head, "there's a venerable logical error for you: *post somnium ergo propter somnium*; sequence proves consequence; the cockerel heralds the dawn, hence its song must have conjured the sun. Really... and you with pretensions to philosophy."

"Yes," I said uncomfortably, feeling something of the force of his rebuke. "But they do seem, at least in retrospect..."

"*Seem?*" he growled playfully. "And here I'd hoped you'd be able to judge precisely from the phenomenal feelings of the situation... its distinctive qualia." He lowered his head pensively and, after a few moments, added, "Of course, I suppose that that begs the question—it's an obvious *petitio principii*. What really distinguishes a dream from wakefulness, after all? If experience is, say, just the phenomenal translation of some occultly noumenal *res ignota*—and I'm not saying it is, I'm simply posing the question—where can we really locate the boundary... the point of quantitative intensity within the qualitative continuum that marks the division between what we call dream and what we call reality? In a sense, the whole world in that scheme is the dream of the representing intellect. Or, better, the *figural* intellect." He paused, gazed at me for a moment, and then sniffed tentatively at my shin; then he sighed again.

"What?" I asked after another moment.

"Just trying to discern your mood."

"From my scent?"

His brow wrinkled and a small wince of disappointment appeared on his face. "Of course. How else? There's a reason why the olfactory is called the most divine of the senses."

"I believe that's actually said about vision."

At once the look of disappointment dissolved into an expression of affectionate mirth, and he shook his head wonderingly. "Primates are so adorable. What nonsense. What sense is feebler and more fallible? The eyes take in only surface impressions, and are so easily deceived by masks or shrouds or peculiarities of perspective or optical illusions. They're no use at all in the darkness. They're the fools of every false smile, every feigned laugh that conceals a stiletto. But the nose—ah, that pierces every veil of dissimulation, penetrates the night as easily as the day, faithfully guides one through the Stygian darkness or the winding labyrinth, finds out the truth the liar involuntarily betrays, the hidden intent, the secret fear—a man can control his lips, but not his pheromones—and is never prey to false appearances. *In naribus veritas*, as the ancient wisdom has it. It's the only sense that goes right to the core of the self. It's the very window into the soul. *Nasus ad nasum loquitur.* Antony forsook all the glory and power of Rome not for Cleopatra's eyes, but for her nose. No, no—olfaction is, as I say, the most godlike of the senses. I mean, why do you think that all our most ancient terms for spirit, the highest and most divine aspect of life, are also words for 'wind' and 'breath'? *Spiritus, pneuma, ruach, neshamah, ruh, ātman,* and so forth? Because what's most spiritual in us corresponds to the most *spiritual*—that is, the most *respiratory*—of senses. The primacy of the olfactory is attested in all wisdom traditions."

"Yes," I began, "all right, I…"

"That's why so many of them speak of the final union with God as an *odoratio beatifica* or *olfactus glorificatus.*"

"Now…" I paused and tried to recall whether this were true. "I'm not sure I…"

"I mean," Roland continued, "if you were, say, hiding some bacon about your person, and I were forced to rely on my poor, pitiable, credulous eyes to discover it, I'd…" But here he paused, glanced at me suspiciously, lifted his snout and sniffed hopefully about, and then sighed yet again. "Well, I'd have no chance. Vision is nothing but a dream within a dream… Maybe that's why it's so hard for you, come to think of it, to tell dreams from waking experiences. How hard it must be for an ophthalmocentric ape to distinguish reality from fantasy."

"Well, I don't think it's any harder…"

"Fragrance is the single unifying sensorium in which all of reality presents itself to us as an integrated whole, the unbroken phenomenal continuum within which the ordered yet variegated world of experience subsists and persists as a simultaneous apprehension of the senses and mind. Vision, by contrast, for all its importance and for all the loveliness it conveys to us, still knows only the outer appearance, not the unity of the outer and the inner… the deeper connection. Olfactory knowledge is the knowledge of life itself, the vital power animating all things. Visual knowledge takes hold only of… well, not vitality, but only a succession of *tableaux vivants*, so to speak. By itself, the eye is the supreme vehicle of illusion."

"Yes, so you've already said," I interjected.

"That reminds me," Roland said, yawning magnificently, "I've a question that you might be best able to answer, being a Hindu."

"Oh, that again," I said, unable to suppress an exasperated groan. "Look, I'm not…"

"Yes, yes," he said with an indulgent grin. "None of your games now. I have a serious question. Just tell me how you'd translate *māyā* from the Sanskrit."

"Oh," I said, trying to raise the angle of my pillow slightly, "well, it comes from the same Indo-European word as *mageia, magia*—magic—and means something like the power of creation, power to produce… in a metaphysical context, it means especially God's infinite power to create."

"And yet," said Roland, "most of us in the West assume it simply means 'illusion.' Why is that?"

"Yes, well, in a certain school of Vedānta, and then elsewhere, that became its special acceptation. Ādi Śankara certainly used it, not to indicate that the world is unreal, but that our false understanding or ignorance—our *avidyā*—makes us perceive reality as separate from God…"

"*Avidyā!*" It was an almost triumphant bark. "That's precisely what I mean. Your Indo-European roots are showing. 'Not *seeing*,' 'failing to *see*.' Reliance on the eyes cuts you off from God."

"Now, wait…"

"I'm joking," said Roland with a gentle snort. "All the senses dream, I know… or, rather, all dreams have phenomenal forms. Ghostly music, phantom palaces, fragrances from the banquets of the gods… the honey of a dream lover's lips… the thorn-prick of a reverie's rose. I suppose that's why primate culture is so uncertain of what dreams are: whether Thomas Browne is right—'*visions, and*

220

phantasticall objects wherin wee are confessedly deceaved… fictions and falsehoods…'—or whether they're visitations from beyond the Gates of Horn, truths written in the symbolic language of gods and angels, which only oneiromancy or oneirocriticism can elucidate to the waking mind… if there's such a thing as the waking mind." He licked his shoulder pensively, then sniffed at my shin again. "*Cognitio vespertina*, evening knowledge—isn't that the scholastic term for the synthetic knowledge of finite intellects? *Cognitio somnians* might be better. Did Zhuangzi dream he was a butterfly, or was he a butterfly dreaming himself to be Zhuangzi? What's the *ontological* difference between the phantasmic or represented empirical world within all of us and the noonday reveries of some ectothermic animal, like a lizard or a Californian, drowsing in the sun? Really, you Hindus, at least the Vaiṣṇavas among you, might have the best image there is of creation's ground: Viṣṇu fast asleep, in bliss, embowered in the loving coils of Ananta Seṣa, afloat on the Sea of Milk, hearing the sweet lullabies pouring from the great *nāga's* mouths, dreaming all things into being… and, asleep in each of us, that same divine awareness… so that we're nearest God in dreaming within his dream…" Roland raised his eyes now and gazed directly into mine. "Novalis knew—knew what we long for in finding God: that 'last morning… when the light does not scare the night and love away… *wenn der Schlummer ewig und nur ein unerschöpflicher Traum sein wird'*—when that sleep within becomes 'eternal… just an inexhaustible dream.' Maybe the Oceanian aborigines saw it all long ago. Everything comes from the Dreaming… the time before time, the place beyond time… and we dream the world within the greater Dreaming…"

"I think that might be a mistranslation, actually," I ventured, hoping to curtail the rhapsody before it became a symphony. "I think that '*alcheringa*' or '*alchera*' might mean something more like 'eternal' or 'timeless,' among a whole host of other things. I don't speak Arandic, of course, but so I've heard it said."

But Roland took no notice. He merely stretched his forepaws out before him, lay down fully against my legs, and continued speaking, half to me and half to himself: "And we come from there and go to there… and perhaps choose the time of our coming hither and our going hence... and perhaps not. But still... we come from the Dreaming and to the Dreaming we return... all is the Dreaming..."

Here, I believe, I was beginning to fall asleep again, but apparently Roland had noticed and was not yet ready for the conversation to end. He rose up somewhat on his front legs, thrust his snout under the edge of the bed's pallampore counterpane, took hold of the toes of my left foot with his teeth, and gently raised his head until my heel was hovering an inch or two above the mattress; then, carefully but firmly, he shook his jaws back and forth. "Yes, yes, I'm awake," I moaned, pulling my foot away and sitting up fully. "You don't need to do that. It hurts, you know. Your teeth are very sharp."

"I shall desist," he said, with a touch of courtly magnanimity in his voice. "But tell me: How did that feel? Could you tell whether that was real or a...?"

"Yes, of course," I said, trying not to betray my annoyance.

"Isn't it curious," he said, resuming his resting posture and gently licking my outraged toes, "that only in the modern world have dreams been so thoroughly sequestered from your species' understanding of reality—except, of course, by certain schools of psychotherapy, most of which, apart from the Jungian, reduce the significance of dreams to subjective experience only? At one time, the fluid boundary between the waking and sleeping worlds was much better appreciated, and hadn't petrified into a wall of granite. People understood so much more keenly that the dreaming intellect is simply one open to deliverances from other dimensions of reality... other regions of universal mind. Everyone felt it rational to view dreams—or consider the possibility of viewing them—as objective communications from somewhere beyond the close boundaries of waking consciousness. Aristotle wrote three separate treatises on the topics of sleep and dreaming and of prophecies that come in one's sleep, even though he was inordinately disposed toward a naturalizing explanation for most of the phenomena he considered. So too Cicero, in his treatise on divination: he may ultimately have rejected most oneiromancy as fanciful speculation, but he nonetheless reverently recorded Poseidonios's three classifications of dreams inspired by the gods..."

I breathed deeply. "You know, I'm familiar with all of this already. You needn't recite…"

"Ah, then, you can correct me if I'm wrong," he said, rolling to his side so that I could massage his chest with my now rather damp foot (which of course I began doing). "As I recall, the classifications are as follows: dreams in which the mind really perceives certain truths by virtue of its innate kinship to the gods; dreams prompted by incidental contact with the deathless spirits that naturally throng the air, who are bearers of symbols of truths otherwise hidden from us; and then dreams in which the gods directly address the sleeping mind, particularly when the dreamer is nearing death, in which they communicate truths about the future. 'They say the tongues of dying men enforce attention, like deep harmony,' after all."

"'Where words are scarce, they're seldom spent in vain,'" I said, completing the quote (as best I could recall it). "Anyway, yes, all of that sounds right."

"Not," added Roland, momentarily waving a paw in the air to signal that he was saying something significant, "that I believe any particular categorization of the oneiric realm is to be credited overmuch." He lowered his paw and, for a second or two, meditatively nibbled at its nails. "What I find interesting is the sheer effort of observation your kind was willing to lavish on dreams, as paths of entry into deeper—or, at least, different—forms of communion with reality, and how pathetically that sane impulse has been attenuated in the modern age, to the point that most persons regard dreams as irrelevancies or, at best, symbolic manifestations of their own little private psychological histories and nothing more. It was not ever thus. We have dream guides from Egypt and Babylon and Assyria that are millennia old—some as many as four millennia, in fact. And think of how many ancient oneirocritical theorists applied themselves to delving into those shadowy depths… those divinely nocturnal mysteries. Antiphon, Demetrios of Phaleron, Philochoros, Chrysippos, Poseidonios again… Artemidoros, of course. And think of those wise souls who heeded the messages their sleeping minds received in the night: Marcus Aurelius taking medical advice from the gods in dreams, Dio Cassius discovering his vocation as an historian by virtue of a divine communication in his sleep, Plutarch taking the advice of a dream-augury to abstain from eating eggs, Galen receiving instruction on surgery from the gods while sleeping..."

"Yes," I said, conscious that these expatiations appeared to have no natural terminus in sight, but also feeling the gravity of an incomplete night of sleep dragging me down. "But, of course, I'm already familiar with all of this. And it's rather late..."

"Quite so," replied Roland, apparently not taking the hint. "One of my favorite among ancient oneiric taxonomies is that of Macrobius. You know the one I mean,"

"I do," I said, "so..."

"As I recall, he enumerates five species of dream. The two most trivial or incidental forms are the *phantasma* or *visum*—mere 'apparition,' that is—and the *enhypnion* or *insomnium*—'nightmare'—neither of which should be accorded any prophetic meaning, and either of which one may safely dismiss as no more than a perturbation of the senses and imagination. But then, in more or less ascending order, come the three orders of dream that convey truths that must be heeded. There's the *oneiros* or *somnium* proper, a nocturnal 'perplexity' or 'enigma' wherein truths are couched in strange and baffling shapes, under palls of ambiguity; such a dream is always in need of interpretation by someone adept at the art. Then there's the *horama* or *visio*, the dream that's really a prophetic vision, wherein one glimpses events that will—and do—come to pass in the future, whether consequential or inconsequential. Finally, there's the *chrematismos* or *oraculum*, the 'oracular' kind of dream, sent directly by the gods, in which a god, or at least a divine messenger garbed in the form of a priest or a trusted relative or a man revered for his piety, directly and lucidly communicates to the sleeper something that is both yet to happen and of the greatest moment."

"Yes," I said, "that's just as I remember. Well, it's getting late..."

"I'm not sure that any catalogue of that sort really encompasses all the possible ways that the dreaming mind can penetrate the veil hiding reality's other side from us. It's enough to know, as Porphyry says, that that veil grows thin before the attentive soul, and betrays glimpses of what lies beyond it. Though normally, he adds, the veil obstructs vision, and is called 'ivory' on account of its opacity. There's the old typology of the ivory gate and the gate of horn, of course."

"Yes," I murmured helplessly, lying back on my pillows again.

"It's all quite important, though, isn't it? I mean, Porphyry is right that all truth is in some sense a *mystery*, in the proper sense of the Greek word: something closed in, within the holy of holies, concealed from vision by that sacred curtain. It's only when the soul is able temporarily to disengage itself from the body's pulses and powers in sleep that it can gaze—or at least peer intently—into hidden things, though never in the mode of absolutely unveiled apprehension. There's always some measure of darkness, something between the soul and the truth that calls to it. Still, one must attend to one's dreams even so, or one won't be able to distinguish those that are truly portentous from some momentarily enchanting nugacity of the roving imagination."

"Of course."

"Your hero Synesius of Cyrene, bishop of Ptolemais, affirms that dreams often foreshadow or disclose the shape of the future, and at other times impart vital information, like the correct cure for a certain malady. At still other times, he says, they reveal things to us about ourselves that otherwise we wouldn't know—the way a dream of the Muses, for example, might apprise the dreamer of his poetic vocation."

"You think Synesius is my hero?"

"Your model, at any rate," Roland replied: "Your ideal of how one should deal with the superficial differences between Christianity and paganism, for instance."

"Ah. Right. Yes. No doubt." I affected an unnecessarily loud yawn. "My goodness, look at the hour." There was no clock visible in the room just then, as it happened.

"You're very unsubtle," remarked Roland, at last acknowledging my hints. "I'll leave you to your repose soon enough. I know it's good for your health to get a full night's sleep. And who knows? There are healing dreams, I hear. It's a pity, really, that there's no temple of Asclepios in the vicinity, where you could slumber alone on some propitious night, awaiting a divine dream—a fine refresh-

Roland in Moonlight

ing night of mystical *incubatio.* Or maybe a temple of Imhotep, if you prefer a more Alexandrian setting."

"Yes, a pity," I replied, scarcely audibly.

"We can resume the discussion anon," he added. "In the meantime, I'll continue reading up on the classical Chinese *zhan meng shu*—the art of interpreting dreams, that is—as well as the various classifications of dreams. So far, I've really memorized only the three-dream system, the *san meng*, as described in the *Zhou Li.* Let's see, there are dreams merely caused by other forces or events, *zhi meng*, and then bizarre dreams or dreams in which one dreams one is dreaming, *ji meng*, and finally dreams in which the dreamer is truly visited by and communes with gods and demons and ghosts and other spirits, *xian zhi*—or, rather, dreams in which one's spirit wanders from one's body and visits those gods and spirits. But there are so many other systems as well: one with four classes of dreams, *si meng*, one with five, *wu meng*, one with six, *liu meng*, one with nine, *jiu meng*, one with ten, *shi meng*, and then ever so many other classifications, and each has its own metaphysical, spiritual, psychological, and even medicinal associations and concepts. And I've only begun to dip into Chen Shiyuan's great compendium, the *Mengzhan yizhi*—which means…"

"I know…"

"…*The Exalted Principles of Oneirocriticism.* I think that that might be the key to the entire Chinese science of *shenyou*, 'spirit-wandering.' That, by the way, may be the correct description of the matter. Maybe dreams should be seen as ventures out of the flesh into other realms of reality, rather than merely deliverances and visitations from those realms. And maybe all reality as we know it is simply a matter of *how* the spirit wanders, in the landscapes both of dreams and of the waking world. All of which brings one irresistibly to Owen Barfield…"

"To…?" Whether I actually uttered the syllable or only tried to do so I do not know. As Roland was speaking, I was inexorably sinking back into sleep, and now was quite powerless to arrest my descent. I heard him issue a last quiet, perceptibly fond laugh. A moment after that, I felt him lick my affrighted toes two times more. Then I heard the soft, muffled reports of his paws striking the carpet as he leaped down from the bed. Soon thereafter I was adrift in a dream of my own (something, I hazily recall, involving a river, a boat, a talking willow tree, and—perhaps somewhat incongruously—a small pig wearing a pink cravat and playing a melody from a Scarlatti lute sonata on a blue guitar).

XXXVI

W
E DID NOT resume the conversation, in fact, for some considerable time. We discussed other topics, I imagine, but it becomes difficult to remember our every discrete encounter during this period. Life had now settled into a more predictable routine, and the sense of imminent catastrophe had begun to recede, and hence a great many of the details of daily existence no longer stand out clearly in memory. In the fall, I returned for the first time in many years to the annual convention of the American Academy of Religion to participate in a few panels and deliver a few lectures. I made other visits to various universities about the same time, most of which I have already forgotten. I also participated in another conference at Notre Dame, this time on the sciences and religion, sat for some television interviews, and began appearing on radio and podcasts again, and wrote the better part of a novel as a diversion (I would complete it later). And it was a mellow autumn that year, crimson and tawny and purple under skies of pearl-gray or silken blue, perfumed at evening by wood-smoke, occasionally glazed by cool and gusting showers. In many ways, the feeling of normal life had been restored to me.

In quite different ways, however, there was an eerily fantastic quality about the world to which I was slowly returning, as if during my illness it had undergone some sort of magical transformation—if not in its visible aspects, at least in its spiritual basis. I watched as what seemed at first an utterly preposterous presidential campaign was run by an impossibly stupid, cruel, graceless, racist, sociopathic, openly fascistic buffoon—a confidence man known for his conscienceless rapacity, a serial business failure, a ridiculous creature of "reality" television, a notorious sexual predator, an inarticulate and functionally illiterate dunce, an inexhaustibly overflowing cesspool of spite—whom I assumed could never win the loyalty of any appreciable number of voters. If nothing else, he had all the effervescent charm of a bloated corpse suddenly surfacing in a shallow pond. Even his physical appearance was clownishly revolting: those close-set, squinting, angry little porcine eyes; that thick, glistening, oily coat of ochre lacquer slathered over those sagging cheeks and dangling jowls; that cartoonishly scalloped and jutting chromium carapace of dyed hair; those plump, puckering little Betty Boop lips constantly writhing up against one another like a pair of copulating slugs; those grotesquely tiny, moist, doughy hands; that pinguid blancmange physique, like a waddling morass of plaque and edemas; the unalleviated glare of brute stupidity on that ravaged face; the weirdly sexless mewling of that petulant, vicious, whiny voice. More to the point, his entire campaign was so soaked in hatred and lunacy and mendacity and loutishness, and his personality so soaked in unalloyed evil, that it seemed obvious to me that he could never gain sufficient support to rise to high office. Surely even our damp, dismal, bedraggled remnant of a living culture, I told myself, could never allow that to happen. In my perhaps blinkered fashion, you see, I had formed a rather clear impression of what I supposed to be his natural constituency (wife-beaters, Nazis, inbreds, cannibals, feral troglodytes, Satanists, human-pig hybrids, Satan, the walking dead...), and it simply did not seem nearly large enough to win a national election. And yet, throughout the primary season, I saw him relentlessly advance through the ranks of his rivals all the way to the Republican nomination. Soon, moreover, I began to learn of how much support he enjoyed among white American evangelicals and conservative American Catholics (proving again that Christianity has never quite reached these shores). Still, I was sure that this bigoted, ridiculously painted idiot could not win it all. Admittedly, he was running against a uniquely uninspiring opponent—a typical Goldman-Sachs, Military-Industrial Complex, "moderate" Democrat, with a documented contempt for those "deplorables" who had the temerity not to be drawn to her cosmopolitan sanctimony like moths to a flame—but she at least bore some resemblance to an adult human being. The sheer mediocrity of her appeal, I assumed, would win the day against the shrill, hideous spectacle presented by the degenerate imbecile on the other side. And so, confident in the eventual issue of the contest, and now living in a state where a Republican victory was already assured, I did as I always had done before and voted third-party (for the Green candidate, to be exact), as my fruitless but persistent biennial protest against "the system" and against the backwardness of both major parties. Ah, what innocent idylls! What days of wine and roses!

Late in the afternoon on the day following the malignant dullard's enormous loss in the popular vote but victory in the Goddamned Electoral College, even without yet knowing the sheer magnitude of the cataclysm his presidency would be, I found myself sunk deep in the Slough of Despond. My initial, self-righteous reaction was simply to tell myself that there was a great deal more profound stupidity and brutality about in America than it was comfortable to contemplate. But neither stupidity nor brutality, nor even the two in combination, could account for the magnitude of what had happened. Somewhere among those millions who voted for this transparently evil, heartless, and imbecile man, there were quite a few otherwise good and decent persons, who somehow had failed to see what I thought could not fail to be seen. Perhaps in our virtual age most of us choose the realities we dwell in: worlds within worlds, echoes within echoes, fantasies within fantasies, forever recapitulating themselves and mutating and spreading. And, truth be told, I could probably have named a good two dozen or so contributing causes if I had been pressed to do so, running the gamut from the understandable (the relentless destruction of the working and lower middle class economy by decades of rapacious neoliberal orthodoxy) to the utterly deplorable (white tribalism). Even so, just then I felt as if this were a new epoch, arrived all at once without any visible cultural precursors. Had I spent more of my waking hours online, I might have known better. Soon I would learn for the first time of the political evils that had been incubating in the swamps and charnel-pits of the virtual world, of the rise of a new far-right far out past the margins of civilized society, of the connivance of right-wing media and foreign powers in the manipulation of desperate, ductile, but politically enfranchised minds. I would learn also to despair of the possibility of any sane or virtuous human community in the age of the internet, and to recognize that the progressive cretinization and barbarization of *homo interreticulatus* is both inexorable and incorrigible. I would learn also just how much evil there was in the spiritual sewers of America for this despicable oaf to summon up, and just how little conscience, honor, or probity was to be found among elected Republicans.

Of course, at that point I could not foresee just how many horrors this creature would perpetrate, directly and indirectly—the stolen children, the lives destroyed or squandered, the violence and the terrorism, the corruptions and ceaseless lies, the attempted *coup d'état*, and so on—but I could sense that a national catastrophe had been set in motion. What was then apparent was that, quite expectedly, the mid-twentieth century struggle of *Kultur* against civilization had been renewed on American soil, in alliance with reinvigorated native racisms, and at a moment when civilization as a whole had already been reduced to a pathetically tabescent vestige of itself; and that a new tribalist nihilism and diabolical nationalism, masquerading as forms of "populism" and patriotism and piety, were making war on every social expression of charity, nobility, and wisdom. Everything seemed, just then, to have been plunged into darkness.

Except, I should say, for that autumn sky. As I was walking Roland through my neighborhood, on a now brightly sunlit afternoon, two hours or so after a minor rainstorm had blown through the area, I was momentarily arrested in my stride by the sight of a lovely opalescence high overhead, set off against an immense cumulus cloud of luminous white; and a few seconds later, as the sun emerged from behind another, more tenuous cloud, the twin arcs of an enormous, shimmering double rainbow became visible. It was stupefyingly beautiful. A strong breeze suddenly shook the branches of the trees lining the pavement, sending down showers of cold, sparkling raindrops and leaves of brilliant yellow and red. For a moment, I considered letting go of my depression. I even considered allowing myself to see the rainbow as a felicitous portent of better days to come, even as another part of my mind was tempted to read it as a smirk of celestial irony.

When we had reached the house and Roland had, as he always does, gone to apprise my wife of his return, I went to the back yard. From there the rainbow was splendidly visible, high above the bright collage of fallen leaves at the far end of the lawn and the towering trees in the cemetery beyond our high wooden fence. I seated myself in one of the deck chairs on the veranda and merely stared up at it. I was tired, however, not having slept much the night before, and soon, predictably, I dozed off.

XXXVII

I T WAS THAT familiar, plush, plummy voice that woke me again, perhaps less than an hour later. "You mustn't mourn for your country," it was telling me in a gentle draft of warm breath near my left ear. "You never felt much devotion to it to begin with."

I opened my eyes. It was still day and the sky was still bright, but the rainbow had faded. I turned my head and saw Roland backing away from my chair, removing his front paws from my armrest, and smoothly dropping down to the veranda. He seated himself on his haunches, staring off into the blazing colors of the treetops as they steadily and languidly shed leaves like tongues of flame on the dead beneath their boughs.

"No," I said, "not as such. But there were things I liked about it that may never have been real… or as real as I'd thought they were, at least. It's the cruelty that depresses me. It's the fear for… for my son, if the world is turning… harsher, crueler…"

Roland sniffed idly at a passing gust of wind. "Even so," he said, "it was ever thus. The evil is always there, just below the surface of things, held in abeyance more by custom and comity than by the rigors of moral codes and religious beliefs. Apes are apes, after all, even if the *bien pensants* among them are often insensible to how ponderous the weight of that phylogenic history can prove at times. When someone comes along who blithely discards or defiles those customs, with sufficient wantonness and coarseness, invariably you'll find that there are hordes of your fellow bonobos all too ready…"

"Sorry, " I interrupted, "if you recall, I'm not a bonobo."

"Forgive me," Roland replied. "I'd forgotten. Though I shouldn't have. Bonobos wouldn't have elected such a man. But, anyway, setting all those precious little pedantic distinctions aside, there are hordes of your kith all too eager to lapse gratefully into unapologetic barbarism. It's the cultural counterbalance to the tendency of

233

others of your kind—the builders of ivory and ebony towers, the morbidly reflective—to lapse into decadence."

"Is that the danger I run, you think?" I asked, cocking an eye at him.

"In your more problematic moments, yes," he replied, quite blandly. "But the only proper response to moments of crisis like this, when everything seems poised on the edge of ruin, is always the same."

There followed one of those infuriating silences that typically succeed Roland's most tantalizingly enigmatic remarks.

At last, I gave in with a sigh: "Well, what is it?"

"What's what?" he asked without looking at me.

"The proper response... to moments of crisis... like, you know, *this* one?"

His sigh was deeper than mine had been, as if it genuinely pained him to have to state the obvious. "Why, to seek righteousness, of course. To love justice. To seek to become one of the truly upright and virtuous souls—a *tsadik*, as it were. Indeed, to seek to become one of those righteous ones for whose sake God suffers creation to continue to exist, a 'righteous one who is the pillar of the world,' the *tsadik yesod 'olam*. And then to seek others of your kind to aid you in the great work of the *tikkun 'olam*, the world's restoration, and in the gathering up of all those burning sparks of the *shekinah* that were lost in the shattering of the vessels, and that now lie seeded throughout the darkness of this lower reality. There's no other course."

"Have you been reading my books on Qabbalah?" I asked.

"Yes," he said, "along with several others I've ordered through your various online accounts."

"You've what?" I said with a small groan. "Look, you know we try to keep a budget."

He appeared not to have heard me. "Of course, I might just as well have said that you should strive to become a bodhisattva in this *kalpa*, one who refuses to enter into nirvana until all other sentient beings precede you, and until all the hells, all the narakas, have been emptied: Arbuda, Nirarbuda, Tapana, Nebraska, Saṃghāta, Sañjīva, Tampa Bay... all of them."

"I'm neither a *tsadik* nor a bodhisattva," I said.

"No," said Roland, with a queerly emphatic note in his voice, "definitely not. What I said was that you can strive to become one. Take this moment as an occasion to remember what a passion for justice feels like, or used to feel like back when you were young and idealistic, and deadly serious spontaneous moral indignation was second nature. Goodness, go back to your elementary school days, when you were constantly writing stories and book-reports about slavery in this country and the massacres of native peoples and…"

"How on earth do you know about those?" I asked, turning my head to stare at him (rather incredulously, I am fairly sure).

"I found some in old boxes," he remarked casually. "I have to say, there's something… sweet about the thought of you at the age of ten choosing to write a book-report on *Bury My Heart at Wounded Knee*, and in such a voice of theatrical moral outrage. Sincere, mind you, but theatrical. Or the story you wrote about the escaped slave and his little sister…"

"I remember that…" I said. "Yes. That was for Mrs. Levine's class… fifth grade…"

"If you say so. In any event, that's my advice. Take what lies ahead as an occasion to remind yourself to love justice and mercy as much as you can. It's the only path to sanity. Moreover, it's what's required of you now. Not to repine at history's wild vicissitudes, but to think and speak and act as one whose name is worthy to be spoken in the heavenly places. It's also efficacious to do so. The world that exists is the world that we all together—or all in proximity to one another—imagine it to be. To seek to look with charity upon all things is the first step in the labor to reimagine and thereby to remake all things into vessels of charity. This is the most basic law of the coincidence of epistemology and ontology. It's like that rainbow you were looking at a little while ago."

"It's…?" I settled back into my chair. "All right. What's it have to do with the rainbow?"

"Oh, I was merely put in mind of Owen Barfield's use of the rainbow as an exemplar of the mind's participation in the construction of reality."

"I recall you bringing him up before…"

235

"I'm not a disciple or anything of that sort," Roland hastily added. "For one thing, he's too prone to speak in terms that sound like a representationalist account of our perceptions of reality, even though that's precisely *not* what he's getting at. It somewhat obscures the ontological side of that participation when he does so. Even so, his point remains a solvent one, no? That the rainbow as such doesn't exist in itself, simply by virtue of the diffraction of light through vapor droplets, but is the result of a participatory—even nuptial—union between consciousness and being? And that, no less than the rainbow, all phenomenal reality is also participatory? Everything's all, in some sense, a poetic achievement of the congress of spirit—which is invisible nature—and nature—which is visible spirit. Again, though, as I say, he sometimes inadvertently makes this sound like something of a Kantian claim about the apparatus of perception rather than the much more radical claim about the inseparability of consciousness and being that he means to make."

"This doesn't really seem to be what we were just talking about," I remarked, somewhat hesitantly. "I noticed the reference to Schelling there, by the way."

Roland nodded. "I've been reading quite a lot of Schelling lately."

"Anything in particular?"

He smiled, somewhat shyly. "Well, as it happens, *Clara*. Oh, and the *Weltalter*."

"Interesting," I murmured.

He rose from his haunches, stepped down from the veranda, turned his snout sideways, thrust it into the grass, and then grace-fully collapsed on his side, turning over onto his back and wriggling energetically back and forth. "Ah, that's lovely," he said with a small growl of pleasure. "There's nothing like a grass-bath after a gentle rainfall." When he had been at his ablutions for nearly a minute, he rolled back onto his side, facing me, stretched his limbs, sneezed twice, and then lay still with an expression of perfect contentment on his face. "You see," he said when a few seconds had passed in silence, "I've been thinking about dreams and wakefulness a great deal since we talked about them... oh, it seems ages ago now. I find a great deal of appeal in Schelling's notion—at least, during certain phases of his thought—that our rational faculty is preceded by, and

arises from, the *Ungrund* of the unconscious mind, and that in a
sense the vast dark ocean of the unconscious must withdraw itself
to make room for the existence of the small, brightly lit island of
rational consciousness. Rather like the *tsimtsum* of God's *ohr Ein-
Sof* to make room for creation. It doesn't quite accord with my own
metaphysical premises—at least, I wouldn't grant that the difference between the conscious and unconscious minds is really a difference between the *rational* and the *irrational*, properly speaking—
but it's thrillingly mysterious and lovely even so. For myself, I'd prefer to speak of the difference between the Dreamtime and the time
of *māyā*, and from there..."

"You're being a bit promiscuous with your syncretisms, aren't
you?" I interrupted with a laugh.

He closed his eyes and deeply drew in the fragrance of the grass
through dilated nostrils. "I certainly hope so," he then said. "I also
very much like his description in *Clara* of those moments of sleep
that come just before dreaming begins, when we half consciously
glimpse the seeds of our personalities buried in the soil of the
unconscious mind, and know that at death they'll achieve their full
growth in the perfection of our true identities. And I'm especially
enamored of the *Weltalter*'s treatment of clairvoyant and magnetic
dreams, and the ascending stages of portentous dreaming, right up
to the ultimate oneiric state that we can't remember afterwards
except in fragments—the state of free communion with the spiritual, archetypal, angelic world at the apex of subjective mind."

"All right," I said. "This still doesn't seem to be germane to..."

"No, it isn't," he said, turning upright and raising his eyes to
mine. "My apologies. I'm wandering off on a tangent, I fear. No,
what I meant to say when I mentioned the rainbow was simply that
you mustn't despair of the world about you simply because it fails to
meet your expectations, or because the frame of social reality seems
to have shifted when you weren't looking and become something
unrecognizable to you."

"It amazes me," I said, quite sincerely, "how well you read my
thoughts at times."

He smiled indulgently. "Primate psychology isn't a particularly
complicated or abstruse study. In any event, what I mean is that you

can always do your small part to reconstitute the pattern of the world through the energy of your own consciousness. See the world differently and a different world will emerge to be seen. If only... if only you had the immediate intuition of this truth that canine culture has never forsaken... even the rationalist spaniels and skeptical Airedale terriers and dourly pragmatic dachshunds among us. Remember, as I've said, so much of what we take to be the limits and configurations of the real are only the conventions agreed upon by those whose perceptions shape that reality. All the history of your race, after all, is the history of consciousness constantly revising the nature of... well, nature... that of the world and that of yourselves. Why, consider how different the humanity that looks upon the cosmos as a system of machines is from the humanity that was once able, almost effortlessly, to descry the gods in all things. Think of what's become of your kind ever since you erected an impregnable partition between the historic and the mythic, and in the process reduced the latter to quaint tales and meaningless fables and petty psychological allegories. At that very moment, the free communication between the world of the five senses and the world of the Dreamtime was almost entirely disrupted, and reality as your kind knows it withered and solidified into the meager, mechanical effigy of nature that so many of you now mistake for Nature as she truly is. Nature always loves to hide, yes. But how heavy, how opaque... how like *ivory* the veil of Isis has now become. There was a time when the mythic world and the world present to human minds were not so cruelly separate, when time didn't flow in a merely linear sequence of causality, when Indo-European tenses weren't fixed in a rigid structuralism of past, present, and future, when..."

"What?" I asked. "What was that about tenses?"

"Sorry," he replied, idly nibbling a few blades of grass. "A needlessly recondite philological point. All I mean is that when, say, Plutarch reported that there was an island west of Britain where Kronos slept in a deep cavern of stone that shone like gold, confined there by Zeus under the watchful gaze of the giant hecatoncheir Briareus, fed by birds with ambrosia whose fragrance pervaded the whole island, and that in his dreams Kronos foresaw all the future events that Zeus intended for the world, and that prophecies were harvested from those dreams and delivered by intermediary spirits… well, what he reported was verifiably true. One could indeed have found that island if one sought for it in just the right frame of mind, at just the right moment, when the rays of the sun struck the ocean waves at just the right angle. And one could have found the titan sleeping in his cave of gold—the great fallen king of gods and men—if one knew how to look. Not precisely on this side or the other of the wall between dreams and waking reality, but in that still accessible realm and at that still locatable juncture where the two merged and flowed into one another, and where the Dreamtime and circadian time ceaselessly blended with and sustained one another."

"I see…"

"And, of course, on the other side of that juncture, quite out of sight to us now, lies the paradise of the before-time… the Eden that we can all remember but never recall… the terrestrial Gan Eden, as well as the heavenly Eden of the 'olam ha-ba where the righteous will gaze upon the divine chayot… and the Sumerian Dilmun… and the Hesperides…" His voice was taking on an almost hypno-tized quality, as if he were drifting away irretrievably into his own thoughts.

"I'm still not entirely sure what this has to do with what's put me in this mood," I remarked, loudly enough to call him back from his deepening trance.

"What?" he said, raising his snout from the grass and looking at me again. "Oh, yes, well, I mean only that you mustn't sit about in sackcloth and ashes for the next four years, lamenting the death of a civilization that was never very civilized to begin with. Seek ye first the Kingdom, after all—a Kingdom that is, it turns out, inside of you. Seek to enter the visionary company and…" But now his brow furrowed as some other thought evidently crossed his mind. "You know, it's all very vulgar, isn't it? The human notion of civilization, I mean? Especially in the modern age? I mean, it seems to me that a civilization exists—and is truly great—precisely to the degree that it succeeds in retaining and preserving memories of that other, more original reality that now lies on the far side of the Dreaming, and translates those memories into great poetic feats of imagination… into great art and… into profound and inexhaustible symbols. And that's not always something that can be measured purely in terms of its material expressions, can it?" He looked far away, toward the now faintly roseate western sky. "Of course, it's easy to equate civilization with material gigantism and technological mastery, but all of that's often contingent on material conditions and possibilities. Some peoples have achieved incomparable greatness without ever embodying that greatness in tactile or visible artefacts, principally because circumstances were less than propitious for building on a grand scale, or even for surviving at much above the subsistence level. Rather, they've done all their building, so to speak, in the spiritual realm. Consider those peoples whose culture best nurtured and protected that fragile, elusive memory of the Dreamtime, the aboriginal peoples of Australia. And, yes, I know that 'Dreamtime' isn't a literal rendering of '*alcheringa*,' so you needn't mention it again."

I lowered the hand I had just raised and closed my mouth.

"The world of their poetic visions contains incalculably complex and exquisite structures of spiritual creativity—prodigious dreamscapes composed out of the impalpable but imperishable stuff of imagination. Theirs might be one of the most arduously achieved civilizations ever known, and yet where are its monuments in this world? By comparison, Manhattan is nothing but an infantile exercise in physical accumulation—the sort of thing that impresses the savages you'd find in a neoconservative think-tank or some Ayn Rand institute, but nothing more." He lowered his head morosely. "Then again, of course, civilizations like that—the kind that exist only in the inward realm of vision—can soon enough be exiled altogether from history. They may be perpetual achievements, but they aren't necessarily perennial facts about the world we know. They too can be driven off into the realm of the mythic, sealed behind the doors of the temple, in the now inaccessible inner sanctum of the mysteries. Think—just think—of how much was lost when the Western barbarians came, and began to destroy the patiently accomplished agronomies of the native peoples of Australia, which had been the principal physical manifestation of the spiritual tact that made those peoples at one with their land. And consider how much continues to be lost as the children of those ethereal civilizations are still today being drawn away into the shrill, brittle, ever altering spectacle of modernity… into a world that never dreams, that's always savagely awake… always awash in a grim fluorescent glare that makes everything look leprous…" Once again his voice suggested that he was floating away into his own reflections.

"Well, what can one do?" I said, again a little loudly.

"I mean, Mungo Man was interred with full funerary rituals some 30,000 years ago or so. Who knows how ancient a civilization it truly is… how long its dreamscapes have overlain the landscapes of Australia?"

"Indeed," I said.

He yawned, shook his ears vigorously, sneezed again, and then continued, now in a more conversational tone. "And I have no doubt that, during all that time, aboriginal shamans—'clever fellows,' or whatever they're called—have continued in the same fashion to undergo the same spiritual transformations, and to be lifted up into the same heavens. Surely they've kept open those ancient avenues to the 'Father of All'—to Ungud, or Mangela, or Nambakela, or Daramulum, or Baiame, or… well, whatever name he's called by—all that time, century upon century, without ever wavering from their holy calling. They've also kept alive the memory of the great Rainbow Serpent—Jarapiri, Kunukban, whatever—winding his way across the continent and creating its landscape as he went. And isn't that simply the mythic tale, the true tale, of consciousness shaping the world it inhabits?"

"Is it?" I asked.

He turned his eyes to me again. "You know, we all come hither into this world from the Dreaming…"

"So you've said."

"…and go hence again into the Dreaming, when the *birrimbir* soul returns to the heavenly realm and the *mokuy* soul departs into the darkness… the nothingness."

"I see."

"We were all there, you see, in the beginning, and we'll all be there again at the end… and even now we're there. At least, so it's said by some—that, after the mortal body is buried, the *ulthana* or spirit rejoins its *arumburinga* or spirit-twin in the timeless realm."

"I don't believe I'm familiar with any of that," I remarked after a moment, trying to recall whether I had ever before heard of the notion. I sat forward in my chair. "That's very interesting, of course, because it's…"

"Because it's reminiscent of the gnostic idea of our spirit's heavenly double or twin," Roland interjected.

"Yes," I said, "precisely."

He nodded knowingly. "Quite so. The Gospel of Philip, I believe, and the Hymn of the Pearl, of course. And, needless to say, there was Mani's celestial twin. But isn't it obvious, really?"

"Isn't what obvious?"

Roland turned his face to the western sky again. "That each of us has a true self 'there above'—the self each of us is *sub specie aeternitatis*… the eternal truth of who we are, freely consenting to our own existence in our own first beginning, freely rejoicing in our own consummation in our last end. Both before and after our life in this world, always already complete. As Plotinus said, there's that aspect of our souls that never descended, that forever looks upon the naked beauty of the noetic world. That's, for each of us, the true self, from whom each of us has been temporarily estranged and to whom each of us shall eventually return."

"Well," I said, "it may be obvious to you."

He sighed again. "I admit, I do have a certain advantage where these matters are concerned. Much more than your kind, dogs have retained the ability to gaze into the glass of possibility, to peer into hidden…" He paused pensively. "Tell me," he suddenly said, "have you ever used psilocybin?"

At this, I was genuinely taken aback. "What? Why do you ask that?"

He looked at me with a small but obvious knowing smile. "Don't be evasive. Have you?"

"Well… not *psilocybin* as such."

"Some other hallucinogen then? Mescaline? Or raw peyote? LSD, perhaps?"

I smiled feebly. "The last, in fact. Back in high school… and college. Many years ago. Why do you ask?"

"Oh…" He sniffed at his own right shoulder and then breathed in deeply. "You really should try rolling around in the grass just now, while it's still just damp enough and so very aromatic. You can't imagine how invigorating it is."

"Perhaps in a little while," I said. "But you were saying…?"

"Oh, I was just thinking of shamanic trances, vatic frenzies, journeys into the spirit world… Dionysian transport, even… and of how much of human religious experience has been aided by psychotomimetic drugs or intoxicants or mortifications that alter brain chemistry. It really is all about breaking down the walls that your kind erects between ordinary consciousness and extraordinary vision. Deranging the machine so that the spirit can break free momentarily from its pitiless regularities. Mind you, the same is true of the ecstasies of art, the sacred elations of dance and festival, all forms of poetic inspiration and celebration. You're always striving for the rare and inspired moments when those walls begin to disintegrate, and when you can catch an unobstructed glimpse of the land beyond… and can step out of the confines of the finite ego into the vast territories of universal mind. That's certainly what your great uncle and great aunt were thinking back in 1956 and again in 1958, when they traveled to Taos and experimented with peyote."

"*What?*" I sat further forward. "Did they? Did they really? How would you know that?"

Roland rose, turned his body about, sat again, and looked at me as if once more making some silent mental adjustment to his general evaluation of my wits or character. "I do think you might occasionally have read some of Aloysius's papers. You profess to have been so fond of him."

"I was. That's why I'm hesitant to learn more than I might want to know."

He looked at me with an expression of gentle vexation. "You needn't fret about that. And you shouldn't be surprised. As I've said, Aloysius always longed to find a way back to a world that *spoke*, that *communicated*. He was inspired to make those expeditions to the Southwest, you see, by the appearance of Aldous Huxley's *The Doors of Perception*. I'm afraid, however, that I've discovered no real record among his papers of what revelations he may have received—or what your great aunt Polly's experiences were, either. Well, except that both were made rather ill by their first samplings of peyote. I

243

know only that your great uncle professed to have been deeply moved by certain things he saw in his altered states of consciousness. And he left behind at least one poem written in one of those states." "Is it any good?" I asked.

Roland took a deep, meditative breath. "That's not the point, really. It's interesting as a testament to something really experienced, I think, but ultimately incommunicable. You can look for yourself, though. It's right there next to you." He gestured with his snout just a few degrees to my right and somewhat downward.

I turned my head to look and for the first time noticed the slender, blue plastic binder lying on the veranda not far from my right foot. I picked it up, wiped the slight moisture from its underside on my trouser leg, and opened it. I stared at Roland again for a moment, hesitating, but then looked downward. The binder held perhaps ten sheets of paper, all obviously pdfs of typed pages, the first two of which read thus:

Dream-Language Dithyramb
(*or, Ode: The Demiurge and the Aeolian Harp*)

Beauty and the music of the air
Disturbed by visions and by tendencies
To rearrange the sleeping tangle of her hair,
To name the music and the beauty's mildness:
For sun on windowpanes, now bronze,
Divides her world from light of any color
But this splendor, and the shadow of her body
Paints its cool and fluid figures on the wall.

Still beauty underlies the wind's deft melodies.

Such is the shadow, such the light, the dream, the dolor,
And she turns the deep red shadow of her body
Toward sleep (as a leaf might turn toward night)
Where the music must forever fall:
Such the dolor, shadow, dream, and light.

The somber moans of viols as the hours pass:
What beauty here beyond all ravishing,

TOWN

What glowing fruit of day on what green vine
Will catch those sallow glimmers from the edge of night?
It will not bear night's shadowing.
And night the color of full grapes with dark blue skins,
And fragrant of the sea, salt-white with soft green foam.

How can she know the beauty of her body fall,
Its fullness like the ripening yellow
The sun has burnished on the clustered fruits,
Pendant in her dreams? Now she descends to silent worlds.
She is conscious of strange music,
She is aware that lush green shadows grow
Between her and the evening world beyond
The window and the murmurings of pine.

There is laughter in the darkness of her sleep:
She sees recumbent Adam, naked, prone:
Who rose out of his dreams, the wild fruit of his fantasy,
To take and taste, to gaze upon and nourish sight:
Sweetness of blossomed air, of shining body out of light:
But hers the dream sustaining all, creating beauty,
That deeper down and at the green abyss
Becomes the source, from the unfelt, as music.

The flushed sky glows upon its silver loom, and no one can
Unthread the strands of red from violet night:
Her sadness stays, for still she hears
The strains of song receding from the light,
The winds that stir the harp's taut strings.
And so what world there is to live upon,
What truth there is to know, can now
Rise only from her dream:
The air is emptied of its light:
Her bright body knows the glory of such flowering.

The date at the foot of the page was September 1956. After having
read it twice, I closed the binder, shrugged, and sat back again in my
chair.

245

"Any reaction?" asked Roland when some seconds had passed.

"Well, it's not exactly 'Kubla Khan,'" I replied.

He smiled wryly. "Its composition was, however, interrupted by the arrival of a man from Porlock. Selling tallow, I believe."

"Well, that's certainly a coincidence," I said with a meager laugh. "I sort of like the penultimate stanza, I think."

"That's definitely where the... *feel* of the thing seems momentarily to become intelligible. Something about the feminine, consigned to secondariness by a certain kind of mythic perspective or... I don't know, mythopoetic consciousness, but actually being the deeper, more original source of the reality we dream into being... the divine wellspring. Your great uncle's inner goddess myth again, I think. Who can say? In all fairness, Aloysius never made any great claims for the poem. He kept it because, as he said, when he was writing it, and for as long as his chemical transport lasted, he felt sure he knew exactly what it meant, and that it all made perfect sense, and expressed exactly what he had seen; but then, when he had regained his normal state of mind, he had only this souvenir of his journey into the other world, but no clear recollection of what it represented."

"Of course," I said, "it's always possible it never meant anything, and his wits were so addled by the drugs that he temporarily couldn't distinguish profundity from gibberish."

Roland began to smooth the fur of his chest with his tongue, somewhat more deliberately than usual. "No," he said, lifting his snout again after some seconds, "I don't think that's quite right. It's not quite... babble, is it? It's much more like something genuinely glimpsed, genuinely caught hold of for a vanishing instant. And then, of course, *she's* there."

"She?" I asked.

"Yes, you know, the 'she' who shows up in so many of his poems. *Her.* The one he longs for with that strange ache, part memory, part anticipation of something unforeseen... part worship."

I looked down at the binder, still resting in my lap. "I don't know," I said. "At least I can say it has the feeling of a dream. A disconnectedness, that is, that might have felt more continuous and intelligible at the time, under the influence. But... why exactly did you bring this to me now?"

"Oh, I didn't," he replied. "It was the next poem—the one directly after that one, written a month later—that I meant to show you. I thought it particularly *à propos* to your mood... and to the cultural hour."

I opened the binder again, found the pdf of the next poem, also typewritten, and read:

Tiberius on Capri

Depraved, unthinking animal who drag
    Your swollen limbs and girth across the grass,
Noisome, indolent, and strange, arbiter
    Of all our many destinies, retire
And go again to your damp lair, the cold
    Bright quietudes where monstrous deities are bred.
A sea of writhing shadows turns about
    Your head, a crowd of dim and distant forms
Perturb your memory's hazed horizons.

The children's ruthless laughter at the sea's
    Warm verge invites you to recall sweet thoughts
Hidden deep in senile forgetfulness:
    Coarse urgings of the flesh, the rich delights
Of boundless cruelty—"Fling the slanderer
    Headlong from the cliff!"—O, ravenous wolf!
Incapable of dreams or of ideas,
    Gross lout, murderer, gaping brute, how can
One such as you imagine that when once
    The dreary drumbeat of your life has ceased,
You will be called "philosopher" for this,
    Though all fled before you as from the soft
Stalking of some inexorable beast?

"I see," I said on closing the binder again. "A bit like Robert Graves, maybe. Definitely appropriate to some degree, I suppose. But a poem about Caligula or Nero would be even more so."

"Sadly," said Roland, "there's none to be found among your great uncle's literary remains."

"In truth, it's all still too flattering. The reality of the moment is far more squalid."

"*D'accord*," he replied quietly.

A distinct blush of pink now pervaded the western sky and dyed the edges of the white and lavender clouds overhead. "The days are getting shorter," I observed.

"And who can say how long the night will prove?" Roland mused. Then, after several seconds of silence, he said, "Shall we go in now? We really should all decide on what's for dinner tonight."

"Yes," I said, "I suppose we should."

And doubtless we did, though here memory fails me.

XXXVIII

WINTER CAME, and the dry, bitterly cold air was a trial for my lungs, though one perhaps not as severe as that of the previous winter. Then spring arrived in moist, fragrant, floriferous splendor and lingered for months, in a way it never does in Maryland. I had a new collection of colleagues at the institute, every bit as delightful as the first had been, and representing an even more diverse array of disciplines. My own project deepened further, began to crystallize around certain themes that I had initially imagined to be only accidental to its design, and took on ever more vividly Neoplatonic and Vedantic colorations. I finished the writing of two more books, unearthed a comic children's mystery novel that I had written with my son when he was eleven years old, persuaded an old friend of the family to illustrate it, and arranged for its publication with a visionary editor. My health continued to show improvement, if not miraculous at least encouraging. And at some point I agreed to return to the institute for one last year, this time not as a fellow but in the role of a deputy director of the undergraduate research assistants.

As, however, I would no longer be an endowed fellow of NDIAS, I would no longer be entitled to free university accommodations, so it became necessary to rent a house. We found one a few streets away from where we had been living, on a pleasant avenue in a neighborhood of older homes and copious trees, and signed a lease for a tenancy beginning in April so that we could make our move from one home to the other in stages over the course of a few months. The new house was constructed on three levels, which made it less than ideal for my mother, but it had an annex at the back—a kind of airy sunroom with a sliding glass door on one side and a rear exit opening out onto a wooden deck—which we decided to make into her bedroom. By that time, it had become obvious to me that her next room would almost certainly be the last room she would ever inhabit, and this one seemed more than ordinarily cheerful. Behind the house, moreover, all around that deck and enclosed in high wooden fencing, was a garden, well kept by the owners of the property, adorned with some young fruit-bearing pear trees, but otherwise positively begging for my wife's loving horticultural attentions.

Sometime in the waning days of the semester, I took stock of the journal for which I had been writing for many years and reluctantly concluded that its current editorial policy was a cautious but firm embrace of political and religious positions I thought not simply wrong, but positively evil. The senior editors had even publicly pledged themselves to the cause of the degenerate sadistic racist child-abducting moron in the White House, thus simultaneously destroying the last vestiges of the journal's reputation and probably securing themselves berths in hell. So, reconciling myself to the loss of regular revenue, I severed all ties with the publication. This would lead to some bad feelings, and even three comically inept attacks on my next book in the journal's pages as retaliation. Estrangement soon became enmity. But that was, as yet, all in the future. On the afternoon when I sent off my email of resignation, the only feeling of which I was aware was an acidulous melancholy. I found myself recalling much better days, in different cultural circumstances, and the friendships that had existed then, when amicable ideological disagreements were still possible, because the politics around us had not yet become a matter of open spiritual warfare, and because one faction had not yet explicitly allied itself with the devil. Now, sadly, everything had changed. Apparently it had been changing for some time but I had been too involved in my own concerns and fixations to notice.

XXXIX

I T WAS IN THE EARLY HOURS of the morning following, if I recall, a long day of moving beds and bookcases and books and papers into the new house, near to the time of our final departure from the house by the cemetery, that Roland and I next had a long conversation. At least, I believe that was when it happened, because I was sleeping in the guest room when he woke me—licking the lobe of my left ear with the tip of his tongue and occasionally taking it gently between his front teeth and tugging at it—and I would only have been there because I was exhausted and wanted to retire early, and it happened to be situated in the quietest and most secluded part of the house. "What time is it?" I mumbled, raising myself into a sitting position. It was dark, but not absolutely so. The thin muslin curtains admitted just enough light from the direction of the campus that the white of Roland's fur was visible as a cloud of smoky silver, and his eyes and nose gleamed softly out of the shadows. He had withdrawn a few feet down the bed. "It's too early to be getting up," I remarked in a plaintive tone.

"It's past three already," he replied. "You've had more than five solid and fortifying hours of sleep."

"That's not nearly enough," I moaned.

"Now, now," he said, "don't be petulant. You don't want to be accused of sloth, do you? The ancient Romans always rose well before dawn."

"And retired soon after dusk," I replied. But I knew that it was best to surrender, as long experience had told me that Roland would go away again only when he had satisfied himself regarding whatever thought or perplexity had prompted him to wake me. So I heaped all the pillows on the bed together behind me and lay back against them in a reclining position. "All right," I said, "what's the matter? Is there something wrong?"

"A question of vital importance."

"One that can't wait till...?"

"One that can't wait at all."

I closed my eyes. "All right, then," I said, "what is it?"

"Do you believe in the possibility of multiple worlds?" he asked, a distinct note of urgency in his voice.

I hesitated to reply. I could not quite see how this was an issue that needed to be addressed without delay, no matter the hour. But I also knew that any protest on my part would be of no avail. "Whatever answer I might give to that would have to be qualified by a number of considerations. Are we talking about Everettian quantum mechanics? Or is this a more general metaphysical question? I mean, I suppose that if one wanted to affirm classical theism one could say that there are infinite possible worlds, and that in the divine supereminence all of those worlds are in some sense actual and really exist..."

"I believe," Roland interrupted with a hint of impatience, "that one will find that, where logic's concerned, the physical and the metaphysical versions of the problem coincide. That's rather the point of my question, you see."

"Oh." For many seconds neither of us said anything. As always, though, I was the one to capitulate. "Can you explain?"

Several more seconds passed in silence before he replied. "I can, I suppose, but it occurs to me that I should probably explain how the question came to me before considering its possible answers. Otherwise, I fear I'll leave you behind."

"Oh, well," I said, "if it's a complicated sort of thing, perhaps we'd better wait till later after all. I really am very..."

"It all came to me," he said, "as I was considering that elegant little personality test I devised—you know, the one that can tell you almost everything about a person's temperament, sensibility, and character from his or her answer to three simple binary choices."

"Have you told me about that before?" I asked, certain that he had not.

After a momentary pause, he said, "Perhaps I haven't, now that you mention it. I certainly haven't put you to the test, so I suppose not."

"Well, what is it?" I asked, now genuinely curious. "I mean, what are the questions?"

"They couldn't be simpler," he replied: "Bach or Mozart? Tolstoy or Dostoyevsky? Lennon or McCartney?"

I opened my eyes, but in the darkness I could not see whether his expression was an earnest one or was instead that mercurial smile he wore whenever he was gently mocking me. "Those are the questions, are they?" I asked after a long pause.

"Yes indeed."

"And you can tell an enormous amount about someone from how he answers them?"

"Definitely."

I exhaled slowly and audibly, fluttering my lips as I did so, mostly in impatience with myself: I knew that I needed to go back to sleep, but also that I would not be able to do so until I had made sense of this. "It's not a question of choices between one's loves or hates, is it? Or between which one in each pair is 'good' or 'bad?'"

"Obviously not," he replied in a scoffing tone. "How could it be? Consider the terms of the choices. It's a matter of one's preferences between differing manifest excellences, not a choice *for* or *against*. That wouldn't tell you anything about anyone. At the very minimum, one expects anyone to know that, say, Martin Luther King Jr. was a better man than Hitler. But so much is revealed when one must choose between different kinds of perfection."

"Yes, that makes sense," I said. "Well, then, for me the answers would be clear: Bach, Tolstoy, Lennon."

"As I already knew," he said. "In any event, I happened to be thinking about that test, and all its implications, at just the same time that I was pondering a few of those questions that naturally occur to one in the dead of night. You know what I mean: Whether, for instance, Heisenberg's matrix mechanics is just a strategy for saving the appearances, rather like Ptolemy's cosmology. Or whether George Sanders and Tom Conway really were brothers, and not just the same glum, cynical chap in a partly unresolved superposition state, with two only partially decohered wave evolutions—on the one hand headed toward a death by his own hand (out of ennui), on the other toward death by cirrhosis (out of ennui)—rather as if Schrödinger's cat were to live out two continuous evolutions in a single macroscopic space."

253

"That seems very unlikely to me..." I began.

"And just then, no doubt through an accidental convergence of all these disparate trains of thought, it occurred to me that there's an argument for the reality of God from the Beatles."

For several seconds, neither of us said anything. I knew that he had left the remark dangling between us like a cat toy in order to force me to ask him to enlarge upon it, but I was resolved that, on this one occasion at least, my will would prove more redoubtable than his. I failed, of course. "All right," I finally said, "what is it?"

"Well, you're no doubt aware of how some philosophers of religion, in that quaint and credulous way they have, argue for the 'existence' of some 'entity' they call 'God' from the extraordinarily fine calibrations of all the cosmological constants that make this universe possible."

"Yes," I said.

"Not that such constants aren't suggestive. I just object to the crudity with which analytic philosophers of that sort tend to conceive of God."

"Naturally," I said.

"But my point is that one of the ways in which skeptics on the other side answer this argument is to argue that our 'Goldilocks' situation in this universe seems amazing to us principally because we assume it's a one-off affair, rather than one among an innumerably great number of universes, perhaps being ceaselessly generated by fluctuations in a 'quantum foam.' Now, I'm not sure if that's a successful response or not, as I haven't the patience for the mathematics necessary to calculate the probabilities of those constants. I mean, there may be levels of improbability so great that they exceed the conceivable stochastic limits of even infinite iterations. Drop a million nickels from an airplane over the Arizona desert and it's *logically* possible that they'll all end up resting upright on their edges in a thousand neatly serried rows, ordered chronologically by their dates of issue. But I daresay that even an infinite number of repetitions of the exercise wouldn't achieve that result. Though perhaps I'd have to ask a set theory specialist..."

"I think I'm getting a bit lost here," I interjected.

"Mind you," he said, "I'm also not sure how much I trust in any

254

arguments from statistical quantification. It's always a strange sort of fiction, isn't it? The statistical mean, that is? A sort of Euclidean abstraction of generalities, useful when describing—not explaining, that is, but describing—a distribution of possible results. I trust in the particular, however. A poem is the truth of poetry. And, after all, I have Aristotelian tendencies—as distilled through Neoplatonism of course—and so I'm content to say that perhaps a universe is of its nature a certain set of rational relations that 'naturally' subsist in any cosmological context. So, well, cosmological constants might simply constitute the equation, so to speak, that a universe is."

"Well, that's..."

"But then there are the Beatles. That's a level of improbability that, to my mind, may very well exceed any plausible set of purely fortuitous results."

I tried again to make out his expression in the darkness, but it was impossible. "Not Bach?" I said. "Or Mozart, for that matter?"

Now I did see, if only in murky outline against the dim glow from the windows, the familiar disappointed shaking of Roland's head as once again he found himself obliged to guide me step by step to a conclusion he thought should have already been obvious to me. "No, certainly not. Individual genius, no matter how prodigious or colossal, is statistically uninteresting—nugatory, in fact. The fortunate accident is always a possibility of random chance. *Un coup de dés* and all that. It *must* sometimes occur, if only to define the limits of the statistical curve; but, no matter how far outside the norm, it's not outlandish as regards the mean. But here we're discussing a confluence of possibilities so unlikely as to defy the credulity of even the most superstitious materialist. Lennon and McCartney meet as boys in postwar Liverpool and want to start a band, and they just happen to be arguably the two most astonishingly gifted natural songwriters of their generation, as well as among the most capable of constant innovation and development in style. What other band ever boasted two song-writing talents that prodigious? And then, along the way, they pick up a guitarist who just happens to be George Harrison, who will himself become a songwriter of extraordinary originality and range. Well, it simply can't be accident. It's what Fred Hoyle called a 'put-up job.' There must, it seems, be a designing intelligence behind it all."

"I see," I said after a moment, not certain whether I found this line of reasoning persuasive. "I do have to admit that the Beatles do somehow feel... *necessary*," I mused. "At least, it's hard to imagine the world without them. But that's partly, surely, because they so influenced the way we hear melodies, and write them, and the way we construct songs, and the sort of chord progressions that arrest our attention, and the..."

"Yes, yes," said Roland. "That's all true. All those lovely modal melodies especially. The Mixolydian mode seems especially pervasive. 'She Said She Said,' 'Tomorrow Never Knows,' 'Paperback Writer'... 'Within You Without You,' of course. Oh, and 'Doctor Robert' and 'If I Needed Someone.' And that magnificent Mixolydian bridge in 'Rain.' And, of course, the oscillation between Mixolydian and Dorian in 'Norwegian Wood,' for instance, or between Dorian and Aeolian in 'Eleanor Rigby.' Though all their melodies were remarkable, whether modal, major, minor... I wonder why they didn't include 'Rain' on *Revolver*..." His voice trailed away.

"I've never heard you speak so warmly of popular music before," I said.

There was a long, somewhat uncomfortable pause. "Why shouldn't I?" he eventually asked. "Surely you don't think me the sort who disdains the popular on principle. Whatever's done well is admirable. Whatever's done superlatively well is high art. And to have produced that many distinctive and original melodies with that many imaginative modulations and chord structures and so on, and in less than a decade together, was to have done something superlatively well. Anyone who dislikes the Beatles is a philistine."

"I notice," I said, "your test doesn't include the always burning question of my youth—you know: Beatles or Stones?"

"Of course not," he said with an air of indifference. "That's not a choice one should have to make. Apples, oranges. Chuck Berry, Buddy Holly. Scarlatti, Handel. Watteau, Chardin. And it wouldn't tell me anything. If you feel you must prefer one to the other, all that means is that you suffer from a needlessly constricted sensibility."

"All right," I said with a yawn. "Well, thank-you for explaining it all to me. I'll just try to get more sleep now if…"

"But that's merely what *led* to my question. The issue of many worlds, you see, has a far wider scope for me than any dreary calculus of physical or historical probabilities. The metaphysical implications are, to my mind, far more exhilarating… and troubling." I felt him settling himself on the bed by my feet. "I've been pondering Wheeler's Delayed Choice proposition. Far more consequentially, I've been pondering the violation of Bell's Inequality. I mean, locality is clearly done for, at least within the typical physicalist way of approaching these things. And I don't know what difference it makes to presume or to reject 'hidden variables' once that fact's been established. And… you see, I do think I believe in a real collapse of the quantum wave-function. I just think that all the variations of the basic double-slit experiment still make that inevitable. And I still think that Eugene Wigner was right in thinking that consciousness does actually play a necessary role, and I think it's able to do so precisely because it's not confined within any system of physical causality mediating between quantum and classical scales."

"You don't think that maybe the whole issue of the collapse might be done away with by a sound theory of decoherence, then?" I asked, feeling myself being drawn against my better judgment into the conversation after all.

Roland snorted derisively. "I don't see how that would really dispel the measurement problem. I don't see what difference it makes theoretically. Of course, that goes right back to the whole issue of multiple worlds, and the possible multifurcation of reality in moments of measurement, and… well, I suppose it would neatly explain away the apparently superluminal instantaneity of effect in entanglement. But for now I withhold judgment. It does occur to me, however, that so much that's paradoxical in the standard model of quantum mechanics wouldn't have seemed the least problematic in antiquity. There's something at least instructive in that."

"How so?" I asked, shifting myself into a somewhat more upright posture on the pillows. "What do you mean?"

"Doesn't it seem to you that part of the enigma of the quantum realm lies as much in how we think about causality and actuality as in the actual results of observation?"

"I should think so," I said, now finding myself genuinely interested. "Go on."

"I suspect that a good number of modern tendencies of thought cause us to see problems where we might otherwise not. I'm not saying that those problems aren't there to be seen. But it's a matter of what questions you ask, and with what presuppositions. One modern tendency is to think of potentiality only in statistical terms, as a mode of logic but not of ontology. Another is to think—even when quantum theory should have disabused us of the prejudice— that all real causality must be somehow mechanical, a transfer of energy operating within the physical constraints of spacetime. It was very different for, say, the ancient Aristotelian who understood 'causality' primarily as a system of rational relations, *aitiai*, and thought of the most basic kind of material causality—*hylē*—as a real principle of potency awaiting the impress of a formal cause. For him, it wouldn't have seemed at all paradoxical to find that there's an instantaneous correlation of determination between two entangled entities when one of them is observed, because formal causation isn't a physical transfer of energy, but rather a rational specification that's transcendent of time and space, the immediate translation of potency into actuality—an event both logical and ontological. Nor would a good late antique Neoplatonist necessarily have recoiled from the thought that the instant of formal determination and the instant of conscious observation might be one and the same event. And, of course, it shouldn't be inconceivable to us now that consciousness operates at an oblique angle, so to speak, to the texture of spacetime, like a formal cause impressing itself instantaneously on that fabric, in a way that would have no unfolding temporal history of physical processes within the continuum. Since form's a principle that seamlessly unites the ontic and the epistemic—that is, one and the same form actualizes both material and mental potency—it's not all that mystifying that observation should be the real occasion of the collapse of the possible into the actual. Seen that way—I mean, seen in a way that allows for the modal distinction between potency and act to be understood as a real ontic distinction—there doesn't seem to be much difference between the Copenhagen version's collapse of the wave function and some Everettian divergence of universes. I mean, so long as one sees the measurement as indicating the divergence of an actualization from a real realm of possibility that otherwise retains its purely potential modality."

"Do you think," I cautiously interjected, "that perhaps, without knowing it, some theorists are heading back in that direction? I mean, in the way that so many increasingly speak of quantum theory not as a theory of physical states as such, but as a theory of information? Information understood both as, in some sense, an intrinsic property of quantum events and also as our knowledge of those events? I'm not sure I understand where it's going, but it may suggest a more… imaginative approach to potentiality and actuality."

"Perhaps," said Roland quietly. "But, of course, many of those approaches use 'information' to mean what's wholly situated in the initial quantum state, but then progressively diminished for us as the superpositions decohere. Information is what's sifted and separated and, so to speak, epistemically *diluted* by its ascent into higher scales. That's not the same as seeing the quantum realm as being informed by a higher actuality. For them, I think, 'information' is an alternative to the potentiality wave, whereas you're talking about 'information' as what's *gained* in the collapse of the potential into the actual. The logic is reversed."

"I suppose so," I said.

"That's more than a semantic difference," he said. Then, after several seconds, he added, "That, I suppose, is another distinctively modern tendency of thought—to presume that physical explanation always properly takes the form of a reduction of phenomena to their most basic material ingredients, and to whatever physical forces might apply exclusively to those ingredients. That's the narrative of absolute emergentism… total composition from below. And with that comes the myth of irreducible emergence—understood as a purely mechanical process—and specifically the irreducible emergence of phenomena from lower into higher scales. And, of course, analogously, your kind has learned to think of phenomenal reality as only the emergent representation of a qualityless realm of pure extension and force, and to think of mind as nothing but the faculty that accomplishes that dissimulation, and so too see the world in which you live and move and exist as a congress of ghosts... qualitative phantoms marking the absence of the quantitative really real. But nothing simply *emerges*. Phenomena are *formed*. They always have a final cause, a rational maximum of their intrinsic possibilities, so to speak, which is native to the formal properties individuated in them. And the quantum realm is nothing but the first responsive level of potency as a real mode of being, the analogical boundary between nothing and something. That seems obvious to me, at least. The old metaphysics is still illuminating. I mean to say, the realm of the phenomenal is the realm of the finite and the determinate, which is the realm where the principle of non-contradiction necessarily obtains, and so where every superposition of possibilities must yield to a collapse into singularity in order to become anything actual. But that realm exists in the interval, the *metaxy*, between two realities where non-contradiction doesn't hold sway: the infinite simplicity of the divine, which is a *coincidentia oppositorum* in which all is forever always actual, and the infinite indeterminacy of *materia prima*, in which all is always only possible and in a state of 'informational' superposition... infinite patiency, awaiting formation. And our consciousness participates in—is a vehicle of—that gracious descent of the light of the former into the darkness of the latter. The infinite potential of the lower order of being is able to exceed the determinate realities of finite actuality only because it is more originally a mirror of that infinite actuality of the higher order, that *actus purus* there above, from which comes the power that makes prime matter *this* or *that*. And that nuptial union between possibility and the actuality it reflects is something that happens here below whenever mind *attends* to reality."

"Ah," I said, sinking back onto my pillows, "that seems like it would be a hard sell among modern physicists."

"I'm not interested in being a salesman," said Roland. "My interest isn't scientific, after all. I'm just as happy to call that interval between infinite actuality and infinite potentiality the realm of Fairy, or the Dreamtime. I do wonder, though, whether the actualization

260

of a world in the conventional consciousness of any given age might
have a retroactive effect. Whether the past is in some sense changing
with every new conformation of the cosmos in thought. Or perhaps,
it might be better to say, whether the past as we know it, and as it
connects to the conventional picture of the present, is changing. I
mean, we know that in a sense entanglement is as much a temporal
as a spatial inseparability and…" His voice trailed away. "Anyway,"
he resumed after a few moments, in a tone that suggested he was
chasing some distracting thought away, "I'm not sure that 'many
worlds' explanations of quantum effects really allow us to ignore the
role of consciousness in wave evolutions. And that's true of 'many
minds' explanations too. For one thing, I don't think that consciousness is a mechanical thing that can become entangled with a particle
and multifurcated along its various consistent histories. I think that
the mind's intentionality is an act of *attending* to an object, and that
in doing so it actually determines the object as something available
to attention. Until then, all those histories *really* exist as potentialities, but thereafter one of them exists as an actuality. It seems to me
that otherwise there wouldn't be a change induced in observable
physical effects in, say, the double-slit experiment—between, that is,
the visible manifestation of an interference pattern and the visible
absence of such a pattern. If observation somehow induces a divergence of the observable—even if one means by that only the collapse
of information into a decoherent spectrum of different evolutions of
the wave—there was still a single world in which the wave function
was an observable unity and then, as a result of observation, and all
at once from one end of reality's wave function to the other, there
wasn't. There's a local collapse of the *reality* of the undular into that
of the corpuscular *because* the mind attends to its object. Given that,
why should I grant that the consciousness of the observer isn't
the efficacious power that makes this world out of that one? I can't
conceive of an understanding of measurement that allows me to separate the act of consciousness from the actuality of being. Consciousness *is* being, so long as one remembers that potency and act
are *ontological* modes, as I say, not just logical modalities. I don't
think that there are multiple worlds *in actu* here in the realm of the
finite. I think that mind participates in composing the whole history

261

of a particle, just as it is always doing for the world as a whole—plucking the rare flower of the actual from the wild, untended, fertile gardens of the potential. Conscious attention, ontic determination—where's the line to be drawn between them? What's the difference between saying there's been a collapse 'out there' and saying there's been an awakening of the mind 'in here?' Knowledge is itself formation—the passage from potency to act in the mind—and there's no surprise in learning that it's the same as the passage from potency to act in the world. Again, of course, the world that's thus produced is a collective convention of attention, but maybe not absolutely bindingly uniform. That's why dogs, for instance, or isolated primate visionaries like Blake can still find the way back to the abodes of the gods. In every moment, all souls are seeking the path to a shared frame of perception, but some souls happen upon other paths... other doorways."

Unwillingly but resignedly, I was now thoroughly awake. "It would be amusing to think," I said, "that the defeat of Aristotelian physics by the mechanical paradigm might be succeeded by a vindication of Aristotelian metaphysics in the quantum paradigm."

"As specified by its Neoplatonic interpretation, of course," said Roland.

"Of course."

"Of course, in that sense the collapse of the wave function would be only an exquisitely acute manifestation of something happening in every instant. The vast ocean of the world of indeterminate possibility is forever disappearing into the narrow channel of the world of determinate actuality. And, of course—and perhaps this is the most Aristotelian thought yet—if one assumes the arrow of time to be itself only an effect of that actualization, as the form taken by that collapse, but otherwise reversible in the realm of the possible, then the course of the collapse comes as much from the future as from the past. More so, as final causality is the rational terminus that determines which formal determinations are to be extracted from the indeterminacy of the possible. And that fits rather neatly with the notion that entanglement occurs as much along the fourth axis of spacetime as along the other three."

I glanced toward the window. The light seeping in through the flimsy curtains had not noticeably changed. There was still time to sleep away the rest of the early morning, if I could bring the conversation swiftly to a close.

"You move with disarming ease between relativity and quantum mechanics," I remarked.

I heard him sigh deeply and felt him stretch out along the length of my leg. "Well, doesn't the stable fixity of the formal and material axis of reality require the energy—the *energeia*—of the efficient and final axis, in order to be set into motion... in order to *become*? What is structure without force? I prefer to say that Parmenides and Heracleitos must embrace... that Apollo and Dionysus must together provide both the orderly measures and the wild frenzy of the cosmic dance of generation and destruction. And we see this even in reality's subtlest and most minute choreographies when we apply our minds to the sub-atomic realm, every time the whole flowing reticulation of undulous possibilities is suddenly pulled taut into a fixed corpuscular weave."

"All right, then. Well, if that's all..."

"Needless to say, that also fits in nicely with my contention that the world produced by mind is always also in the process, perhaps, of having its past reconstituted, rewritten... or, rather, reperceived... in such a way that things once possible become practically impossible for conventional consciousness. Hence the history superstition—the belief that there's such a thing as the 'true' historical narrative of the past that can be distinguished, in every age reaching all the way back to the beginning of the universe, from a 'false' mythical narrative. Modern thinking, uniquely, with its mechanistic prejudices, abstracts the poverty of the historical out of the superposition of narrative pasts and thereby reduces myth to pure fantasy. But you can't suppress those other worlds forever, or even completely. They still wait there, pressing through—at least, till the last shaman or mad visionary, the last blessed lunatic, the last Blake or Kit Smart, has turned to dust. The last terrier, the last dolphin, the last grey parrot. The last octopus. Yes, for most of your kind today the gods are lost in the collapse of the potentiality wave... banished like the gods of Epicurus to the ontological interspaces. But now and then, in different guises, they find avenues back to manifestation... to *theophaneia*. At one time, theophany was ubiquitous. Human consciousness, in looking at anything and everything, intended also the dimension of divine splendor in everything and so again and again parted the veil hiding the gods, and allowed them to step forth in all their glory. But, as I say, that past has been reconstituted now, and the unity of the tale has been discriminated into temporal history and atemporal myth. And so the gods live on in their full radiance in that other, forgotten, unforgettable past that we all really share, and still know in that now occult dimension of mind that still dreams the potentiality wave—where Odin hanged himself for nine days upon the wind-shaken world-tree Yggdrasil, pierced by his own spear, and where Nachash walked on God's holy mountain in the stones of fire, and where Adonis slain by the boar lay in the arms of Aphrodite, and where Arthur sleeps in Avalon. That's where the gods of lightning and thunder and rain conquered—and still conquer—the monsters of chaos: where Indra slew the great serpent Vṛtra, and Perun the great serpent Veles, and Zeus vanquished the serpent giant Typhon, and Ba'al Hadad defeated the great sea-serpent Lotan, and Teshub slew the great sea-serpent Illuyanka, and Yahweh subdued the great sea-serpent Tehom or Leviathan, and Marduk slew Tiamat, and Thor will one day slay the mighty world-serpent Jörgmungandr. There too is the forest where Gilgamesh and Enkidu stripped Humbaba of his seven mystic radiances and killed him, and where they defeated and slew the Bull of Heaven. There the Vanir and Aesir fought their ancient war, and there lies the plain of Mag Tuired where the Tuatha Dé Danann defeated the Fomorians, and where..."

"I think I understand," I said, at last unable not to interrupt.

After a moment's silence, Roland gave vent to a loud, prolonged yawn that dissolved in a small but sonorous groan. "Yes, sorry," he said after a moment. "Anyway, I imagine my point is obvious."

"It... is?" I asked. "I'm afraid I may have lost sight of it."

"Only that what for us is a vanished possibility is always in some sense actual in God. In fact, that might be our best modal picture of God. As the infinite act of mind who is also the infinite act of being, he has no 'real relation' to this or that world as something over against himself. So what would the difference be for God between

TOWN

'imagining' a world, so to speak, and creating? All realities are com-
possible in the divine nature, and so also actual in the divine nature.
That creative *potentia absoluta*, or *māyā* or *śakti* or Sophia—that
eternal divine *dynamis* that is the source of *to dynaton* here below—
isn't merely some logical or statistical possibility. It is for us—to
us—that the collapse occurs, as a measure of our freedom as finite
beings in our own rights. But the collapse isn't a *pathos* for God as it
is for us. It literally makes no difference in him."

"It sounds vaguely Spinozan…" I began.

"No," Roland instantly interjected. "The collapse is real enough
and isn't necessitated. Creation really occurs *as* creation, as other
than God even in having its life and movement and existence *in*
God. In God, yes, it is God, but in itself it is not God."

"Still, *can* there be freedom in such a scheme?" I asked.

"Of course. The truest freedom imaginable. For one thing, consciousness and the rationales informing its intention of the world
aren't simply the inevitable consequences of prior physical causes. It
really is mind that induces the reduction of potency to act—or,
rather, the collapse of the wave-function. Within the physical continuum, understood as a spatiotemporal totality, everything is
determinate perhaps; but consciousness doesn't belong to that continuum, but rather forms it from outside… from elsewhere… from
the Dreamtime. It stands between infinite potency and infinite act
and participates in the poetic labor of bringing the world into
being, in every instant, out of inchoate possibility into determinate
substance, as it seeks its natural end in the goodness and truth and
beauty of the divine nature. It's the demiurge, looking up toward
the eternal splendors, and then looking down to catch their reflections in the dark waters of the possible."

"So…" Now I raised my head from the pillows again and stared
once more toward the foot of the bed. At last, Roland's features had
become faintly visible in the mild, pre-dawn light, though not well
enough for me to discern an expression. I saw only the persistent
gleam of the eyes and nose, the slight luminosity of the white fur of
his snout and upper body. "So you're saying that we're in some
sense co-creators with God?"

"Isn't that the most primordial impulse of any rational nature?"

he said. "To know reality by making it within consciousness, and thereby to reach out to the one who makes all things in and through our making? Why should we think that our knowing reality is a separate, private representation rather than a direct participation in the very 'Let there be' of Genesis?"

"God creating by creating gods who create...?" I nearly whispered, sinking further back into my pillows, now beginning to feel sleep stealing in on me again and wanting to do nothing to chase it away.

I felt Roland rising unhurriedly to his paws again. "As any Qabbalist might tell you, the infinite and formless *Ein-Sof* is present in all manifestations of the divine power, all the *Sefiroth*, even if it's present as that which is also always withdrawing to make room for the created. That withdrawal, that *tsimtsum*, is also an ever more intimate approach, an ever more transcendent immanence, *interior intimis nostris*. It makes room for us to make that openness into a world." I felt the weight of his body lifted from the mattress by my leg and heard the soft report of his paws on the carpeted floor. "The paternal *archē* is fully present in its *logos* and thereby in all the *logoi* of created things without despoiling them of their creaturely freedom." His voice was receding as he walked toward the door. "Brahman *nirguṇa* is pervasively present in all the radiant powers and manifestations of Brahman *saguṇa*." His voice was fading away as he retreated down the hallway. "It's in all of us, and we are called to see it..." And then he was too far away for me to hear him any longer and I began to drift down toward sleep.

Suddenly he was speaking to me again, from the open doorway: "Oh, I just remembered why I originally came in here."

I moaned. "None of that was your reason for waking me?"

"Hush now," he said gently. "You need your sleep. I just wanted to let you know that I've finished editing the final form of your great uncle's prelude to his otherwise unfinished epic poem. I know you're aware of that piece at least. It's slated to appear in another issue of the Maryland Archivists' journal. That issue won't be wholly devoted to Aloysius, like the last one dealing with his verse, but it's still a singular honor for the old man's memory I think. You'll find the text on your desk."

I realized that I had never seen that earlier issue, or even been aware of its release. "Wait…" I said.

"Really, you need to sleep," said Roland. "You really shouldn't be up at this hour after yesterday's labors, you know."

"I… I…" I began to protest, with more than a hint of indignation of my voice.

But he was gone again. I removed most of the pillows from behind my head, turned over on my side, and struggled to fall asleep again. I must finally have succeeded, since I vaguely recall opening my eyes sometime later to the full light of late morning.

XL

A S IT HAPPENED, I did know about Great Uncle Aloysius's immense, unfinished, discursive epic *Theophaneia*. He had discussed it with me more than once, and not long after his death Great Aunt Polly had shown me several pages of the manuscript, which existed in such a variety of versions—all of them festooned with revisions and often illegible marginal notations—that I had assumed it would be impossible to abstract a single completed text from the welter of its pages. He had written it in heroic couplets—with occasional minor violations of the form—probably because of his special devotion to Pope ("The only Pope to whom I would ever bend my knee," he would quip in his rare fractiously sectarian moments). Its title was a reference to the yearly unveiling of the sacred images in the inner sanctuary of the Apolloneion at Delphi, to celebrate the god's return at the end of winter, and it was intended to consist in a series of allegorical visions supposedly vouchsafed to the narrator by the old gods. The only more or less finished section of the poem was its long prologue in three cantos, which bore the title "Melancholy"; and even that existed in seven or eight variant texts, as far as I recall.

Moreover, the history of the epic's composition could scarcely have been more irregular. Aloysius worked on it chiefly over the course of two long retreats, some thirty-one years apart, to the little hamlet of Cambridge on Maryland's Eastern Shore, in Dorchester County, along and spreading away from the southern bank of the Choptank River (not actually a river, but rather an immense estuary of the Chesapeake Bay, excellent for sailing). The Bentleys kept a small house there, a few miles outside of town, as well as two sailboats at the local marina. He wrote the first version of the poem while staying alone in that house during the summer of 1920, when a fit of deep depression had driven him into seclusion. I know I have said that his conversion to paganism was, in his eyes, a natural and

268

TOWN

largely uneventful transition; but he did mention now and then that his complete commitment to "the way of the gods" was occasioned by a brief "passage through dejection." When pressed for details, he would say only that during the most crucial year of his conversion he had been suffering from a kind of anomie occasioned by his abhorrence of what he saw as the special evils of modernity: the disenchantment of nature, the reduction of the world to a soulless machine, the hideousness of modern architecture, the decline of the arts, the rise of a crass materialism. And this dark mood, he said, had been exacerbated by any number of recent events: the Great War, the Spanish Influenza, the Volstead Act, and so on. I think it safe to say, however, that a very great part of his depression also had to do with Deirdre.

Whatever the case, he had come to believe by that time that the pathologies of modern society could not be healed by what remained of "cultural Christianity," which he regarded as a hopeless historical paradox. He saw Christendom as an impossible alloy of the gospel of humble love and the violence of imperial order, one that had been imperiled from its inception by internal tensions and forces of dissolution. And its natural sequel, he concluded, could be nothing other than the prolonged death-rattle of that defective accommodation and a gradual but inexorable descent into total nihilism. The god of Christendom, he had come to believe, had failed, and was now a lost cultural possibility, and was perhaps one that never really could have come to inhabit history in any but an ambiguous and always fugitive form. Only if the old gods returned, he decided, would the world be able to speak to Western humanity again. But an intellectual conviction is not yet faith. When he arrived on the Eastern Shore, he was a pagan merely by disposition; by the time he left, he was a pagan in his heart; and his poem was meant to describe how he emerged from doubt and despondency into that condition of radiant cheerfulness and "heathen grace" that characterized him throughout his later life. But he set the project aside on returning to the western side of the bay that same autumn, intending to resume his work on it later in the year.

Instead, he left it much as it was until inspiration visited him again, in the summer and fall of 1951, which he and great Aunt Polly

269

spent in that same small house outside town after he had secured a semester's sabbatical from Johns Hopkins. It was then, it seems, that he at least produced a reasonably finished version of the prologue. The effect of the long delay between the initial and final forms of the text, however, was a certain heterogeneity of narrative voice. When he wrote the first version, he was young and unmarried and the little house was entirely isolated. During that summer, when his loneliness became intolerable, at least at a physiological level, he was perfectly willing to resort to "boughten love"; and happily there was a very pretty and cheerful barmaid named Mary in town who, though certainly not a professional working girl, was not in the least offended by the emoluments he provided her on the mornings after. There was also another girl named Betty, who worked at the cannery in town and who took a somewhat more frankly mercantile approach to the transaction, and on whose services Aloysius called two or three times. (I knew all this from my great aunt, who in her carefree and bohemian way took a manifest delight in recounting her husband's sexual adventures in the days before she captured his heart and assorted other organs.) In any event, this younger version of Aloysius remains the putative narrator of the poem, although even then the self-portrait is an intentionally distorted one; the Aloysius of the poem is unkinder, more splenetic, and pettier than my great uncle ever really was. I assume his plan had been for this only semi-autobiographical protagonist to be transformed into a better man over the course of the epic by virtue of those divine visitations, rather like Scrooge after his adventures with the three visiting spirits.

When he finally got around to writing the final form of "Melancholy," however, to the degree that he ever did, Aloysius was a middle-aged and married man who I can say with some confidence had never once, in the course of a long and deliriously blissful married life, strayed from his own wife's bed, or invited anyone other than her into it. The Bentley house, moreover, though still remote, had acquired a few neighbors. A scattering of new homes had been erected in the area, all decently distant but palpably present nonetheless. One was even visible, if only just barely, from the front porch, on the other side of a large fallow field and a woodland spur

270

of tall deciduous trees. Another lay at the end of Dark Road, the country lane where the house stood, and was occupied by a retired couple whose company both my great uncle and my great aunt found largely insufferable, and who appear in the final poem in distinctly unflattering (albeit fictionalized) form. More to the point, the Second World War had provided Aloysius with an entirely new gallery of horrors to contemplate—new atrocities, new evidences of the barbarity of modern technological society. I know that his dismay at the revelations regarding the death camps at the end of the war had, on my great aunt's account, practically paralyzed him emotionally for better than a year, with frequent descents into abysmal despair. But he was also haunted for a long time, and in quite a different way, by reports of the mercilessness of the Allied program of fire-bombing civilian Axis cities at the end of the war; he was especially disturbed by the destruction of Dresden, a city he had visited and loved as a graduate student. And this is reflected in the finished form of the prologue. So, as it happens, is his profound distaste for a still emerging avant-garde in the arts, the description of which could only have come from the latter period of the poem's composition.

Thus, in the finished product, the narrator turned out to be a curious conflation of the young, somewhat callous libertine of the first draft and the aging, somewhat saturnine cultural recusant of the last.

In any event, I found the text of "Melancholy" in a manila folder on my desk when I went to my office in the enclosed foyer a little past noon on the same day as that early morning visit from Roland. It was a stapled Word document of eleven pages. I only glanced at it then, however, as I had more moving to do. But that evening, not long after dinner, I returned to it and read it through. I did so again an hour later. I have to say, I rather enjoyed it, even if I might have blotted a few lines myself. I regret, I suppose, that Aloysius's great project never came to full fruition. It was not necessarily a tragedy that the prologue was orphaned from the larger work, since it can stand on its own. Still, it might have been more edifying, at least from my perspective, to see the somewhat unattractive narrator of the prologue gradually evolve into a figure more like the generous and jovial soul I know my great uncle to have been.

XLI

Melancholy: A Prelude

I: The Fall of Night

The lambent sapphire of the sky of day
In trembling streams has melted quite away;
The West now dons crepuscular attire
And wraps himself in gold and crimson fire;
The chaste moon through the turquoise twilight pours
Her pearl-pale light upon our lustrous shores,
And by her glassy essence opaline
Makes strand and surf with iridescence shine;
And silver stars, cold, fair, and wanly bright,
Are scattered on the sable cope of night.
Here where eternal order marries time,
The sky is beautiful, the sea sublime:
On high, the *primum mobile* rotates,
In my great clock the moment pendulates,
And downward through the heavens' aethers flow
Sidereal magics, guiding earth below.
   The westward wind is fragrant with fresh brine
And perfumes from the swaying groves of pine;
Here on the Eastern Shore of Maryland,
Where mighty trees above flat acreage stand,
The stridulations of the insects make
A music full of bliss and ardent ache.
Gold fireflies glisten on the wine-dark night,
And float, and burn: small gems of ghostly light.
I take up—hearing ocean's surge afar—
My ruddy wine, my smoldering cigar.

272

TOWN

My great bay window open lies—I gaze
Out over fields dissolving in a haze,
Far past the forests of whispering corn,
Beyond our tributary waters' bourn,
To where the world's dim margins softly gleam
And moon-bright billows blend in Ocean's stream.
There silhouetted on night's blue I see
The stern colossus of my black gum tree.
The rarest airborne orchid of the night,
A Luna moth, floats by, jade-green and white.
All should be peace within, the fretful heart
Should rest in idle calm, and fears depart—
And yet it is not so: my thoughts are grave;
It seems that I am melancholy's slave.

I am, it's true, no stranger to bleak moods:
I'm rendered atrabilious by bland foods;
Without my true, my blushful *Hippocrene*,
I find I suffer an excess of spleen.
Why, at their best, my humors are deranged,
My wits disjoined, my faculties estranged.
But something worse than mere imbalanced blood
Has sunk me deep in melancholy's flood,
And borne me on its currents deeper still
To death's dim portal, stripped of hope and will.
For when my mind to those dark pools descends,
And down black Phlegethon my spirit wends,
My milder fits may dissipate at once;
If not, my soul a black abyss confronts
(Lugubrious doubts, regrets, and morbid fears
Provoked by nothing, then a tide of tears).
There's no prescribed escape from this chill void,
Not in occultist Jung or ghastly Freud.
I pore through pages ancient and abstruse—
At least they have some diagnostic use—
And yet no ready remedy I see
Described in Burton's great *Anatomy,*

Roland in Moonlight

Or old digests of antique medicine,
Alchemic manuals, treatises on sin,
Discourses on the stars, profane or pure...
No explanation—no, nor any cure.
　I tread the narrow ridge of my despair
And wonder, should I now resort to prayer?
I sway above insanity's dun lands
And crave some kindly angel's staying hands.
I could in this, my rural wild retreat,
Become a hermit—meditate, entreat;
I need no Thebaid whither I might flee.
But sadly I am poor in sanctity.
I am no holy man, I've no vocation,
Nor any gift for struggling with temptation.
Ascetics, with their adamantine wills,
Grow hard among their spirit-haunted hills,
But should to me the feeblest wight appear
My prayers would cease, I'd shriek and run in fear.
So many demons rack the mystic's night:
Pride, sadness, wrath, the worm of appetite,
The noonday devil (*accidie*), desire,
And visions of the everlasting fire.
Should I contend with that chthonian host,
Ingloriously the field would soon be lost.
But—worse than cowardice or devil's ploys—
My greatest enemies remain my joys:
My tempers mingle in a giddy whole,
A humor wildly swinging pole to pole,
For when I'm not despondent or morose,
My animal vitality is gross.
A creature of the senses, I adore
My liquor cabinet and humidor:
A warm seraglio each appears to me,
In which my regal lusts should wander free;
I quench my thirsts in rich, nectareous wine,
I sip sweet cordials, on rarest viands dine;

TOWN

As for those appetites that women sate,
I dance and, when convenient, copulate.
(From unspoiled local girls I can, sans risk,
Embrace some alabaster odalisk,
Then send that well-paid blossom floating home
On morning's pearly tide of gushing foam.)
I am a ship adrift on passion's seas;
My slightest want I'm eager to appease.
A wanton born to privilege and pelf,
There is no pleasure I'll deny myself.
I am a roisterer, a sybarite,
Orgiastic Bacchus, drunken with delight...
    And then Prometheus, torn by eagle's claws,
Not knowing my transgression, or God's laws.
    If only I could isolate a reason
For this my soul's long pestilential season,
Say why this murksome shadow falls athwart
My heart's meridian light, its garden court,
I could, I think, throw off its tyranny,
And walk the earth again, august and free.
    Tobacco's opiate, abetted by drink,
Makes me vertiginous. My senses sink.
Lulled by these potent nepenthes, I feel
A languid Ixion on a sluggish wheel.
    And has some god or angel heard my plea?
I slip the bonds of time and I am free.
The minstrels in the trees have ceased to sing,
The pendulum rests poised in upward swing.
Now spins a merry misrule through the spheres,
The pathless stars derange the days and years;
The past, the present, and the world to come
Dance madly to a Dionysian drum;
The secret depths of time disclose to me
Things hidden in the folds of destiny;
Shapes flicker in my glass of vision, shine,
I swoon, I float, I laugh—I am *divine*!

Roland in Moonlight

Ah, but the fancy passes and I sleep
Below the thunders of the upper deep.

II: Late Morning

Drunk from the torpor of midsummer light,
I should be free from demons of the night—
The throbbing bombinations of the bees,
The treetops swaying in the humid breeze,
As woodbine's balm comes dropping through the air—
A day too heavy for such heavy care.
   Yet still the shadow lurks within and tells
My secret mind of all its million hells.
   It is a gentle madness makes me write—
So let no man my savagery indict.
In certain souls the wisest can discern
Two great ferocities—two fires—that burn:
One to create, which overleaps with joy,
And one, in sorrow, only to destroy;
The former sets the restless spirit free
In a quiet rapture, guileless subtlety;
The latter's filled with rages, fraught with dooms;
The one transfigures, the other consumes;
Yet they are intermingled by degrees,
In mild or violent volatilities.
Nor dare we hastily discriminate:
A lovely work's oft vivified by hate.
(For fallen souls eternal forms can know
In dim unlikeness only, here below,
And eros in the arts, just as in love,
Still needs the flesh it seeks to soar above.)
Thus, though I strive for bright marmorean calm,
I cannot hide what animates my song;
I must acknowledge whence these verses well:
An anger in my heart as deep as hell.
Why ever not? I feel I may requite
As I'm requited—quaff my cup of spite.

TOWN

I'm brusque and vehement, impetuous, rude,
Stubborn, intractable of habitude...
I'm not the kind who happily palpates
My fellow man; so much upon me grates:
The trivial popinjay whose only passion
Is never to fall out of step with fashion,
Collectors of plebeian bric-a-brac,
That local farmer's son whose jaw hangs slack,
A feigned affection for the *avant-garde*
By bourgeois frauds who came to art *trop tard*,
Mad visionaries, mirrored in whose eyes
Malignant portents vex the burning skies,
The mountain climber, young, devoid of fear,
The moron who thinks Shakespeare was de Vere,
Free Masons, crooners, Presbyterians,
Bicyclists, people always making plans,
The sweet, the cute, the winsome, and the droll,
That banking clerk who looks just like a troll—
The terraquatic globe to me oft seems
A jungle that with noisome vermin teems.
    And, oh, my neighbors down the shady lane,
Proud of their stucco palace without stain,
Their stocks, their bonds, their lawn, their vintage cars,
Their framed signed photographs of movie stars.
I cannot bear his hale and hearty ways,
His hand clapped on my back, his empty praise,
His bulging neck, his rubicund complexion,
His certitude of his divine election.
And she, that dropsical drabogue, his wife,
The pillar and the torment of his life:
Her stern but flabby jowls, her suet face,
Her icy yet *gelatinous* embrace,
Her form orbicular, and yet amorphous,
Her thick eyeshade, the color of a porpoise,
Her distaste for the poor, her raucous cheer,
Her voice, loud as a crow's and as severe.

And yet so small, so dainty in her way,
A garden gnome half-molded in wet clay…
Perhaps there is some charm, *je ne sais quoi,*
In all that tremulous *avoirdupois,*
The raven nimbus of her plastic hair,
The inner waste her empty eyes declare,
Her lipstick such a shocking shameless red,
The eager nodding of her vacant head…
　I should not be so cruel, nor condescend.
They do no harm, I say—none does offend.
　I have grown saturnine, I must admit:
I think the moving finger has now writ,
That all the West is wrapped in swelling gloom,
That we are racing heedless to our doom,
Lured on by Sirens that we can't resist…
I am, I think, what's called a "pessimist."
To me our culture seems the foulest midden,
Where innocence and love are now forbidden,
As dreary as the meanest rustic hovel,
As boring as the modern English novel,
As insubstantial as a hungry wraith,
Vindictive as the God of Christian faith,
Where nothing noble lingers, no love higher
Than barbarous materialist desire,
Where ceaseless hunger for mere acquisition
Drives on a world of dazzling inanition,
Nor seeks for beauty's transcendental font,
Nor lifts the soul beyond each transient want…
　Not that I crave some cheap autumnal glamor.
A whore "philosophizes with a hammer."
The grim appeal I'll never understand
Of Spengler's *Sunset of the Evening-Land.*
The prophet's mantle gladly I decline,
So too the Pythia's frenzy sibylline.
Still, I have seen the glory of the West
Sink—gutter like a candle wind-distressed—

278

TOWN

In empty eyes, as sterile as the moon.
We'll cease to be quite human, very soon.
  At least such is my fear, my heart's abuse,
The tireless talons of the bird of Zeus...
  I've been that thing—our time's servilest dog—
The futile academic paedagogue,
And learned in "major" universities
To keen civilization's obsequies:
I've wept to see my lectures swallowed whole
Into a dark blastema of a soul,
Poured forth that wisdom on whose tree I've bled
Into a nodding vacuum of a head,
And watched the healing lights that heaven's sent
Meet simian gazes of bewilderment.
I cannot blame those children: poverty
Is not the pauper's fault—not usually.
But in them there perhaps gestates a race
Wherein the human visage has no trace:
Just faces capable of vacant stares
And heartless leers, brute grins devoid of cares,
Compassion, wonder, joy, or tenderness.
I fear their lips can curse, but never bless.
Their yearnings are inane, their humor crude,
Books rot in dusty dank desuetude.
They do not know romance, their love is cruel,
Each is Narcissus bent above his pool.
These are those Last Men Nietzsche warned us of,
Those heroes of contentment and self-love,
With hearts like twisted mirrors, in whose glass
Deformities and lurid colors pass.
  Such hideous tastes take root when cultures gloam—
Think decadent and blood-besotted Rome!
All through the rolling ages empires rise:
Each thinks itself immortal, and each dies,
And, at its vespertine eclipse, the earth
Awaits with fearful heart some new Beast's birth.

279

Roland in Moonlight

Perhaps—to wax a little Yeatsian—we
Are drawn on to a monstrous destiny,
And darker worlds, decreed by ruthless fate,
Within our eventide now incubate...
  Of course, you may be well-advised to laugh,
Ignore my ravings, call me a moon-calf;
You might remind me gently that "The herd
Loves things barbaric, garish, and absurd!"
And note, with knowing smiles, wry and patrician,
"Among that kind one always finds perdition,
And woe betide the culture that's arraigned
For games whereby the mob is entertained!"
  But think of our "high art," if still I may
Apply that term to such advanced decay:
Ours is an art of concepts, not of skill,
The product not of vision but of will,
And even then those concepts are obtuse—
Ponderous minds don't fly when they're set loose.
Thus we admire—we must do as we're told—
Blank canvas, or a urinal of gold,
Dismembered mannequins, three rusting pails,
A plastic torso punctured by steel nails,
Profanities on cardboard, childish spatters,
Just meant to shock... Why not, when nothing matters?
A splendor that would seize us from without
Might cast the ego's self-regard in doubt,
So "artists" celebrate emancipation
From talent, vision, and imagination.
See! Lurking in the shadows, gaunt and cruel,
Some drooling German "artist," a pale ghoul...
  No, no, I cannot bear to dwell on this:
One step the more, I'll sink in the abyss.
  My friends have always said I'm delicate.
Here in this peaceful place I'll hebetate.
  In my remote Arcadia, I can see
The brightest gems of ornithology:

TOWN

Bluebirds, in sparkling splendor winged and crowned,
Among bright pyracantha berries drowned;
The ruby-throated hummingbird whose flight—
So sweet to hearing, but eluding sight—
Becomes a vibrant stillness as he sips
From trumpeter-vine blossoms' chaliced lips;
The saffron-yellow goldfinch sings his song,
An ostinato stream, rippling along;
The great blue heron's dusky cerulean;
The milk-white egret's sheen like porcelain;
The scarlet cardinal's liquescent trills,
As crimson dawn is breaking on our hills...
   (Whereat the captious reader should complain:
"The Shore is flatter than a windowpane!")
   Well, I admit, I could not find a rhyme
Appropriate to my sea-level clime;
I here repent, for I require no device
Of art to praise this earthly paradise.
Just now a citron-blazoned swallowtail
Across my garden flutters, starts to sail,
Then vanishes amid rose-haunted shadows,
To float off to his honey-colored meadows.

III: Late Afternoon

Depression is voluptuous, and one must
Resist its lure, its charms, its fairy-dust.
Hence, lest one be reduced to base inaction,
One makes a moral labor of distraction:
To flee this last temptation and its snares,
One summons lesser dragons from their lairs.
This hale seductress fears one war-machine:
Games of the idler and the libertine;
Thus by one's carnal revels one is saved
From sins immeasurably more depraved.
To drink, tobacco I again resort,
Carouse and—in my modest way—cavort;

Roland in Moonlight

Autochthonous delicacies delight
My trencherman's—my *gourmand's*—appetite;
Once more I'll summon to my shady bower
That lovely, blushing, meretricious flower…
   The day is still quite warm, not harshly so,
And from my porch I hear the river flow.
Nearby the Lesser Choptank's currents roll.
There is still time for a riparian stroll:
Three hours until I dine, two till sky's blue
A pale lime green and purple blush subdue.
I'll amble with the pilgrim's barest goods
Between the river and the skirting woods—
A good cigar, a flask of scotch, and thou—
And pen my verse below the black gum bough.
I'll walk to where the low slope of the land,
Before the ocean, melts in splendent sand…
   Sometimes I think I see the dryads flit
From bole to bole, or on high branches sit.
They are but figments, who would me beguile;
No sprites enchant this forest umbratile,
No naiads haunt this undulating rill
Whose sighing shoals the booming froglets fill.
I'd dally with the fairies, dance with fauns,
Join their carousals till the morrow dawns;
But we have chased them from our hills and dells—
Forsaken them for our bright plastic hells.
   Still, as I wander, my mind wanders too,
Imagining the game I never slew:
In daydreams I now play some great Orion,
A predator, a brute, a tawny lion,
Or reckless Actaeon by the goddess smitten,
Or some deer-hunter in a mythic Britain:
The old New Forest's trees, fabulous suns,
The shade where still the magic White Hart runs;
A quiver full of arrows, thickly quilled,
A doublet whereon blood is often spilled;

TOWN

The flush, the quickened, then the slackened pace,
And all the sweet elations of the chase;
Dew-silvered woods; the mist-gray light of dawn;
The violet shade; the grazing doe and fawn.
Then morning's sky puts off its somber hue
And through the branches breaks a fiery blue;
The mournful belling of the stag, the bays
Of loping hounds, the sun's green-golden rays,
The plash of ferns, the splash of blood, the gleam
Of silky sunlight in a stony stream;
The arrow loosed, the dreadful wound, the horn
Whose echoed note grows ever more forlorn;
Until at last the quarry's flight is stayed,
And silence fills the green sun-dappled glade...
　　O Artemis, I'd meekly face your wrath
　To glimpse you rising naked from your bath,
　And like the wounded doe or sling-felled dove
　Be torn asunder by the hounds of love.
　　I could be very happy in this place,
Absorb its lethargy, its glacial pace.
I know the seasons as they play upon,
These fields and woods, I know the flirting sun.
I know what figures fill the turning year,
And so can meet the future without fear...
　　I see myself in late and leafless fall:
The ground-mist spreads its gossamer pale pall.
The woods are now the color of soft lead,
Except the ghostly sycamores outspread,
Which take into their palsied, white embrace
The cold and briny light of empty space.
A blue and silver smoke drifts languidly—
Sweet redolence of oak and hickory.
In softly incandescent nacre skies
The griseous clouds, through which a lone crow flies,
Grow great, and dark, and ominous of rain;
The air has metal's taste and ashes' stain...

283

Roland in Moonlight

I see myself in scintillating winter:
I see the shining bright icicles splinter,
The glistening blue-shadowed glaze of snow,
A hollow drift, a wind-upswept plateau.
The trees are sheathed in ice from winds grown bitter
And hem the sky with their white diamond glitter;
Drenched in prismatic light and cobalt shade,
The treetops form a crystalline cascade...
    And then comes warm satyriatic spring—
Silenian woodnotes from the forest ring...
    Continuing on, I see the sprawling ocean,
The surge of its eternal massive motion;
From here, sky's blue looks richer on the waters,
Like the Aegean, where romp Poseidon's daughters.
Upon its pearled horizon billows coil
And glimmer in the sun like silver foil.
The nymphs sing sweetly in their limestone caves,
While ceaseless thunders roll across the waves.
I see beyond the misting gauze of rain
A rainbow's gleam, a sky like cymophane.
An opalescence rims this spume-drenched world.
Blue lightnings glitter, down from heaven hurled...
    Impossible, I think... I cannot speak...
I fear my dreams at night... The future's bleak...
Oh, we've seized fire from heaven, from Jove's hand.
The gods withdraw. We've cursed the sea and land.
    Steel bridges, emblems of our race's might,
    Became thin strands of silver in the night,
    Stretched out below the airmen's misty wake
    Like fragile threads a careless hand might break:
    Frail gossamer, laced on the vitreous seam
    Of Elbe's ancient, deep, and doleful stream.
    "In Dresden town, my love, in Dresden town,
    The shining flakes of fire came raining down;
    We gazed into its heart of gold and red,
    While small flames danced upon the stones and fled,

284

TOWN

And melted in a mystic, streaming blue,
Transparent fringe of light, of heaven's hue:
The honey-hued combustion of the world
Beneath high clouds whence thunderbolts were hurled.
Oh love, my love, such sweet contentment flowed
Through nerves and veins! And how the grim earth glowed,
All wrapped in sun-bright filaments of fire,
The Stoics' eschaton, the great ecpyre..."
One could go mad, you know, on days like this.
I must resolve to seek out sensual bliss.
   There is here loveliness enough to fill
The hungry heart, and all its violence still.
I've music, books, tobacco, harlots, wine—
I walk, I read, I smoke, I dream, I dine.
Only an insensible dolt belittles
The lush delights of our rich local victuals:
The muskrat, goose, and lordly terrapin,
White sugar-corn, and lean, tart venison,
The fair rockfish whose flesh could not be moister,
The succulent blue crab, the mollient oyster...
   But now I risk, I fear, waxing absurd.
Great Zeus! In thy hard mercy, send thy bird!
   A melancholic, but not lame or halt...
The air is sharp with the cruel tang of salt...
   How fierce my demon when he vaunts and raves...
How wild the joyous sparkling of the waves...
   I shall be well, if I can only sleep...
A crystal swell folds up the azure deep...

XLII

I WAS, IT SEEMED, standing in my garden, gazing through shifting curtains of mist at the muted yellow of a flowering forsythia. I seemed to know that it was only a little past dawn, on what I believe was the last day before our final departure for our new house. I might have gone inside after a moment had I not heard the garden gate behind me swinging on its steel hinges and then the soft click of its latch. When I turned to look, I could initially see nothing through the haze; but after a moment a small figure appeared, at first like a wavering phantom, then assuming the solid, mottled, familiar form of Roland. Dangling from his mouth by a thick, dark red cord of braided silk was what after some seconds I recognized as a Japanese *koto*, though one of unusually small design. On seeing me, he started back slightly, furrowed his brow, then strolled over to the low wooden veranda and gently set the instrument down. Returning, he stared at me thoughtfully and said (sounding even more like Laurence Harvey than usual), "You never rise this early. Is all well?"

"Yes," I replied, in an unexpectedly hoarse voice, "I think so. I don't recall…"

But now he was energetically sniffing at my left hand.

"Honestly," I said, "nothing's wrong."

He sighed, gazed intently upward into my eyes for a long uncertain moment, and then said, "Very well. Actually, your fragrance is healthier than it's been for some years." Then he began to turn away.

"Wait," I said. "Where have you been, with… that?" I pointed at the *koto*. "I don't think I've seen you with it before."

He turned to me, smiled enigmatically, and sat down upon his haunches. "I was afraid you'd ask." He shrugged. "It's something I occasionally do. I spent the night in the hall of the local *daimyo* performing passages from the *Heike Monogatari*… the battle of Dan-no-ura, to be specific… and…"—he lowered his eyes somewhat bashfully—"declaiming some of my own verse."

286

"There's a local *daimyo*?" I asked.

He raised his snout, his head at a quizzical angle. "Of course. Who do you think makes sure the local peasantry plants enough glutinous rice for wine... or protects them from the depredations of the *yakuza*?"

"Oh. Yes... I suppose that makes sense."

He nodded. "These are parlous times, you know. It's an age of faction and fallen houses and, as a result, roving unhoused *ronin*."

"Your verse?" My drowsy wits had only just caught up to his words. "You write poetry?"

Again he looked away, somewhat reservedly, the faint smile still on his lips. "I keep that side of my life quiet. Actually, last night was a celebration of my most recent volume of haiku."

"Your... your most *recent*?" For the life of me, I could not recall his ever having mentioned any such publications in the past.

"Just a hundred poems, one to a page, each with an English gloss at the foot."

"You wrote them in Japanese?"

His eyes met mine again, now with his customary expression of longanimous affection. "Of course. It's not a form that suits other tongues."

"What are they, um, about?" I asked feebly.

"Transience," he replied mildly. "The evanescent moment, the fading day, the ephemeral blossom. I try merely to capture the delicate essence of a passing moment—its tone, its texture, its exquisite impermanence—and something of that anguished yearning for eternity that's expressible, mysteriously enough, only in images of transitoriness." He sighed deeply and shook his head. "Who knows if I succeed? How can any artist share more than a distant, dying echo of his inspirations?" He paused for a moment, met my eyes searchingly, and then—almost shyly—dropped his gaze again. "I could recite one for you... if you'd like. There's one perfect for this setting."

A thrill of sentiment passed through me; I felt genuinely touched. "Yes, please," I said, "if you would."

He smiled that restrained smile once more, straightened his back, stared away into the pearl-hued emptiness, and spoke in a clear, measured voice:

Cool mist at morning,
Trembling leaves gleam with dew—*Ah!*
An earthworm's fragrance.

He fell silent, continued gazing away for several moments, then bowed his head meditatively. "Well?" he asked.

"Yes," I replied, a bit uncomfortably, "I see what you mean about… it suiting the scene."

After a moment he raised his head and, with a suspicious scowl, asked, "Nothing else?"

"I don't know," I replied. "I mean, for me that last line… isn't so evocative."

"Don't be absurd," he said with a curt laugh. "It's the piquant master-stroke. What captures the feel of the morning more than the fragrance of earthworms—that strange, sharp, vinegar-and musk pungency, those hints of clay and minerals, that faint soupçon of scorched saltiness…?"

I swallowed awkwardly. "You see, I don't have your nose."

He stared at me a moment longer and then shrugged wearily. "No, I suppose not. It's like describing a sunset to someone blind from birth." He took a deep, ruminative breath. "Of course, we've discussed all this before, but it remains a constant source of pity for me. For instance, I imagine that if you were to thrust your face into those forsythia blossoms there and breathe deeply, expecting some pleasing floral perfume, and your nostrils discovered instead what you would perceive only as an absence of any conspicuously gratifying fragrance, you'd interpret it as a defect of the flower—or at least a privation. You naturally crave delicacies, sweets, sumptuous dainties—don't we all?—and your undiscerning nasal palate registers the absence of any superficially appealing scent, whether exquisite or garish, simply as a kind of vacancy of sensuous experience. So much of the olfactory texture of reality is beyond your ken. And your hearing is scarcely any more acute. It's tragic in some sense. It pierces me at times to think of it. If only I could convey to you the full diapason of aromas from which the whole phenomenal order of reality is woven—the richness, the depths, the contrasts… the intricate reticulation of different strands of odor. If I could only com-

municate to you the subtle shadings of redolence that cling to—and
define—the edges of every leaf, the surface of every stone, the deep
wellsprings of scent that overflow the very pith of things, the great
floods and the small tenuous rivulets of pure fragrance... But...
well, there's the tragedy of insular consciousness for you. There's
why all great spiritual traditions know that only at the ultimate
ground of the unity of all consciousness is there true knowledge of
reality." He shook his head despondently. "Of course," he said, his
voice assuming a somewhat more conversational tone, "translating
the poem into English also detracts from its effect considerably."

"I imagine," I said.

"But that's a perennial problem—mediating between tongues,
cultures, sensibilities... souls. Certainly all my labors of translation
often feel like attempts to change iron into satin, or butter into
wine."

"Do you do much translating?" I asked.

"My, my. I'm divulging all my little secrets today," he said with a
snort. Then he sniffed at the grass at his feet, bit off a few blades,
chewed them slowly, and swallowed. "In my small way, yes. I'm
working on certain unjustly neglected epics: the *Punica* of Silius
Italicus and the *Dionysiaca* of Nonnos. Admittedly, in the former
case the neglect is more understandable: the enormous length...
and some of the same aesthetic oddity as Camões, with that uneven
mix of historical and mythical materials. And Nonnos is certainly
the more important and absorbing author. I mean, where would the
best poets of late antiquity have been without him—Dracontius,
Musaeos, Colluthos—or the Byzantines—Planudes, Genesios? But
how to render his language into another tongue? It's so rich, diverse,
gorgeously involved and imbricated—he was the greatest virtuoso
of *poikilia* ever—and his... well, his Gongorism, for want of a less
anachronistic word, is more beautifully and perversely complicated
than even the most bombastic Alexandrian grammarian's allegory
on the alphabet... or of whatever else. And that's a daunting truth
for the translator to confront. How is one to capture that wild
polyphony? How is one to match that mighty tempest of verbal
invention in another tongue, or with anything like a comparable
combination of precision and flamboyance?" He shook his head,

perhaps a little morosely. "That's why there's no good translation of Virgil—so much is in the pure music of the verse."

"True."

"But the problem's deeper than that," he continued. "If translation were just a system of mechanistic correspondences, one sign for another, for which one could devise non-semeiotic algorithms, then maybe... But, no, that's impossible. Translation is about meanings, and so the whole enterprise is dependent on a kind of spiritual tact—or on functioning spiritual senses, really, able to perceive implications, atmospheres, nuances... not only what an author expresses, but also what he doesn't need to express. One renders discrete words into their most plausible equivalents, but by itself that accomplishes nothing. One *translates* the text as the product of an intentionality, with a purposive dimension that one has to share in to understand the work at all. That's why there'll never be a computer program for real translation. One has to know the whole before understanding the parts, and more than the whole before understanding the whole. One has to intend the author's intention, and that means in part retreating to a level of consciousness prior to individual identity."

"I'm not sure..."

But Roland was now too preoccupied with his own thoughts to notice me. "We've talked before, I know, about the irreducibility of intentional consciousness to material forces—its teleological orientation toward a transcendental horizon beyond nature, its origination in a pure awareness prior to empirical identity—and about how the whole world of nature is constituted only in the relation between these two poles outside of physical nature..."

"I believe..."

"That's where the real work of translation is done: that original pure act of consciousness, more inward than our inmost, higher than our utmost, to which the mystics ascend by going inward. Oh, you know, Eckhart's *Seelesburg*, or whatever word he used, in the heart of which dwells the *Fünklein Gottes*. Or the *ātman* that's more original in its universality than the *jīva* in its individuality. Do you know the Sufi idea of the seven layers of the soul?"

"Yes, I do. I..."

"The more one descends into the *nafs*, the higher one rises, and the nearer one comes to the hidden garden, till one reaches the secret soul, the *ruh sirr*, which remembers God, and beyond that— more inward yet—one draws near to the secret of secrets, the *sirr-ul-asrar*, where the divine spark shines. Then, of course, there's the Qabbalistic hierarchy of *nefesh*, *ruah*, and *neshamah*, which you sometimes see assimilated to the Aristotelian scale of vegetal, animal, and rational soul. But that's a mistake. *Nefesh* already possesses all the faculties of a sensitive, deliberative agent. It's more like a distinction in spiritual aptitude, like the ancient Christian hierarchy of somatics, psychics, and pneumatics. Everyone has a *nefesh*, but *ruah* and *neshamah* are of more celestial origin, and in a sense descend into the living soul. Some say the *neshamah* really only takes up its habitation in the greatest of mystical adepts. Some believe, in fact, that it's only the *nefesh* that ever suffers transmigration—*gilgul*— from one incarnation to another—though that's not the view expressed in the *Ra'aya Mehemna*, of course. And, too, other schools speak of two yet higher souls, the *Chaya*—the eternally living soul—and then the *Yehidah*—the unique soul, the one, the end that awaits humanity perfected, the highest unity with the divine power itself, the first manifestation of the *Ein-Sof*... a divine spark that's also at one with the *keter*, the crown of the sefirotic tree..."

"Yes," I said again, "this is very..."

"Or think of Teresa of Ávila's interior castle, with its seven chambers, and the divine throne at the center... Well, it's somewhere in those inner realms that translation occurs because, the more deeply one enters in, the more expansive one becomes, the more the veils of our small exclusive empirical egos fall away before the naked light of that original and ultimate truth. That's also where all art is born, violating the boundary between the calculating mind and that purer dimension of consciousness where one finds the transcendent ground and end of mind not as a concept, but almost as an immediate intuition. That's why the true artist is to the philosopher as an angel to a worm... and why a true translator is someone who drinks from that same spring."

Roland fell silent. I stared at him for several seconds through the slowly drifting mists, and then said, "You're a very unusual dog."

He raised his eyes and looked at me with an expression some-where between disappointment and indulgent fondness. "You know," he said, "I realize that remarks of that sort are well-intended, but they also reveal some unreflective and distasteful prejudices." He sighed yet again. Then he rose, bestowed a mollifying lick upon my hand, trotted over to the veranda, retrieved his *koto*, and contin-ued on toward the back door of the house.

PART FOUR

GARDEN

XLIII

A S I WRITE, it has been more than three and a half years since we took up residence in this house. It has proved a pleasant home, although the world beyond its walls has grown grimmer with each passing month. The administration of the slobbering, slouching, whining, brutish, tumid, psychopathic simpleton in the White House has drowned civic life in a ceaseless stream of atrocities, pollutions, perversions, cruelties, lies, and violence. And the legions of his most faithful and belligerent followers have proved beyond any reasonable doubt that gross credulity, viciousness, bigotry, cowardice, stupidity, vulgarity, and hardness of heart are far more pervasive of whatever remains of American society than any of us cares to admit. Nothing that that orange distillate of psychic and spiritual sewage has done or failed to do with his powers—no act of monstrous mercilessness, no gigantic feat of lethal ineptitude or dereliction of responsibility, none of his venal corruptions of government institutions, none of his perpetually overflowing personal crudity and idiocy, none of his tens of thousands of preposterous and degrading lies, none of his assaults on civic decency and virtue, no expression of his sheer, unadulterated foulness—has dissuaded them from their devotion to his cult.

And then, of course, the pandemic began in February of this year. Since then, my family and I have been more or less confined to this house. In some ways, however, as the world around us has grown colder and darker and crueler, our private world has grown richer, or at least more concentrated in its graces and delicacies. The garden has become, in many ways, the heart of our home, and so beautiful and placid a retreat that the world outside its high wooden fencing often seems like little more than a dark rumor. It is almost as if the persistent and terrible pressures imposed on everyone over these past few years have served to transform our ordinary domestic existence into something ever more precious, like plain coal transformed into an ever purer, ever more dazzling, ever more infrangible diamond.

I am getting far ahead of myself, however. Our time here did not begin quite that idyllically. It was no more than a few months after our resettlement that we realized we would require regular medical assistance for my mother; and it was only another month or so before we realized that soon she would require hospice care. Fortunately, in South Bend one can receive such care at home, and so my mother was never in any danger of dying in some bleak institutional setting, as my father had done. A hospital bed was installed in her room. Oxygen tanks as well. Two nurses and a practical care worker began visiting her in regular daily shifts. Her medications became more numerous, as well as progressively more palliative and less therapeutic. And, as had been the case with my father, her mind slowly began to abandon the present and to swing ever more freely between the distant past and eternity. She too began to converse with presences unseen by us. My nephew came for an extended visit, and my eldest brother flew in from Norway for another. My other brother made plans to come near the end, but was too late by a day.

But, again, I am moving too swiftly ahead. I should note that our first Christmas in the new house—and her last in this world—came and passed pleasantly, and she was still sufficiently *compos mentis* to enjoy it.

There came a day in late winter that was unseasonably balmy. My mother had required more than the usual medical assistance to deal with her pain and restlessness, but when at last she was able to sleep I went out to sit on the steps at the end of the deck and to gaze up into the high, leafless branches of the tall trees on the other side of the fence and into the mild lustrous blue of the sky above them. The garden was not yet in flower. For perhaps the first time I felt the nearness of my mother's death with piercing certitude, and had a sense that she was also aware of it. I may, in fact, have begun my grieving precisely then. Whatever the case, as I was sitting there, Roland ambled into the garden from the door at the side of the house and sat down in the grass, perhaps five feet from me, staring up into my eyes. I smiled at him and invited him to approach with an outstretched hand. He rose and came to me and I began scratching him behind his ears. As I was doing so, however, I realized that the features of his face had undergone a subtle but distinct transformation, one that had obviously been going on for some time but that I was only noticing now. The two irregular ellipses of dark brown that had once formed that strikingly bold carnival mask around his eyes were now receding, leaving behind something more like their gauzy outline and a haze of smoky charcoal gray. He was aging. Of course, I already knew this. But until now I had noticed no signs of it, and certainly not this palliation of his facial fur. And all at once a pang of sorrow overwhelmed me. Somehow, while I had succeeded in largely preparing myself emotionally to confront my mother's mortality—in part I suppose because my father's prolonged decline had taught me how to pace myself—I was utterly defenseless against this sudden realization that my dog had passed into and perhaps a little beyond middle age. Admittedly, he was only seven years old at that point, nearing eight, and for a dog of his size that meant that his dotage was still a few years off. Even so, I felt tears springing to my eyes, and I closed them and bowed my head. I continued to smile at Roland and to scratch him behind the ears for some time. Soon my body began shaking and the tears flowed freely for a while, and I rested my head against the railing of the steps until the tremors passed. Then, wiping my eyes, I rose, and Roland and I went back inside together.

XLIV

IT WAS IN THE GARDEN again, three days or so later, this time well after dark, that I found Roland settled on his haunches and bent over three sheets of paper laid out in a neat row on the deck, inspecting them by the bright light of the security lamp at the back of the house (which I was sure I had not turned on). Two manila folders were lying a few feet to his left. I do not now recall how I came to be there, but I was still wearing my daytime clothes and was holding a cup of coffee in my hand, so I had clearly not yet gone to bed. There was a slight chill in the air, but my well-worn casual suit jacket was more than sufficient to keep me warm. I believe it must have rained earlier in the day; at least, there was a dense surface fog covering the grass around the deck and rising to the topmost of its three steps. It glowed an uncanny white in the light of the crescent moon overhead, shining fiercely and edged in burning blue, like a blade drawn white-hot from the forge. The stars were sparkling with an almost unnatural clarity, as if the sky were a great lens in which they were being magnified.

"May I ask what you're reading?" I said after several moments, drawing up one of the folding chairs, seating myself a yard or so from where he was crouching, and sipping my coffee.

He briefly pursed his lips, then licked his nose twice, then turned to stare at me with an expression of frank amusement. "Just at the moment," he said, "I'm looking at two specimens of truly execrable nonsense verse. Execrable only in the benign sense of 'so silly they're good,' you understand."

"Ah," I said. "Yes, my great uncle did have a pronounced taste for…"

"Oh, the author isn't Aloysius," Roland interrupted. "You wrote them."

"What?" I set my cup down on the deck by my feet and leaned forward. "Are you sure?"

"See for yourself," he replied, rising to his feet and taking two steps back.

I leaned further forward and, after a moment, I could see that the texts (obviously poems) on the first two sheets of unlined white printer paper did indeed appear to have been written in my distinctive and somewhat absurdly ornate italic hand. "May I?" I asked, not waiting for a reply but instead rising and gathering both of them up.

"Be my guest," said Roland with an increasingly wicked smile. "The first, the one based on the Duchess's song from *Alice in Wonderland*, looks like something you might have come up with late at night after one too many glasses of wine."

I resumed my seat and no sooner had I begun to read than the occasion of composition came back to me. Roland was not far off the mark, as it happens, though the culprit had in fact been a third snifter of cognac.

> Damn parents who misname their lad
>   Osbert or Plantagenet,
> Or Peveril or Galahad,
>   Because they think it elegant!

> CHORUS:
> Waugh! Waugh! Waugh!

> Now "David," one cannot deny,
>   As names go, is a sober one.
> How grateful to my parents I
>   They did not call me Auberon—

> CHORUS:
> Waugh! Waugh! Waugh!

"Well, you mustn't judge me for a bad joke produced when I was in my cups," I said. "How on earth did you come across this?"

Before answering, he altered his position on his haunches somewhat and then scratched his right ear with several vigorous strokes of his rear paw. "Oh," he said when he was finished, "I found them among some of your *disiecta membra* in one of those sealed file boxes you brought out of storage after we settled here."

"Sealed? You don't mean you opened it without asking?"

"I opened all of them," he replied blandly. "And, yes, I see why that surprises you. The mailing tape you used on them *was* rather difficult to break through. I probably should have asked for assistance."

"No, I mean..."

"But it was worth it. I found all sorts of little treasures." The smile returned to his lips. "Some of them were delicious."

"Oh, now, really..." I began.

"I found the other little ditty there more touching, though. Apparently it's a song you wrote for your son when he was—what?—perhaps two years old. Which, I know, is still quite young for one of your kind. And, from evidence internal to the text, I deduce that in those days one of your hypocorisms for him, sweetly enough, was 'Paddleduck.'"

"Oh." I gritted my teeth slightly. "One tends to call one's children some very stupid things. Especially when they're very small. And he had a toy duck, you see, and..." But I was distracted from whatever else I was going to say by the second poem, which I had just slipped from behind the first and laid atop it.

(*To be sung to the tune of "Wild Colonial Boy," but at a somewhat faster, more martial clip than is customary.*)

My name is Patrick Paddleduck, the king of all I see.
O come ye princes of the earth, swear fealty to me!
My rule is wise, my justice mild, as all good men attest,
For I am Patrick Paddleduck, the Emp'ror of the West!

Now, many are the rivals to the throne I rightly hold,
But to revolt by force of arms usurpers make not bold,

GARDEN

For legends of such fearful might have so long gone before
The great lord Patrick Paddleduck, invincible in war!

My soldiers are as numberless as sands beside the sea.
Before the tempest of their swords all enemies must flee.
But none need fear the hand of wrath when once the battles
  cease,
For I am Patrick Paddleduck, magnanimous in peace!

For several long, reflective moments I said nothing. I was remembering my son at that age, very small, peering out at the world through his bottle-glass spectacles, absorbed in the serious business of floating a small rubber toy duck on the surface of a large rain puddle in the lawn of the house we had in Princeton during our year there, a long time ago. That was the day, I believe, when I employed that idiotic sobriquet for the first time.

"You're not drowning in sentiment now, are you?" Roland asked at last.

"Perhaps I am," I replied. "Why shouldn't I be? Time... time passes so damned quickly."

"Please, I encourage it, so long as you come up for air before it's too late."

I turned my eyes to the third sheet of paper, still lying on the deck. I could see even from there that the text was another poem, this time typewritten. "Is that also something of mine?"

Roland shook his head. "Aloysius," he said. "When did you last use a typewriter?"

"Some time in the early 1990's," I said. "But I still have papers from those days stored away."

"Indeed you do," he said. "But that there is a poem your great uncle wrote around 1934, and then typed out some twenty years later. I only brought it along to re-read because it has a Homeric theme, and I've been thinking a good deal about Homer lately." He raised a paw invitingly. "Please, have a look."

When I had taken up the page from the deck, I saw that it was a printed pdf.

301

Roland in Moonlight

À Propos d'Akhilleus

Thetis, silver-footed, did you intend so fierce a child,
So wild a spawn of Zeus, great thunderer on Ida's slopes?
The fashionable salons will not admit him, the best
Hotels refuse his reservations.

                   See how—in the brute
Immensity of his running stride, savage eloquence
Of his loud tormented roar, his huge appetite for slaughter—
A lion stalks, tawny in his splendor, his thick limbs bedewed
By blood. He rushes down upon the Trojan heroes,
A tempest of rage, a tourbillion of murder, now crushing
All who fall before his pitiless blows, his spear of bronze
And sinewed ash. Not even Xanthus with its yellow flood,
The outrage of its risen surge, engorged with blood and screams,
Beating down upon him—shimmering, brilliant, and vast—
Can quell his bestial rage. The fires of heaven attend him.
He is shining violence, bright flashing death, great Ocean's
    scion,
Companion of flame. Carnage and cruel nobility are
The single pattern of his fate, the story that he weaves
As it is told of him. Goddess of the bright sparkling tides,
The spindrift spray, can you not gently bid him to relent?

For the secret of your son, O lovely Thetis of
The glittering tread, is silence, a stillness underlying
All his rage, as he dwells upon his nearing death. Doomed
To brief and blazing greatness, his soul floats upon the depths
Of time. The horizons of his world are close, and he knows
At once—with an abiding certainty and cold disdain
Of the form his life must finally assume—his fate:
Everlasting oblivion and everlasting renown.

"I see," I said when I had finished. "And you say you're… thinking
Homeric thoughts just now?"

"Well…" He lifted his eyes to the sky overhead. "Homeric analogies, it might be better to say. Epic forms, at least. You see, I'm immersed in translating an epic just at the moment, and I find myself unable to decide among the possible styles I might adopt in order to capture something of the force and beauty of the original in the rather limited medium of modern English."

"Oh, yes," I said, laying the pages aside on the deck and retrieving my coffee. "Nonnos, wasn't it? Or…?"

"No, no," said Roland, "that's all done and delivered. It's already with the copy editor at the press."

"It's…?" I felt, I confess, more than a little surprised.

"No, now I'm dealing with a far thornier set of textual difficulties. The linguistic and aesthetic gulfs are immeasurably vaster." He lowered his eyes again, stared away toward some far corner of the garden, and shook his head musingly.

I was genuinely mystified. "What's the epic, then?" I asked. "Something Persian? Or Japanese?"

He smiled again but did not look at me. "The *Lykiad*," he said. "At least, that's one version of its title."

Even more confused now, I searched my memory, but in vain. "Is that some obscure Hellenistic work? Or Byzantine?" I asked at last. "I've never heard of it."

Roland breathed in deeply. "Spring is near," he said. "And, no. Forgive me for using a Hellenized version of the title, but the original would be unintelligible to you. And, while you may never have heard *of* it, you've certainly heard portions of it declaimed. I myself remember well when, as a puppy, I first heard certain of its stanzas sung in the lovely haunting voices of the coyotes who roamed the mountain south of our cabin in the woods."

"Coyotes?" I cast my mind back to those eerie keening choruses in the night, drifting down from the wooded ridgeline. "I had no idea. Well, then… what's it about?"

"It's the great and ancient epic of my people," he replied, "far older than any recorded history, written or oral. It emanates from the earliest days of our civilization. It's the story of the father of our race, the demigod wolf Lykos—again, pardon my Greek. In my ancestral tongue, his name would be pronounced…"—and here Roland lifted his snout, parted his lips, and gave vent to a kind of low, musical, moaning howl in three distinct syllables, terminating

303

in a slight, shrill bark. "In any event, it's his tale, in thirty-two exquisite and haunting cantos. It begins with his conception, in a place called simply the Endless Steppes, when a cloud in the shape of a wolf settled upon the peak of the holy mountain where the gods and celestial spirits walk and, by that coupling, became great with child. Sixty days later he emerged full-grown, the first and greatest of the wolves, his fur the color of the sun, his eyes like fiery diamonds. It tells also of how he made a mate for himself by calling her forth from the divine waters flowing down from the summit of the holy mountain, and how he fashioned the first wolf-pack from earth moistened from those same springs. And it recounts a whole host of his legendary adventures, and those of his kind as they multiplied and created a vast empire for themselves in the Endless Steppes. There's the tale of how his wife was abducted by the Rabbit Demon King of the far southern wastelands and how he rescued her by defeating seven magically protected rabbit demon champions, one after another, by virtue of both his strength and his cunning."

"Rabbits?" I asked.

"Rabbit demons," Roland corrected me. "Far more terrible and wicked beings. Giant things with flaming eyes and razor-sharp incisors. It also tells of how he entered the realm of the great Black Squirrel of Death, dark lord of the underworld and psychopomp of all vermin, and bore away that terrible king's golden wand. That was the wand, you see, with which the Black Squirrel guided the souls of departed rodents to his realm, and it had the power to fascinate and enchant any soul, and lead it wherever its bearer might list. Lykos used it to lure the Black Squirrel's armies of hell-squirrels to their destruction in the sea. The poem also tells of Lykos's great contest with the bear-god Megalarx, which lasted twenty days, and which ended with Lykos triumphant; and then it tells of how the antagonists thereafter became the fastest of friends, and pledged themselves in brotherhood to one another, and fought side by side on many adventures. At last, however, Megalarx was slain through the treachery of an evil squirrel who had been magically transformed to look like a bear-cub and sent by the Black Squirrel to exact vengeance for Lykos's plunder of his wand and the destruction of his armies. That's actually one of the most tragic and moving moments in the whole epic. Shattering, in fact."

"I can imagine," I said.

"*Squirrels*," he muttered in an uncharacteristically truculent tone. "Oh, well, really…"

"But it's not just a narrative of adventures and wild escapades. It's also a great religious, philosophical, and moral treatise, full of enlightening discourses. You see, Lykos is revered among my kind not only as a mighty hero, but as our great and enlightened teacher and lawgiver. The poem tells of him proclaiming the first legal code governing clan and pack, and recounts how he laid the foundations of our culture and customs. It also includes all twelve of his greater discourses, known now as the *Sutras of the Luminous Wolf Wisdom*, which contain those spiritual truths that inform all canine religion. They include only the exoteric doctrines, admittedly, as the greater mysteries are reserved only for the most committed of spiritual adepts. But they're awe-inspiring teachings for all that—on overcoming illusion, and defeating the demon-squirrel of ignorance, and mastering the passions, and obeying reason, and practicing compassion. I imagine they might strike you as somewhat Mahā-yāna in their morals and metaphysics. Certainly, some of the later Central Asian recensions of the poem, like the very interesting Sogdian variant, incorporate quite a few Buddhist terms as equivalents of many of the most important concepts advanced in the discourses, and the effect is anything but discordant."

"Remarkable," I said, perfectly sincerely.

He turned his eyes to me and stared in silence for several seconds, as if pondering his next words carefully. Then, with a distinctly diffident air, he said, "The last canto is called 'Of His Great Compassion and His Descent to the Wretched.'"

"Oh?" I said. "What's that about?"

Roland's expression became almost tenderly wistful. "Humanity," he said quietly. "You. Your kind. The canto tells of Lykos coming upon a wandering band of wretched, hapless, bipedal simians somewhere on the Endless Steppes—savage, uncouth, languishing in such a state of olfactory debility as to be virtually incapable of feeding themselves. At first, he was tempted to turn away in distaste. The sordid spectacle of these shambling, misshapen, feeble brutes repelled him. They weren't only ridiculous; they were rebarbative to look at or to smell. He wasn't even tempted to do them the honor of running them down and devouring them, like noble antelopes; given their clumsy gait, they wouldn't be able to make a real chase of it—certainly not over any expanse of ground, and certainly not with the grace and power of any of those splendid, nimble, powerful creatures that the gods created for the Great Hunt. He would have thought it degrading to feed on so maladroit and helpless a prey. And yet, as he contemplated them, his divine intellect perceived in them a kind of rare promise, and his heart was moved with compassion. He saw also that these creatures had somehow lost their way— had become estranged from the world all about them—and realized that none of their extraordinary promise would bear fruit unless they were patiently guided toward higher things, and taught the arts of social love, of community, of hunting properly, of personal hygiene, of religion and law. And so, one day, he gathered his most trusted earls and most beloved disciples about him and declared to them that it was his intention to go down among these creatures, to assume for their sake a humbler, less terrifying form, one at once wolf and not wolf, and then to undertake the great task of leading them—gradually, unwearyingly, generation upon generation— toward the highest possible realization of those potentialities that slept within them, latent, like seeds beneath the winter soil. He declared his resolve to go forth from himself. He who was the first and greatest of the wolves—the 'Wolf Who Was in the Beginning,' as he was styled throughout the Endless Steppes—would now become dog and take up his dwelling among humankind. By his willing, self-outpouring transformation from the lupine to the canine, he would be able to bring enlightenment to these poor naked apes. His people begged him not to depart from them. He promised that he would come again to them, on that day when the great Wolf of Night would swallow the sun and the world would be fashioned anew. Until then, though, he must pursue the course he had set himself. 'For my heart has been wounded with pity,' he told the Great Pack of the Endless Steppes, 'and fain would I die rather than bear that wound unhealed. I must go down now to this savage and

suffering people, wandering in darkness and despair, these mysterious orphans of the land and the sky, and must wean them from their
rude and violent ways, and lead them upon a better path, even the
path of enlightenment; else I shall myself be lost.' And so he went.
The epic ends—and I can't even begin to communicate the sheer
poignancy of those closing lines—with the image of Lykos walking
slowly away toward the tribe of Man, gradually taking the form of a
dog as he goes and at last disappearing over the horizon while his
whole people raise their voices to the vast sky of the Steppes in lamentation." Here Roland ceased speaking, and it seemed to me that I
caught sight of a tear glinting in the corner of his eye.

"I believe you," I said after many seconds of silence. "I'm moved
just by hearing about it."

"Oh, but how to capture that beauty and that grandeur in a
tongue so devoid of... nuance, subtlety?" he said. "How to give
some impression of the cadences and melodies and glissandi of that
noble verse in a wholly alien medium? English encompasses an
entirely different set of sensibilities. And every human language,
being a fallen tongue, subsists in so different a semeiotic economy."

"A fallen tongue?"

He wagged his head vigorously several times from side to side,
shaking the tears away. "Yes," he said at last. "There's a kind of fall-
enness in all language, I suppose. At least, there can be. Words, if
they become too detached from the living symbolic system of revelation that nature is, and are no longer rooted in any system of cosmic correspondences, invariably wither and die. And any language
can become alienated from its natural wellsprings. All human language exists at the threshold between nature and culture, and a very
delicate magic indeed is required to guard that boundary without
allowing it to become a total alienation. All of nature is logos, of
course; all of it is eloquent of its divine source and end; but how easily your kind loses the connection between nature's symbolic economies and the signs you use when speaking or writing. How quickly
the metaphorical flower, once plucked, wilts in your hand. And
every dead metaphor is the record of a lost communion. The vocation of the poet—the true poet, that is—is to overcome the fallen-
ness of human language, in part through converting words that

merely *indicate* into a music that truly expresses... truly *means*... to overcome the schism between reflective thought and the immediate knowledge of the world... to reestablish communion by subordinating the words one speaks aloud to the silence of the inner *verbum cordis*. And, of course, the truly inspired poet, or truly poetic prophet, is always trying to reach that primordial word that, in being uttered, utters all things into being... the logos that discloses the depths of the origin, prior to this or that primate dialect. That's what fascinated the Jesuits about Chinese ideograms you know—that they aren't transcriptions of phonemes, but rather symbols of concepts. A Platonic form of writing. Edenic, perhaps... or as near as possible." He ceased speaking, obviously lost in thoughts of his own.

"So," I said after nearly a minute, "how will you go about translating it?"

"Hmm?" He turned to me as if he had momentarily forgotten I was there. "Oh, I'm still thinking it through, to be honest. I'll probably go the route of most modern renderings of Homer—to affect a plain, sublime purity of phrasing. I have to say, though, I often wonder whether that tends to perpetuate a modern misconception regarding the language of the Homeric epics, and regarding the general difference in sensibility between the epic and lyric. When you actually look at the Greek, you find a finely-wrought music there, often subtle—not just rolling, resonant, noble diction. There are all sorts of glittering, daedal intricacies and ornamentations. Yes, it's all very grand and stately and sonorous; but it's also often fleeting and delicate and diaphanous. It's an old problem, that— translating *through* our preconceptions of the cultures we're drawing on. There's something analogous in modern translations of classical Chinese poetry. That is, for some reason, we now try to make all of it seem as limpid and simple as Japanese *haiku*. Hence, even a poet as fantastical and Romantic and formally audacious as Li Bai often comes across as a virtuoso of the unadorned and glisteningly transparent. Maybe Pope's Homer, simply by virtue of its grand and ostentatious artificiality, is nearer the true spirit of Homer's verse than any of those more recent, excruciatingly solemn, uniformly sublime translations are. Who really knows?"

308

GARDEN

"Indeed," I murmured, taking a healthy swallow of coffee. "I have to say," I added after a few seconds more, "I'm rather touched to learn that my kind plays so climactic a role in your people's greatest epic."

"You wouldn't necessarily be flattered by the depictions of your ancestors, however."

"Even so."

"You see, our compact with your kind was the greatest epochal transition in the history of our own civilization… even our own physiology and sense of spiritual destiny. The Great Compassion— well, the version of the story in the epic may be a myth or allegory, but it's true nonetheless. And how could we not come to your aid? You were so helpless and wild and so very, very stupid. You would have gone in such catastrophic directions otherwise, especially as regards social intelligence. You—your kind—from the first you had that strange, terrifying, fierce energy within you, that prodigious natural capacity for creation and destruction, but as moral beings you were quite hopeless. For curiosity and inventiveness, you were the most evolutionarily dynamic and… oh, vagile creatures imaginable. But, where moral ingenuity and adventurousness were concerned, you were as sessile as sea anemones. You wouldn't have evolved even the simplest of natural taboos—like, say, not eating your neighbor when you get peckish. And, I assure you, but for our continued efforts among you, you'd revert to that savagery within a generation or two."

"Of that I have no doubt," I said.

"I suspect, moreover, that there's some latent race memory of that long and arduous moral tutelage in your kind. Note how, for instance, whenever we go for a walk together, in wood or meadow or along a boulevard, you're afraid to venture out until you've tethered yourself to me, as if you don't trust yourself to find your way home without my guidance. It's touching, but also revealing."

"You mean, um, the leash?"

"Precisely," he replied, his expression now becoming poignantly sympathetic. "Believe me, I quite understand."

I cleared my throat, a little uneasily. "I think there's been a slight misunderstanding here…" I began.

309

"Honestly, you needn't explain," he interrupted, briefly raising a paw to silence me. "I don't judge. I wouldn't want you to feel like a ship adrift at sea. It's a huge, intimidating world out there, especially for the... well, let's say, for the olfactorily challenged. I expect that, deep down in your nature, there lingers some vague, terrifying memory of the vast openness of the steppes. I assure you, nothing could evoke deeper sentiments in me than does the sight of you pathetically clinging to that stout cord. I cannot help but think of it as your *umbilicus amoris*."

I nearly said something, but then thought better of it.

"You know," he continued after a moment, looking away again, "there are a good number of persons out there who choose—*choose*—to live without dogs."

"I know," I said somberly.

"Where do they get their moral examples? Who are their paragons?" He sighed deeply and shook his head heavily. "Do you think their lives can have meaning?"

"No," I said, "most certainly not."

He nodded sadly. "And yet, perhaps, there can be a kind of grace even in meaningless lives."

"I couldn't say," I replied.

For a long time, neither of us ventured another remark. The moonlit ground-fog eddied lazily all about the deck, its ghostly glow mingling in a pleasantly macabre way with the starker light from the house's lamp.

"One question haunts me, though." Roland finally said, turning a thoughtful gaze on me.

"What's that?"

"What became of your tails?"

"Our...?" I swallowed some more coffee. "Well, if my remote forebears had any, evolution long ago eliminated them."

"But did it?" he said quietly. "Did it really? How, though, I wonder, in the long history of all those syncynic adaptations by which your kind advanced under our guidance—how is it, I have to ask, that the most needful of things...?" He paused, staring at me with a deeply reflective expression. "Yes, I do wonder..."

After a while, beginning to feel slightly uneasy, I observed, "Most evolutionary theorists speak of 'synanthropic' adaptations—the way, that is, in which other creatures have conformed themselves to us, and the way in which we constitute a kind of ecosystem for them."

This elicited only a small snort of laughter from Roland. "It's only that the absence of a tail tends to render your kind a mite emotionally impenetrable at times. It makes you seem unnecessarily furtive, covert... secretive. As though you were ashamed of something." His gaze became momentarily more intense. "Do you perhaps have them amputated at birth? I believe I read something about that in the works of Lord Monboddo, after all—something about midwives discreetly cutting them away. You can tell me, you know."

"Absolutely not," I said. "Nothing's amputated. Tails are just something we lack."

Roland stared at me with narrowed eyes for some moments, but then nodded ruefully. "I suppose that must be true. It's a pity. It's the very tendency of one's tail to escape the control of one's rational faculty that makes it so trustworthy a sign of one's inner states. Tails attest to an openness, a frankness—a sort of noble naiveté—in one's nature. That's why it occurred to me that your kind might choose to have them removed. After all, human beings have good reason to want to hide their impulses. It seems to me that it wouldn't be very strange for you to resent your own inability to govern the wagging of your tails—for you to feel ashamed, that is, of so incontinent a display of emotion's power to throw off reason's tyranny. I believe Augustine talks about that somewhere, come to think of it."

I cleared my throat. "Well, not exactly in relation to tails. Something else. Something analogous."

"All right, then," he said, rising, stretching, yawning. "Would you mind bringing all of this in for me? I've discovered I heartily dislike the flavor of manila folder."

"Of course," I said.

And I imagine we went inside then, but the rest of the night seems to have been erased from my memory.

XLV

WHEN MY MOTHER DIED, the garden was in only very hesitant flower. Spring was still more than a month away, but a week of unseasonable warmth had prompted a few daring bulbs to rear their heads above the soil. During her last days her decline was as precipitate and dreadful as my father's had been, though mercifully she was able to spend them entirely at home, and she finally passed away in her own bed (to the degree that the hospital bed provided by hospice was hers). She—or most of her— seemed to depart before death finally took her; for a time, she held conversations with presences visible only to her; then, at the end, words no longer came to her lips at all, but only occasional strained gasps that irresistibly suggested to me that she was struggling to shed her body. The nurse who was present for her last hours marveled at how long she lingered—which, I have to say, provided me no comfort.

When the moment of her death came, I was absent. I and my son had briefly left the house to take Roland for a walk, and within twenty minutes of our departure my wife phoned to tell me that it appeared that my mother had gone. My eldest brother, I recalled, had once told me that in his experience (from his days before leaving the priesthood) the dying often seem to wait until their loved ones are out of the room and then take the opportunity to slip discreetly away. I called both my brothers, in time to prevent the younger of the two from making his flight to us from North Carolina, scheduled for that very day. Then I began calling other members of the family.

I am not entirely certain how anyone ever learns to speak about the death of his or her parents. To those who knew them, there is nothing one need say. To those who did not, there is nothing that one can. Everything one might try to communicate would be fragmentary at best. So what is there to talk about? My father's genu-

GARDEN

inely operatic bass-baritone voice and fondness for atrocious puns? His kindness to children and animals? My mother's ineffably upper-South southernness and peculiar restlessness of nature? Her only ever partially appeased wanderlust? The psychic wounds my father carried till the end from the Second World War? The equally deep wounds my mother carried from her father's alcoholism? What would it mean to anyone? Moreover, the sudden and total absence of that sheltering past—that living continuity with one's earliest childhood—is a feeling quite without analogy to any other (at least, none of which I am aware). Unlike the far more terrible death of a child, of course, it is an anticipated grief, a "natural" bereavement, and so we accept it and wait for the pain and the now incurable regrets to subside. Still, even so, when it comes it is not at all what we had expected, and there really is no way of describing it—even to ourselves. All I can say with certainty is that it is accompanied by an especially poignant sense—a reminder, really, that we should not need—that this world is only a very temporary station upon the way.

My writing was a comfort when I returned to it. So was my daily solitary walk with Roland.

My mother's remains now rest next to my father's, in the grave-yard of the church in Ellicott City, Maryland where they were wed, some sixty years before my father passed away, and some sixty-five before my mother followed him. Both graves are quite humble, as each requested.

XLVI

THIS IS ROLAND'S BOOK, of course, and I have tried to recount as many of our more significant conversations as I can; but I have omitted many even so, in most cases out of forgetfulness, in some out of discretion. There are confidences that it is always wrong to violate. And here I omit many more, as in recent years we have tended to discuss matters of peculiar privacy. But there was a day this last spring when at last I came to understand, I believe, things he has been trying to tell me for nearly a decade.

There is a garage behind the house, at the bottom of the garden, and one of its lateral walls constitutes part of the property's back fence. Its main entrance can be reached by a grassy access passageway, shared with a few neighbors, but it is no use for parking my car because a large tree—no doubt unplanted or only a sapling when the house was built—stands too close to the overhead door to allow for convenient use. There is a side entrance in the garden, however, and so we use it as a shed for yard equipment. That, however, requires little space, and so I had for a long time assumed that the interior was largely empty. But on that spring day, early in the afternoon, I found myself in the garden, there for no other purpose I suppose than to enjoy the delightful weather and the plentiful flowers and the temporary respite from my computer screen. I really do not recall all the details. But I do recall noticing that the garden entrance to the garage was standing open. I went to see whether my wife or son was there, or whether instead the door had been left ajar by accident and then had swung wide in the breeze; but as I approached I became aware that music—orchestral, melancholy, obviously late modern—was emerging from within; and just as I was reaching the doorway I recognized it as Takemitsu's "Through me flows what you call Time." Then I noticed the soft glow inside. Without announcing myself, I stepped into the dimness. It took a moment for my eyes to adjust, but when they did I was quite taken aback.

GARDEN

There were in fact gardening tools stored inside, neatly leaning against or hanging along the far wall, but otherwise the interior was wholly unlike anything I expected to find. The bare concrete of the floor was entirely covered by neat parallel columns of bamboo matting, in slender oblongs with narrow selvedges of plain ecru linen sewn around their edges. Stretched along the lower half of the opposite wall were a variety of small but elaborately carved Chinese chests, their dark wood adorned with images of dragons and billowing clouds and blossoming trees and bridges over winding streams. Tastefully arranged in the middle of the room were four small teak plinths on which rested various delicate, lavishly painted, glazed Chinese vases, as well as a fifth on which stood a small hexagonal teak lantern whose single flame shone a sultry gold through the yellow patina of its gauzy mulberry panels. Everything was immaculately swept or dusted, and—rather than the dank staleness I had anticipated—a fresh, pleasantly dry, musky fragrance pervaded the air, part sandalwood I think, part the residue of joss sticks that had at one time or another shed their smoke upon the walls and ceiling. To the right, just inside the overhead door, there were four simple straw *tatami* seating mats symmetrically laid out around a low square table of polished teak. To the left stood a tall, narrow, open case of shelves—plain sanded pine stained a light honey color and thinly varnished—extending halfway into the garage from the opposite wall and containing easily half a hundred neatly rolled paper scrolls tied with slender black ribbons. Beyond that was an exceedingly rudimentary oblong table made from the same wood, on which there was another glowing lamp in the same design as the other, as well as a mutedly glossy black Chinese ink-stone and a simple ceramic cup with a sea-green finish holding five or six bamboo calligraphy brushes. And there, perched on a handsome Chinese taboret, wearing an unusually small Confucian scholar's black hemp *yugeon* on his head, its tassels hanging limply down past either side of his face, was Roland, bending forward with another calligraphy brush extending from his front teeth and diligently inditing a sheet of rice-paper with tiny, precise strokes. Beyond him, at the back end of the garage, a sleek, probably German turntable with a spinning LP sat on a simple wooden end-table; two small but

315

evidently good speakers in polished black wooden cases hung in metal brackets on the wall above it.

I approached him cautiously, and for a moment he gave no sign of having noticed me; but, just as I came up behind him, and just as the LP came coincidentally to the end of the side and the arm of the turntable returned to its strut with a quiet click, I heard him grumble something to himself through his set jaws. He gently laid the brush aside with its tip propped on the ink-stone.

"I picked up your scent some moments ago," he remarked in that smooth, Laurence-Harvey-like voice of his. He briefly glanced over his shoulder at me (and I must say he looked quite distinguished in that splendid cap, with its elegantly dangling straps). "And your tread is anything but soft—at least, to my ears." Then he turned his eyes back to the sheet of paper.

Looking at it over his head, I saw that it was filled with descending lines of minute but extraordinarily refined ideograms. "I had no idea you had this... this..." I looked around.

"This scholar's studio," he said, completing my sentence for me. "Yes, I took the liberty of hiring some men to bring these furnishings and decorations in. I had need of a good Confucian retreat. Sometimes I feel an urge to imitate Pu Songling or someone like that... to withdraw into a humble scholar's sanctuary and write ghost stories, or whatever else might occur to me. You'll find the charges on your next credit card statement."

"Oh..." I began, but then simply shrugged. I had grown used to these small fiscal surprises by now.

"Sometimes I have to nourish the Chinese side of my sensibility," he added.

"Ah," I said with a nod. "But I notice the music is Japanese."

"True," he said, tilting his head so that his cap slid off gently onto the tabletop. "I've been listening to quite a lot of Takemitsu lately. Also a bit of Yoshimatsu and Miki, though they're lesser composers. So I suppose I'm also in a Japanese mood. But there's no contradiction. And, anyway, there's no reason why a modern Chinese Confucian wouldn't have a taste for Japanese composers."

"No doubt," I said. Then I noticed a rather large, obviously extremely old volume bound in dark leather, lying on its side in the shadows on the far side of the table, near the wall. "That doesn't look very Chinese or Japanese," I said, reaching for it.

"Oh, have a care," said Roland.

I retracted my hand. "Is it very valuable?"

"I should think so," he replied. "And very fragile. It's an incunabulum. To be precise, it's a Byzantine codex containing Plotinus's *Enneads* in Greek, and it comes from the personal library that Bessarion donated to the Venetian senate in, I believe, 1439. But it's some centuries older than that."

It was a moment or so before I was able to speak; and, even when I did, there was a distinctly feeble quality to my voice. "Are you... playing on my..."

"Simplicity? No, nothing of the sort. Though it's always a temptation."

"Well, how do you come to have it?"

"Oh, you know..."—he looked up into my eyes with the expression of someone trying not to seem too pleased with himself—"I have my connections."

"Who?" I asked, still not quite able to contain the tone of incredulity.

"Discretion forbids me from saying," he replied, turning his shoulders, nimbly leaping down from his seat, and trotting lightly toward the floor-mats. "But let's not worry about that. Let's sit down together over in my little parlor here. I need a break. The taste of dry bamboo begins to irritate the tongue after a while."

I hesitated a moment, cast another glance in the direction of the codex, shrugged, and then followed him. I sat across the table from him, settling down upon the mat in labored fashioned, and not without a few gratuitous groans. The straw fibers crackled beneath me with a pleasant delicacy and their faint, drily sweet aroma rose up around me. "You've made it quite a cozy little studio," I remarked. "I'm envious."

"I'm sorry I don't have any tea made," said Roland. "Would you care for some?"

"Maybe a little later," I replied, looking about and noticing for the first time the collection of lovely, monochrome, deftly minimalist brush-paintings—a sparrow perched on a bamboo branch, a butterfly drifting above a tussock of wild grasses, a distant waterfall casting up clouds of spray, two blossoms on a bough shedding a few of their petals on the wind—affixed by white drawing pins to the wall at Roland's back. "Did you paint those?" I asked.

He briefly cast a glance over his shoulder and then turned back to me with a mildly bashful frown. "Just a few idle daubs," he said. "Nothing worth celebrating."

"On the contrary," I said with perfect sincerity, "they're exquisite. I wish I could master those... those subtle strokes. They're incredibly evocative."

"Well..." Now he allowed himself a slight, satisfied smile. "It's the magic of emptiness, isn't it? Learning to use what's absent from the canvas—from the paper, rather—to suggest immeasurably more than is really there. And, if I do say so myself, it does take a certain lightness of touch... a certain legerdemain, so to speak. *La légèreté de la main*, that is—or *de la bouche*. A good metaphor, really, for so much of reality. Everything is more originally emptiness, after all. And the best proof of this is how near to nothingness we can reduce our impressions of the phenomenal order and still find that the barest hints of existence are sufficient to summon up the whole of things out of the void."

"I suppose that's true," I said.

He cast a few glances about the room. "Don't disdain my wanton combination of Chinese and Japanese aesthetic and conceptual idioms, though," he said. "It's not as if the two cultures were hermetically sealed against one another. Of course, my general preference, like yours, leans toward Japan. I prefer the traditional Japanese search for an ideal balance between nature and craft—or between simplicity and sophistication, or between sublime plainness and beautiful ornament—more affecting than the classical Chinese appetite for an unapologetically artificial union of the exquisite and the opulent. Of course, those generalizations aren't exactly fair, I know. Chinese civilization also perfected certain arts of limpid simplicity. But..." He arched an eyebrow meaningfully.

"I know what you mean," I said.

"Anyway, we're always mixing and matching. That's what culture is, even within native boundaries. Or, rather, what civilization is.

GARDEN

Here I am, for instance, playing the Confucian and writing verse in the style of Du Fu, but..."

"Oh, is that what you're doing?"

The shy expression momentarily returned to his features, but then he gave his ears a couple shakes and continued. "But, of course, you and I are both as much Romantics as Classicists—more so, really—and so more truly ourselves when we're letting our inner Daoists out to play. For all our love of Du Fu's austere lucidity, we need Li Bai's magnificent glittering combinations of the wildly visionary and naïvely sentimental and gaily whimsical to be truly happy... and the mad eruptions and lightning-bolts of his language... and his, if I dare say it, nature mysticism."

"It's true," I said, nodding and taking a deep breath. "But, then also, in Buddhist moods we crave Wang Wei, surely."

"But of course," said Roland. "And, when one's feeling a bit like a Chinese Rimbaud, only Li He or Li Shangyin can satisfy. We all contain multitudes. In our hearts are many mansions, and some especially capacious ones for all three of the Great Sages, and also for their greatest poetic disciples... and poetic apostates, for that matter."

"I certainly hope so," I said.

"Mind you, some of these distinctions are so misleading. I mean, Confucius spoke every bit as often and as mysteriously of 'the Way' as did Zhuangzi or Laozi. And who's to say that all that restraint and propriety of his—'If the mat was not straight, the master would not sit' and all that—wasn't itself an expression of a certain kind of mysticism? Perhaps he confined his positive statements—his *cataphatic* statements—to the realm of civic, social, political, and ethical discourse in order to guard the boundaries of the mysteries... to protect the sacred precincts of the unutterable. *Wovon man nicht sprechen kann, darüber muß man schweigen*, after all. There's more than one way to serve the great silence. Oh!" He leaned forward and placed a paw on the table. "That reminds me: do you think it's possible that, in *Journey to the West*, the Monkey King's misadventures in the Heavenly Court and his eventual expulsion are based on Li Bai's exile from the Imperial Court?"

I pondered this for a moment. "It had never occurred to me," I said, "but it's an attractive suggestion."

319

He sat back again and withdrew his paw. "It is, isn't it? And, really, it would be so fitting." A wistfully fond look appeared on his face. "What a truly wonderful man. He was so perfectly... centered... and so indifferent to all the inane nonsense your species worships—power, wealth... success. He might have been a dog, he was so pure."

"That's high praise indeed," I said.

Roland stared away toward his writing table. "Do you think the legend of his death is true?" he asked after a few seconds.

"You mean the one about him falling out of the boat and drowning in the river when he was drunk, because he had been trying to embrace the reflection of the moon?"

"Well, naturally," said Roland, turning his gaze back to me. "Is there another?"

"No," I said. "And yes, I believe it's true, even if it didn't happen."

At this, he allowed himself an affable smile. "I'm glad you put it that way. That's what I think healthiest about your temperament: you believe everything. Even where religions are concerned, you believe everything."

I laughed. "By which you mean, I suppose, that I must believe nothing as such."

Now the smile dissolved into a look of absolute earnestness. "On the contrary, I mean precisely *everything*. I'm a dog, remember. I'm not susceptible to that human sickness of thinking that religions are mutually exclusive systems of propositions, true *if and only if* all other systems are false. I say, would you care for a few pieces of *yokan*? I have a very fine variety here, sent to me from Tokyo by an admirer of my volumes of haiku."

"Oh, right," I said, feeling my brow furrowing as the memory returned to me, "your haiku... the fragrance of earthworms and all that."

"I'm touched that you recall," he said with a small, ceremonious inclination of his head. "But would you like some?"

"Perhaps when we have our tea," I said.

"Excellent suggestion," he replied. "You know, *yokan* always makes me think of Tanizaki. You've read Tanizaki, of course?"

"Of course."

320

GARDEN

"I don't mean the fiction. Have you read *In Praise of Shadows?*"
"Several times."

"So you'll recall where he talks about eating *yokan* as being like eating shadows, or something like that—how he calls it a quintessentially Japanese candy precisely because it's so... well, so tenebrous, I suppose one might say. Because of its dark translucency. The way it lies on a dark dish all but invisibly in a dim room, and the way it melts on the tongue like a sweet shadow... or like a shadow of sweetness, it's so mild. I don't recall the exact wording, so perhaps I should read it again."

"I recall it," I said. "I love that book. I love the way Japanese culture has always been able to aestheticize everything... even violent death."

"It's so true," he said. "And Tanizaki is right too. There's a special Japanese virtuosity of the umbratilous, the nebulous, the... softly shadowed. It's a sign of true refinement to be able to love shadowy spaces... liminal intervals... places of transition. There's a tacit metaphysics there too, in that aesthetic sensitivity to the dim and crepuscular, and to the moments and spaces of fluid indistinction... the junctures where possibility briefly overwhelms actuality, where anything might emerge, where the mystery of being announces itself in the as yet undisclosed next moment. It speaks of the sheer fortuity of all of the world's beautiful transformations. Dreams overwhelming waking thoughts. Unseen presences overwhelming visible absences. It's—how can a poor dog say it without lapsing into ecstatic gibberish?—it's that lovely floating experience of suspense on the threshold of existence, where it seems anything might come into being. Twilight consciousness. And there's a lovely metaphysical fragility there too, isn't there? A sustained precariousness, as though at any moment the world might melt into potentiality again. Which is itself another revelation of the wonderful needlessness of the gift of being." He heaved an especially deep sigh and his smile became distinctly melancholy. "In the modern world, flooded as it is at all times by shrill, brittle electric incandescences, lit by the leprous white glow of computer screens, we desperately need more shadows... more love of shadow as such. We need those places and moments in which the mind sees nameless things moving in the

321

obscurity, in the dusk, and occasionally even knows itself as conjuring the world out of a more primordial, more timeless dreaming." He fell silent, his eyes turned downward.

It was many moments before I spoke. "I think you found a way to say it very well. You always do. I know exactly what you mean—even if I couldn't rephrase it in any way intelligible to myself."

He raised his eyes and stared intently at me for several seconds, as if once again adjusting his estimation of me; this time, though, I had the feeling that the adjustment was somewhat upward. "There it is again," he said. "You take the sane approach. I attribute it to that Hindu capacity of yours for syncretism."

"Ah," I said. "Look, I keep meaning to set the record straight there…"

He cut me off with a curt, emphatic sneeze. "Oh, I know, I know. You needn't tell me that you're technically not really Hindu… as such. Or Sikh or Buddhist or Hopi or Maori or whatever. I know. As I've told you, however, to the canine mind these are empty distinctions, and I think that, when you depend on them, you make an unwarranted concession to a debilitating misconception about the nature of religious belief. And, amusingly, it's not even a misconception you really hold to—not deep down in your heart of hearts. As I say, you believe everything. You despise doctrinaire religious certitudes, not—as is common for your kind in this age—out of skepticism or incredulity, but out of a superabundance of belief. You don't think that all the varying respectable creeds are true merely subjunctively, so to speak—merely by virtue of pointing with childish naiveté toward some nameless x that they simultaneously reveal and dissemble under the form of an '*as if.*' At least, not exactly. Your heart and mind tell you that they're all in a sense literally true at one and the same time."

"Perhaps you understand me better than I understand myself," I said. "But I'm not sure how literal and symbolic truth are being distinguished here."

"Of course I understand you better than you understand yourself." He gave each of his shoulders several slow, meditative licks. "As for symbols and… facts, I suppose…" He looked at me again. "I'm not really making a distinction, because I see symbols—true sym-

322

bols, that is—not as allegories of realities that they merely *indicate*, but rather as true manifestations of those realities, the essential vehicles by which those realities enter into the world of consciousness—which is the only world that exists. The living symbol is that nuptial place—the conjugal moment—in which reality emerges as at once what *is* and what's *known*. And I think of religious symbolic economies as specific congelations and contractions of consciousness, local dreamscapes or... oh, I don't know... 'mythotopoi,' I suppose I might say, where the mystery truly shows itself. I mean, one can't expect Sophia simply to step out before your eyes naked, can you? The sheer radiance of her beauty would annihilate your kind, what with your fallen powers of perception. Your spiritual senses are too weak for that. You'd be reduced to ashes, like Semele seeing the full glory of Zeus. So she garbs herself in this or that lovely raiment, this or that robe of beauty, and thereby allows you to see her without the experience striking you dead or rendering you deranged. And you, of course, as a creature of this or that time and place, participate in weaving that raiment, according to the standards of form and ornament and expressive motif you understand. So, yes, it's all true in that sense. And each really vital religious vision is true in its particular place, where consciousness at once projects and receives its imaginal or symbolic forms. Peoples and persons are always doing this, of course, some of them with supreme poetic genius. They're always individually and collectively dreaming the space where the divine shows itself—the opening to the divine, the temenos of the temple, the sun-washed, hospitable, marmorean courtyard amid this vale of shadows."

"I see," I said. "And all the manifest—or, at any rate, apparent—contradictions of propositional content between traditions?"

Roland moaned softly. "How Anglo-American," he said with an obvious note of fatigue in his voice. "*Quel dommage.* Propositions are merely symbols too, you know, neither more nor less. They're simply the kind of symbols from which the symbolic surfaces have sadly been effaced, turning them into collections of dead metaphors that, in their very morbidity, look like dry, precise, unsentimental statements of fact. That's why it's always necessary to deconstruct them—to reduce their terms to their secret, hidden, long-forgotten metaphorical and metonymical origins. Only when we properly remember that, say, 'enlightenment' originally refers to a real flash of lightning, and has never succeeded in transcending that symbol, are we protected against analytic superstition."

After a few seconds, I said, "Yes, I suppose that that's how I *want* to see the matter."

"Well, in your case," he replied, "it's all but inevitable. You have very little capacity for institutional loyalty. Certainly you feel no allegiance to the relics—the baptized swords and crowns—of imperial Christendom, much less the degenerate throne-and-altar nationalisms of the Concordats and Pragmatic Sanctions and such. In fact, you have no use for the notion of cultural purity or national identity at all, do you? You're true devotion is to the sheer chaos of cosmopolitan civilization, with all its religious and aesthetic diversities."

"True."

"I mean, if you could invent your own religion, you would. Its scriptures would be nearly all scriptures, and much else beside. I can see it now—the lector at the lectern reading passages from the *Upaniṣads* and Plotinus and *Alice in Wonderland* or *The Hunting of the Snark* and the *Adi Granth* and 1 Corinthians and *The Wind in the Willows*. And the sacrament would be the Japanese tea ceremony."

"Now you're mocking me," I said.

A mercurial twinkle appeared in his eyes, an amused smirk on his lips. "Perhaps. A little. But I mean it as praise too. I mean, your kind, where religions are concerned, tends to see only a diversity of distinct and incompatible systems of *epistēmē*, hermetically sealed against one another, whereas mine perceives complementary forms of gnosis—forms of intimate acquaintance with and assimilation of the truth in its inexhaustible fullness... trails of scent all converging on the same quarry. I mean, is there truly a gulf of difference between Buddhism's *saṃbhogakaya* and St. Paul's absolutely fleshless *sōma pneumatikon*? Or between the transfigured, radiant body of the risen Christ, or at least the resplendent bodies of the hesychasts, and the radiant flesh of Swami Premānanda walking through the marketplace in an ecstasy of love for God's beauty? And who's to say Swami Rāmalingam didn't in fact experience full bodily transfiguration and divinization in this life, growing constantly physically more luminous and translucent as his fleshly body changed first into the *śuddha deha*, the pure body, and then into the *praṇava deha*, the body of the primordial *OM*, and then into the *jñāna deha*, the body of perfect divine grace, or that he didn't finally vanish away one day in 1874 into pure, immaterial, spiritual corporeality, and didn't thereafter appear to his disciples in this… resurrected form?"

"Well, I don't know as I'd…"

"Even if it's not a factual narrative—who can say?—it certainly… certainly *embodies*, so to speak, one and the same truth about the spiritual fulfilment of nature, here and in… I suppose, in the age to come."

"I…"

"And, of course, there are those Tibetan notions of the Rainbow Body—is that a Nyingma tradition? What about Khenpo Achö?"

"What's that?" I asked.

"Not what—*who*."

"All right: *Who*, then?"

"A famous monk of the Lumorap Monastery in Nyarong. He was originally Gelug, I believe, but he was Nyingma too, I believe, in a wholly non-exclusive way. A Dzogchen adept by the end."

For a moment, I perused my memory. "Maybe the name rings a bell. I can't always recall everything I've…"

"Well," said Roland, "it's reported that, when he died in 1998, his face took on a youthful appearance, and the fragrance of holiness filled the room, and music was heard in the air around his little house, and at twilight strange rays of sunlight shone brilliantly from the east for a long time, and five rainbows appeared over the house for many days on end."

"Some of this sounds familiar," I said, vaguely recalling something about rainbows.

"In any event, he too disappeared into his body of light, we're told—his *'od sku*. Over the course of some days, during the period of his funeral rites, his coarse fleshly body grew smaller and finer until at last it simply vanished into a *vajra* body, leaving no physical remains behind."

"And you believe that?" I asked in a rather tentative voice.

Another sustained suspiration told me that I was in danger of slipping back down a few rungs on his scale of assessment. "I've just said what I think. It's a true story, either as both a fact and a symbol or as only a symbol, but in either case it's true. It has to be. It expresses something universally attested in all real religious experience."

Now I was the one to sigh, but only because I was not at first certain what to say. "What's the practical result, though?" I finally asked. "I mean, in Christian thought, the resurrection of Christ was by definition a unique historical event."

"Well, yes and no," replied Roland. "Paul says it's only the first of many."

"Yes, but presumably all those that follow are contingent on that first one, which creates the new reality."

Roland shook his head. "Again, as a dog, I can't reduce an essential spiritual truth to a simple linear calculus of antecedence and consequence. All I can say is that even a revelation or spiritual event that's unique in its singularity can't be absolutely unique in its meaning. There must be analogical areas of spiritual patiency in nature and history, truths already there that provide this new revelation a place of hospitality and shelter—an opening in which to show itself intelligibly—a temenos, as I've said. Maybe that space is just a space of dreams, or prophetic premonitions, but it must be there. The way must be prepared. Otherwise, that singular event wouldn't be a revelation of anything. It would be a pure enigma, irresoluble and, for all intents and purposes, devoid of meaning."

For a time, neither of us spoke. A gentle gust of wind blew in through the door, stirring the ink-paintings on the wall and the sheet of rice paper on Roland's writing table, and bringing with it a mingled scent of lilac and approaching rain. A cardinal sang out somewhere very nearby.

Finally, I spoke. "It's true, as you say, that I can believe everything at once, though I suspect that it's a choice I make principally on account of my unwillingness to relinquish any dimension of anything that I find appealing or admirable... or beautiful. But it hardly seems as practical a way to live as you suggest. Not for my kind, at least. We have to draw some kind of working distinction between the perpetually valid symbol and the historically novel event."

He breathed in slowly and, barely audibly, murmured, "*Sapiens sapiens* indeed." Then he looked into my eyes across the small, shadowy space between us. The soft, sallow light of the lamp glistened on his nose and in his eyes, and in the dimness of the studio the cucullate shape of his ears gave him an almost monastic appearance. "Yes, of course, but a distinction of that kind can't be an absolute division. And any other way of life, it seems to me, is utterly *impractical*. We've said much of this before, but bear with me for a little while. There was a time, again, when your kind was much better able to see the gods—the angels, deified mortals, spirits, fairies, what have you—than now you are. Not because there was a stabler and more open causeway between the two hemispheres of your brains or anything like that, but because there was a wider, more richly populated open causeway between your souls and the cosmos. And those gods—or what have you—were also mirrors of what you are, as spiritual beings, there above. I don't mean they were Feuerbachian projections, figments of alienation or anything of that sort, but rather that they came more easily into full sensuous manifestation so long as human beings were in a state of what Barfield called 'original participation.' Unlike him, however, I don't believe that your kind's estrangement from that original, more vividly theophanic world is simply a temporary stage—a kind of probationary process—on the way to a post-critical 'final participation.' It would be nice to imagine that that's the case, but I fear that the reality will be one of continuing, deepening estrangement, an ever more precipitate descent toward total spiritual eclipse, and toward a final, enduring darkness in which the true light of spirit has been all but extinguished. Then you'll be worse than mere savages. You'll be a race of nihilists. You may even… you may even forsake your moral tutelage by dogs."

"Don't suggest that," I said in a faint voice. "It's a horrible thought. Hell on earth."

"I'm not saying it will or must happen. I'm saying only that the possibilities created by modernity are full of perils. I understand Heidegger's fatuous little *cri de cœur* well enough—'only a god can

Roland in Moonlight

save us.' Now, I can't speak out of any very deep comprehension of apes or apery—I'm not an animal psychologist or a field zoologist—but I assume that for your kind many things that seem like perennial truths in any given epoch are really only fashions of the moment. But, then again, fashions are more than just superficial fads. They invariably express the stage of development at which spirit has arrived in the collective experience of humanity. All consciousness is unified in its deepest source, of course, as I've often said. And so, in an age of unbelief, everyone is an unbeliever to some degree. Belief now requires a decision, and a tacit application of will that never for a moment relents. That's why the fiercest forms of faith in the modern world are actually just inverted forms of faithlessness—forms of desperation masquerading as faith. Archtraditionalism, I mean, and of course fundamentalism, which are in fact manifestations of a morbidly impoverished power of belief, a faith wasted away by inanition and hardened by desiccation, and of a frantic attempt to hold on to relics or remains that one mistakes for living possibilities—the arid rituals and cruel certitudes of Tridentine Catholicism, the infantile literalism of 'scriptural inerrancy,' and so forth. What's a militant Latin Mass Catholic or a white evangelical fundamentalist from Tennessee other than an atheist who's convinced himself that he truly, truly, truly believes by inverting his total, inescapable inward nihilism in the mirror of his despair? He doesn't believe. He merely believes that he believes. Or he tries to believe that he believes. Or he imagines that he is trying to believe that he believes. And... well, the regress is infinite. It's simply the case now that almost every one of your race today—in the modern world, I mean—even the most devout and convinced of them, is more profoundly an infidel. Real, guileless faith in the divinity that shows itself in the evident forms of creation has become catastrophically attenuated, like the fading scent of a chipmunk on the porch after two days of rain. And that's a tragic condition to be in, because the divine dimension is real, and is moreover the deepest truth of your own natures. To be estranged from it is to be shattered within yourselves... to become something less than machines... fragments of machines... a heap of springs and sprockets."

"That all sounds rather hopeless," I remarked after a moment.

328

GARDEN

"I don't know," he said, with a kindly frown. "Probably, but not necessarily. Whatever the case, it's obvious to me that the only way your kind can hope to find its way back to the theophanic cosmos— if you can do so before destroying the world with your profligate indifference to its ecological fragility—is by breaking the hold of these counterfeit forms of faith… these shriveled positivisms and prejudices camouflaged as true belief, and learning to see the whole of reality as a congress of radiant symbols of spiritual reality. And the only way to do that now is to be willing to believe *all* of it—all real religious insights—whether it's Christianity or Hinduism or Australian Aboriginal spirituality or Sioux or Yoruba visionary wisdom or… well, all of it, even while you try to find a stable hierarchy of beliefs capable of accommodating different kinds of symbolic truth. And, frankly, in a global age in which the variety and historical contingency of religious traditions—and even the variety of each tradition's many schools and factions—is something of which we're all ever more keenly conscious, your kind has to learn the art of having faith intelligently. Otherwise, many will never get past the understandable barrier of incredulity thrown up by those who insist that there is only one system of belief—however local and contingent and bearing all the marks of a limited cultural idiolect—that's nonetheless the one exclusive truth of God. To sensitive souls, the sheer arbitrariness of the choice among traditions confronting them, as though they were different systems of propositional claims, must seem to reduce all traditions to accidental coalescences of empty assertions and quaint customs. So believe it all, I say, and thereby recover the proper transcendent orientation of true belief— the *prisca theologia*, so to speak, by which all local theologies must be judged."

"You're not suggesting, are you," I asked, "that religions should somehow evacuate themselves of their doctrinal content?"

"There are essential doctrines in every creed, which are few in number and obvious, and then there are accidental excrescences on those doctrines, which are legion and ponderous, stifling and stupefying."

"But how does one discriminate among them?"

Roland turned his eyes away and upward, obviously looking at

329

nothing in particular. "There's one indubitable and universal religious truth, by which the worth or worthlessness of every other religious claim or practice or narrative is to be judged. To the degree that a religion's teachings are in harmony with that truth, they open avenues of God. To the degree that they are not, they close off such avenues. It's an infallible principle." As is his wont, Roland here fell silent.

My surrender came more quickly than usual, however. "Well," I said, "what is it? This principle… this truth?"

"अयम् आत्मा ब्रह्म," he replied.

"Oh," I said, nodding, "of course. I should have known."

"So, for instance," he continued, "if one looks at certain essential Christian claims, for instance—say, 'God became human that human beings might become God'—well, that's clearly true, and true in countless ways, and we can certify this because it confirms and affirms the one essential truth of religion in a uniquely emphatic and unsurpassably concrete way. It fulfills perfectly the expectancy of nature and history in offering a place of shelter to that revelation. Incarnation, deification, *creatio ex nihilo*, and so on—all of it meets and illuminates the enduring standard. On the other hand, nonsense about the absolute distinction between nature and grace or between nature and supernature, rubbish about eternal hells or predestination, voluntaristic pictures of divine sovereignty, twaddle about merit or about the difference between sufficient and efficacious grace, or evil doctrines of forensic atonement or limited atonement or penal substitutionary atonement—we know that that's all a lot of degrading diabolical unregenerate chimpanzee thinking… squirrelism, in fact, because it fails the test of that indispensable index of religious truth."

"You know," I said, "there's scarcely a Christian faction that wouldn't object strenuously to that way of seeing things. I mean, the order of priorities there—the authority of the principle in general, that is, as opposed to the authority of the unique historical revelation… the unique event."

"Again," said Roland, lowering his eyes and turning to me again, "no matter how singular the event, there must be a place of hospitality already there, in nature and culture, or nothing at all can be revealed. The analogical womb in which the Logos becomes incarnate. The manger of nature in which the Christ child sleeps. This is something your great uncle understood quite keenly, by the way."

This remark, I confess, surprised me. "Really?" I asked. "Aloysius?" I shook my head in doubt. "Surely there was at least one major religion he believed irredeemable. His rejection of Christianity was fairly unambiguous, as far as I recall."

A sly grin parted Roland's lips. "Oh, you're quite mistaken. His view of things was much subtler than you give him credit for. You're correct, of course, that he came to have a distinctly jaundiced view of Christian institutional history, and there were any number of official doctrines of developed tradition—eternal hell, original guilt, blood appeasement, and so forth—that he often denounced as cruel and dark and hideous. But he never lost his reverence for the person of Christ… or, for that matter, for what he took to be the true central narrative of the faith. I mean, not just the compassion and love and Jewish prophetic rage for justice in Jesus himself, but even the doctrinal narrative about divine incarnation and human divinization, and even about God crucified."

"Really?" I said, genuinely astonished. "Are you sure?"

He stared at me for some seconds in silence. "I insist that you read the man's journals," he said at last. "Yes, he could thunder away at what he hated in the religion's historical configurations with the ferocity of a Nietzsche or an Empson. And he didn't spare scripture his detestation. He especially despised the book of Revelation. Somewhere in his journals he says that every now and again he wondered whether he ought to grant it some praise as a kind of surrealist nightmare book, something that might have been written by Boris Vian or Giorgio de Chirico or André Breton at their most bilious and morbid; but then invariably he concluded that it's so utterly devoid of whimsy, elegance, or genuine imagination that it simply can't be tolerated. He called it a cruel and cretinous book that, as he put it, 'has all the spiritual richness of a ransom note sent through the mail in a parcel containing a severed human finger.' He found its imagery puerile and barbaric and its theology loathsome. Far from a great visionary text, he saw it as a clumsy, lurching, viciously stupid political allegory, one whose sensibility never rises

331

above adolescent sullenness, spiced with pervasive sadism, resentment, and malice. Even its otherwise appealing anti-imperialist rhetoric is spoiled by the violence of its final vision of divine triumph. The monstrous figure who goes by the name of Christ in Revelation, who will rule the gentiles with an iron rod, bore to his mind no resemblance at all to the Jesus of Nazareth depicted in the synoptic gospels, and the association of the two in tradition constituted in his estimation a kind of hilarious confusion of *dramatis personae*, as if Iago had been mistaken for Othello. He thought the book's inclusion in the canon one of the great idiocies of the tradition."

"That hardly sounds particularly pacific," I observed. "I mean, I take the point, but..."

"But that was his judgment on one text only—one trajectory within the tradition. In the end, he saw Christianity as a psychologically divided faith, at least as an historical phenomenon. To him, the original morality of Christ preserved in the gospels constituted something of a bizarre anomaly—and sometimes a fruitful contradiction—in the fabric of doctrine, like a fly preserved in amber. 'How can such tenderness and moral purity consort with such barbarity?' he writes at one point. And, again, he was perfectly at peace with the myth—which for him is not to say 'fiction'—of the crucified God who descends to the dead and who shatters the power of the archon of this cosmos, and who overcomes judgment with mercy. And he was more than a little drawn to the mediaeval imagery of the Mother of God as the merciful advocate, the sheltering mercy, the wellspring of compassion..."

"But..." I began.

"I imagine, of course, that in a sense she fitted his own inner mythology of the goddess. He wrote very similar things about the figure of Guanyin."

"But," I said again, "if all that's so, it was never anything he talked about with me. And surely there's no evidence of it in his literary remains."

At this, Roland suddenly became animated, placing his front paws on the table, rising up on his hind legs, and thrusting his snout toward me, coming within an inch of my chin. "You couldn't be more wrong," he said, sniffing energetically at me. "By the way, your health seems restored to roughly 84%, I'd judge." Then he drew back a foot or two, still standing with his front legs propped on the table. "As it happens, there's quite a substantial number of poems and fragments of poems on Christian themes among his papers. And some of them are reverent… even devout."

"That makes no sense to me," I said. And then: "Am I really that much healthier, do you think?"

"My nose is infallible," he replied. "And yes, it does make sense. Your memories of your great uncle have become somewhat distorted by time, I suspect, and so you remember the more garish expostulations of religious distaste on his part, but I imagine you've forgotten a whole host of more moderate, more reflective remarks."

I thought about this for a few seconds. "Perhaps that's so…" I said.

"For instance, there was a long delightful vacation that Aloysius and Polly took to Europe and Turkey in 1978 that prompted him to begin a sequence of poems on Christian themes."

"What?" I stared intently into Roland's eyes now, seeking some trace of mockery, some sparkle of mischief, but could discern only sincerity. "What poems are those? Did he finish them?"

"He finished three of them. At least, they seem quite finished. One is about a Byzantine icon of the Annunciation that he saw in a small church in Venice. And there's one about an iconostasis he found in another church in Ankara, which seems to have been somewhat unusual—uncanonical, for all I know—in the selection of its upper panels. Assuming, of course, that Aloysius's depiction of it doesn't take liberties. He might have been reconstructing a kind of fantasy version of it in memory. I'm not sure." He paused and seemed to be pondering the possibility.

"You said there were three," I prompted him after several seconds.

"Yes," he replied with a nod, "quite so. The third was inspired by a book in French that he found, as it happens, in a bookstore in Istanbul. It was about the Russian church and was by a French visitor to Russia, and it contained the text of an old Russian Orthodox legend about the Mother of God descending into hell, and seeing the torments of the damned, and hastening to the throne of her Son to implore him for alleviation of their sufferings. A bleak thing in some ways, but the image of the merciful goddess or goddess bodhisattva or lady saint going down among the hopeless and lost, and being seized by pity… well, you know how that would have affected him."

I was at something of a loss for words for some moments, but finally said, "I'm truly amazed. I had no idea. Do you think there was some sort of reconciliation with his childhood faith in his later days? Some change?"

Roland moved farther away, dropping his front paws from the table to his mat. "No, I don't think so, not as such. Just a wiser, more capacious understanding of certain things, and maybe an acknowledgment that even his paganism was indelibly dyed with Christianity—that there's no way back to a pre-Christian piety for even the most devout of modern pagans. But, I should note, at the same time that he was working on those poems he wrote at least one on Buddhist themes as well. I'll try to remember to print out copies of those pieces for you later today. They should interest you. But, what do you say we make that tea now? I'm parched. I've a hankering for some Milk Oolong, if that's agreeable to you."

"Always," I said, leaning on the table, raising myself with some effort to my knees, and then rising to my feet. "Shall I go make it?"

"If you would," he said, sauntering away toward the other end of the garage, "and I'll just fetch that box of *yokan*."

I imagine that the tea and *yokan* were delicious, but I have no further recollections of that afternoon. It has been more than a year and a half since then. I do recall, however, that early in the evening I found a red filing folder on my desk in the room I use as my office; as Roland had promised, he had printed out copies of those three poems for me. I leafed through them then, but it was not until late that night, everyone else having retired, that I sat down to read them. I have to say, they were like nothing I could have predicted. They seemed to contain a few heterodox touches, naturally, but even then only of a rather pious kind. And something in them seemed to speak of genuine awe, genuine reverence before a great and still vital mystery. We never really know nearly as much about anyone else as we think we do, I suppose.

XLVII

The Annunciation
(*Venice*)

I: Foreground I

She kneels beneath a sky of gold and gazes
Into his sapphire eyes, and mirrored there
She sees her own rapt calm. She slowly raises
Her chin and draws her cowl about her hair
And parts her lips to speak, but no words come.
Her thoughts are ravished from her by the sight
Of his prismatic wings; she is struck dumb.
He waits, however, ringed in rainbow light,
Framed by those overarching pinions, meeting
Above his cool, impassive stare. And she
Now sees that all depends upon this fleeting
Instant, wherein all of eternity
Lies hidden, hanging in suspense upon
One spoken word. And yet she also knows
That what must happen is already done.

Still, as she looks, the weight of silence grows.

Between her and his dreadful glory looms
Time's fullness: all its empires and its wars,
Its deaths, its countless hopes and countless dooms,
Below the turning, cold, uncaring stars.

The wind's voice rises briefly and then dies.
And still she sees herself shine in his eyes.

II: Background I

Let nothing stir this night:
Naked sky, untilled earth
Disdain the proud delight,
The yielding and the birth
Foretold, the promised cry
Upon the icy air.
"For all that lives must die,
Rejoice and then despair.

"Daughter of calm, not wise,
Child of regret, not strong,
In his celestial eyes
A lie, a fool's mad song."
Or so the winds lament
With bitter howls of rage.
"The world by his descent
Has lost its golden age,
Made pregnant with another yet to start,
And you shall grieve—
                          a sword shall pierce your heart."

III: Background II

"White dove of morning, light to light," so sings
The longing heart in the wasteland of death,
And in the mountains, and by the sea, "come
In gentle visitations, high above
The livid snow in dawn's cold light, and bring
Us tidings that the world grows great with child.
Nothing will perish but shall be restored,
And nothing lost but shall be found again,
And nothing broken shall be left unmended."

GARDEN

IV: Foreground II

The painter has instilled in her a calm:
No fear is visible in her green eyes,
Which seem to look through him, his glassy light.
Her hand, upraised, is like a flower bowed
Upon its stem, and seems so slight before
His glory and immensity of presence,
And yet one sees that he is bound by it
Until she speaks.

              At last, her words break forth—
The image, like a chrysalis, breaks open—
And the winds' frantic ululations cease;
The powers are silent; their heads are wounded;
And now, as she consents to him, and to
The unimagined other, whose strange promise
Comes winged in light, the world she knows so well
Will fall apart, an over-ripened fruit,
As all eternity comes flooding in.

His wings still form an arch above his head,
And shed their iridescence on the air.
His thick, Hellenic hyacinthine locks
Are brown and glisten in his gem-bright nimbus.
She is still bowed before him, looking up,
And yet the adoration flows from him.

For a moment, deep peace envelops them,
Far vaster than time's ages and dominions,
As though its stillness could consume the world.
But then the veil of boundless light is parted,
And he is gone, and absently she gazes
To where his form has faded from the air.

XLVIII

Iconostasis: Lives and Acts
(Ancyra)

*(The design and the conceit: two tiers of icons are set above the royal
doors, depicting Christ and his apostles; below these is another tier of
icons, depicting the patriarchs and prophets, and at its center there is
a strange image of Isaiah lying asleep, one hand folded beneath his
head, his staff laid parallel to his body—almost as if he is dreaming
the things portrayed above him.)*

I: Christ Upon a Mountain, Praying

*(In somnio eius, Isaias Christum in montem ascendentem videt.
Defatigatus et ieiunus, Christus dicit:)*

Dry in the strange twilight between two worlds,
The soul abroad in desert wastes grows weak,
The flesh at last must yield to weariness
And thirst, and break beneath the burden of
Ceaseless prayer. How near the hour when all
Ordained must come to pass... If I must go
The windless ways of death and take my parting,
What worlds will tremble in their love of me?

In his granitic, idle eyes, half-closed,
The shadows of the day were softly passing,
When I approached him where he lay, beneath
The olive tree, to summon him, to say,
"Come and follow me; you must lose your world,

GARDEN

And know not now where you are going. Come. I
Am sorry, but you must understand..." He
Did not: I was the stranger. But again,
It was the strangeness that compelled him. Gold
The work of sun on leaf, the weave of sun
In hair. The call of beauty came to him
In wavering shape. "No more will the beauty
Of death beguile you, no more draw you on."

And after me they followed, each in turn,
The measureless light about them, receiving
All of them in its still, stern, shining depths.
So indiscreet, the holy fire that blesses
By scorching heart and bone...

                    The wind descends
Upon my head; its kiss will brush my lips,
Dry in the heat of that terrible twilight.
And there in agony, transfixed between
Two worlds, I must endure until the last.
The whisperer will say, "All is decay,
Relent." And with the weight of glory great
Upon me, pouring down, the infinite
In torment, they will be struck blind by tears,
Nor knowing how I see the world transfigured:
They will not know—

                "*Eli, Eli*...

                          "...forgive..."

The world's joy now will be all bitterness;
Now they will take up meat and wine, and taste
Nothing but ashes. And the desert winds
Will carry them to nameless lands, to ends
They could not guess awaited them. What deaths
They will embrace, now that life has death's savor!

Dry, between two worlds, weak, between two twilights...

Roland in Moonlight

II: John Upon a Nameless Island

(*Somnium eius permutat: Ioannem in insula sine nomine,
modulantem cum lyra crystallina, videt:*)

I dreamed that in the shadows of a garden
He walked beneath a sky of diamond blue,
And I fell down before him, begging pardon,
Before the dawn, in grasses drenched in dew.
The olive trees were dark but gleamed like silver
Beneath a moon that blazed like molten glass.
He turned his eyes to me and smiled, but never
Once paused as I in silence watched him pass.

I dreamed once more that he awaited me
Upon a shore in some far distant land,
And that I found him there, beside the sea
In twilight, on its cold, deserted strand.
This time he spoke, but I do not recall
His words. I can remember just my fear,
As though before some dreadful city's wall
To whose high gate I would not dare draw near.

I never truly knew from where he came
Or by what right he claimed my faith or love.
To take his hand was to embrace a flame,
For I was from below, he from above:
A pure light of judgment, which none can flee,
Sent down to conquer this world's God, he said...
Whose hidden Father we could never see...
Whose flesh was food... Whose voice could raise the dead.

And still I chase him through this maze of dreams.
His shining form yet draws me on. His light
Alone can part the shadows here, its gleams
My only beacons in this endless night.

GARDEN

III: By the Sea of Tiberias

(*Nunc Petrus, aetate provectus, in somnio eius oritur, et in voce simul defessa et invicta dicit*:)

When we had lost all sight of him in light
Unendurably bright, and turned again
To humble trade, where gray tides wash and sun
Is spilled on pebbled shores, he came to us,
Again a stranger. We had to begin
Again. Again he called us from our fishing.
As before, he was not what we expected.

How dry the season had been, and how empty
All our nets—then, the strange, heart-breaking summons…
He spoke, and all at once the time between
Became as nothing.

               And we at our nets,
On the whitening sea, the barren waters.

Across a charcoal fire that smoldered in
A squalid courtyard, the words of denial
Had fallen from my lips, like traitors' coin,
To glitter in the firelight, and the sorrow
Had riven the deep inward of my heart:
The memory of such terrible love
Denied was burning torment, and I begged
Betrayal be undone.

             So long ago
It seemed, but here by a charcoal fire, on
The wintry dryness of the strand, again
He spoke, just as before: the same love offered,
The same call made, as though the rest had never
Intervened, as if no death could part us.

341

Roland in Moonlight

Now I will go his many ways, be bound
And led where I would not go but for him:
The sheep need feeding, the forgotten are
Alive...

      And the forsaken, too, has found
A home...

      The lost is in his father's house.

IV: The Temptation in the Wilderness

(*Iterum Christum in vastitate cernit; et draco vetus iste, Satana,
dominum ludibrio habet:*)

        Dicit diabolus:

Not sustenance, nor strength, nor empire, nor
The help of God himself will sway you; but
You feed on nothing, rule the wastes, surrender
To forsakenness—think it victory.

Death will overtake you, beautiful mind,
Though now in this nacreous pale dawn, where all
These shadows flow in endless streams, between
Two twilights, you dream of infinite life.

     Et respondet Christus ridens:

Neither life nor kingdom you imagine,
Once having failed that glory and that chorus.
Let all the boundless deeps of death pour in
Upon the desert of the world, and I,
The one upwelling source of all, shall still
Return, and still return, for love alone
Is infinite, and far mightier than death.

342

GARDEN

So go you on, you evening whisper at
The farthest edge of life, desolate remnant;
And when we meet again, below the boughs
Of all eternity's fruit-laden tree,
There, then, I shall unravel all the ages,
And I at last shall tell your tale anew.

XLIX

The Theotokos Visits Hell

I: Hades Clamavit

How hot and dry the winds that bore us here,
These lands where shadows rove and fill the air
With dreadful shapes and moans of lamentation,
Where nothing stirs the desiccated leaves
That cling to tortured boughs of fruitless trees,
And where our only meat and drink are sorrow,
Memory, and hate. When the lightning breaks
Above the barren hills and hollows here,
No thunder stirs the fervid dark; and when
The sterile moon is risen to the height
Of this perpetual midnight, its glow
Is dim, the dull color of blood, opaque.
We have no tongues to sing the songs of praise.
In the depths all are forgotten, though we
Are cursed with recollection without hope.
The godforsaken and the dust and flames
Drift in one constant motion, toil within
Tumultuous winds, icy calms. All are lost
In shadow, indistinguishable from
The writhing smoke. A time will come when all
The vestiges of force that rouse the soul's
Shrill cries will dwindle and be gone, and silence
Will be our dwelling, the voice of our darkness.

O light of mercy, inaccessible,
Will then such suffering find no respite
In all the waste-time of eternity?

GARDEN

II: Hades Lacrimatus Est

Walk, Lady, in the exile of this place,
Whose silence holds no promise, whose sands are
One stark, parched white, whose runnels fill with dust
That drifts in endless eddies aimlessly.
Walk where the voice of mourning swells and dies
Upon the arid and echoless air,
O Lady of the tranquil noon and sunset,
O higher than the cherubim, beyond
Compare more glorious than the seraphim,
Clothed in the sun. These habitations are
The silence bred outside the word, the darkness
That dwells below the light, where rage is all
The passion that can thrive. Where your feet tread
Will flowers break from this hard withered earth?

And we retreat before your glory, though
Its gentle radiance would soothe our wounds,
Could we but come within its circle; but
Our shame, our hate, constrains us, and our dread
Still presses us into the crevices,
And drives us to the shadows to complain.

Walk onward in your brief and shining transit
Through the umbral emptiness and waste.
Your tender loveliness will sway and dance
Upon the trembling flood of dreams
That rushes over us, your beauty burn
Even in memories that feed on wrath.

For in the graceful bearing of your form
The ancient rift between the worlds is healed,
If for a moment, and a mercy glimpsed
By eyes that find in dark their only comfort.
And, even gone, the sight of you recalled

345

Becomes a song that breaks upon this silence
Like a storm of glory, shattering hell,
And lifting up the dead in ceaseless supplication.

L

A S I SAY, my great uncle was not, it seems, quite who I thought
he was. Or, rather, he was more than I knew.

I should not forget the sequel, though. It was nearly a
week later, if I recall, that I found that same red file folder on my
desk. It was late at night—or, rather, very early in the morning. I
remember having been wakened by a dream, not so much disturb-
ing as weirdly evocative; I shall not attempt to recount it, however,
as I could never do so in a way that would convey its peculiar atmosphere or reproduce any of its effect on me. In any event, I
attempted to fall asleep again, but realized after half an hour or so
that the effort was futile, so I decided to work on the editing of my
latest book manuscript until drowsiness might, of its own discretion, choose to steal in on me. On discovering the folder, however, I
opened it eagerly in hope of finding something more absorbing
than editing. To my disappointment, it contained only one sheet of
paper, a short typed page of verse in pdf, dated February 1979. It
was, obviously, the poem of my great uncle's on "Buddhist themes"
that Roland had told me about. And, I confess, I found it to be in its
way no less surprising than the specimens of verse on Christian
themes. There were so many things Great Uncle Aloysius and I
never discussed, it seems. Every person's inner life is a mystery to
everyone else, even to those who know him or her most inti-
mately—which would be the greatest of tragedies if it were a limitation of our natures that should prove final and immutable, rather
than one that we have some cause to hope will one day—on the
other side of the veil or through the looking-glass—fall away.

Roland in Moonlight

Song on the Waking of Maitreya

See this child of unfathomable ages:
Beneath the boughs of fire he must remain
Silent and still…

               He must be uncompelled,
Uncompelled…

           So let him lie, disturbed
Not even by the quietest currents of
The day, the distant songs and dying lights,

That his eyes might open, a blissful blossoming
Of golden flowers, brighter than the flames
The lotos lights upon unmoving waters.

Now let neither joy nor love corrupt him,
Nor sorrow mark his brow,

                   for in his sleeping
Is the seed of promise, and when he wakes—
Oh, when he wakes—all tumult will have ceased.

LI

O NCE UPON A TIME, we dwelled in Eden; but then we were
cast out. We were forced to descend from our mountain
retreat and depart from our unfallen world. For a time,
however, we still dwelled at the margins of our lost paradise, nour-
ished by the fruits of the fertile, alluvial soil between the Tigris and
the Euphrates—or, at any rate, the rich loam of the lower elevations
of the Blue Ridge. But we were driven out again, into a more terrible
exile, becoming wanderers and sojourners in the earth, outside the
gates, desolate, prey to the elements and every enemy, forbidden all
human habitation. Finally, though—or at least for now—we have
found asylum, here in a shady grove; and, in a season of pestilence,
it has become ever more our sure refuge.

I have even come to appreciate the peculiar poetry of the sub-
urbs, I think, at least of the somewhat older, arboraceous kind: aur-
ous sunlight falling across deep green lawns, swarms of midges
shimmering in the still air under spreading branches, the mild
gleams of leaded windows, birds at their feeders, cats strolling at
their ease along pavements regularly split by sprouting grass or displaced by swelling trees' roots, the distant sounds of children and
dogs at play in enclosed yards.

And I think that we have improved our husbandry. We cannot
return to the paradise of our first innocence, but we have succeeded
in capturing at least a faint ray of its scattered glory in the bright
glass of the foursquare fenced enclosure behind our house. There
we shelter Eden, if only as a fragment of itself, as it once sheltered
us. My wife's garden—our garden—now abounds in beauties and
exorbitances and graces that defy description, even the most lascivi-
ously rhapsodic. In the extended springtime or mild early summer
native to this latitude, one need only enter it through the front
gate—passing between the southernmost garden beds and the elevated wooden causeway running beside the house from the pantry's

outside door down to the yard—to be immersed in otherworldly color and fragrance. Vines of morning glory, moonflower, cardinal climbers, and climbing snapdragons have been thoroughly intermingled there, and grow in heedless profusion around and over an arched wooden lattice, and up and along the causeway's railing, and all along the eaves of the house; and if it is early enough in the day, before the moonflowers have closed their petals but after the morning glories have opened theirs, the promiscuous tangles of satiny white, luminous blue, fierce crimson, and luxuriant purple are almost too fantastic to take in. And everywhere else in the garden, the earth is drenched in glory: the dark glowering gold and vermilion of marigolds or the scorched ochre and cinnabar of nasturtiums; alyssum spilling over the grass like frothing cream; the yellow, porphyry, dusky gold, and blood-red of various cosmos flowers, the ivory and gold of Shasta daisies; the twilight purple of languid browallia blossoms and cranesbill geraniums, the soft powdery purple of bluemink, and the opulent purple of heliotrope; calendula in glowing yellow and orange, dahlias of either amethystine purple or Burgundy red, veronicas of marble-blue, azalea blossoms of mauve, white, or crimson; the mingled pastels of hydrangea blossoms, agastache hyssop's columns of malachite green stippled with magenta; the yellow of evening primrose, the dark pink of rose campion; billowing golden clouds of fernleaf yarrow, delicate white mists of lily of the valley, echinacea's palatinate purple hovering like smoke around the garden borders; and all the brightly or sullenly smoldering yellows, oranges, and reds of black-eyed Susans, Siberian wallflowers, and tall plains coreopsis; and on and on. Even the vegetable beds are riots of color—peppers, Asian eggplants, nearly a dozen varieties of tomato, basil leaves, an exotic array of cucumbers... And, of course, the finches and the cardinals and the hummingbirds, the kaleidoscopic butterflies and harlequin beetles, are constantly invading the garden with their own proud flamboyances.

On a particularly lovely spring day early this past April, when all of this magnificence was on full display, I entered the garden by the front gate and discovered Roland seated on his haunches in the very center of the allotment, his back toward the house, his gaze turned up into a cloudless sky of spectacularly pure cornflower blue. A dilatory breeze was stirring the leaves and blossoms, shade and sunlight were flittering and jouncing all around, birds' songs were merging in rippling arpeggios, two or three bumblebees were droning among the flowers. I was wholly awake—neither dreaming nor experiencing one of my 'oneiroleptic' episodes. Every sensation was vivid and clear. I was conscious of all I had done since rising from bed, and of all I intended to do later in the day.

I was also depressed. It was now a month since we had entered voluntary home confinement on account of the pandemic, and I was poignantly conscious that we still had many months—and in all likelihood a year and more—of seclusion ahead of us; and the miserable precariousness and loneliness of our situation was beginning to impress itself on my mind. That was why I had gone to the garden, in fact: simply to take my mind off of the oppressive reality of life in the present. The sight of Roland, however, immediately improved my mood. I went to him and placed a hand on his head. Indolently, he turned his eyes to look up at me, an expression of contentment on his face. I scratched him just above the brows and he closed his eyes in pleasure. When I stopped and withdrew my hand, he opened them again and, after a second, parted his lips. For the briefest moment, I held my breath.

"Are you feeling downcast?" he asked.

"Oh," I breathed quietly, "so you do…" I fell silent.

He returned his gaze to the sky. "It's such a beautiful day," he said. "You shouldn't fret about the plague. All you can do is take the proper precautions and continue writing to support the family. Melancholy thoughts will paralyze your will if you let them."

I swallowed deeply, cleared my throat twice, and finally said, "I suppose that's true. It's just sinking in now, though."

He nodded slightly. "It's been a bad several years for you in many ways," he said. "But it's been fairly miserable for the whole world for going on four years now."

"That only makes it worse," I replied.

"Would you care to join me?" he asked after a moment.

"I'm not as limber as I used to be," I said.

"You're not an invalid yet."

351

Carefully, gingerly even, I seated myself beside him in the tartly pungent grass, near enough to him to feel the warmth of his body, and turned my gaze up to the sky along with his. "The weather's perfect," I remarked. "It's tempting to stay here all day."

"You're not also still dejected about the state of your country, are you?" he asked. "Or of civilization in general? Or of American Christianity?"

"Oh..." I took a deep breath of the delightful air. "Those ships have sailed long since," I said. "That would be like worrying about one's house catching fire when it's already been reduced to ashes. So, no. I'm just a bit despondent about all those who'll suffer the consequences of the collapse—even the ones so deceived as to vote for their own ruin. The old civil accords... well, they're matters of unspoken custom, aren't they? And once they're destroyed... once someone wantonly barbarous or stupid enough, or both, to cast them aside comes along, the illusion is shattered, and the peace can't be restored. So I worry about those I love... when everything seems to be falling apart. My wife, my son... you."

"That's touching," he said, "but you mustn't torture yourself. Nothing really endures, and nothing's ever as solid as it seems. Surely you know that time is an ocean and history a ceaseless storm, and nations and civilizations are only fragile little fleets driven about upon the waves."

"Yes," I said. "I never deceived myself about... about any of it. I mean, to be an American is to spend your life lying to yourself about America, but I was never contaminated by American patriotism. I never expected that a country based on so many historical lies and so many destructive principles would endure endlessly. Honestly. I simply didn't realize how quickly even the illusion could evaporate."

"Circumambient conditions," he replied. "Specific historical environments. Things evaporate very quickly in... xeric regions."

I laughed, a little mordantly. "Exactly the word," I remarked.

"At least, exactly the word that you or I would choose to use," he replied. "In my case, out of precision; in yours, out of pretentiousness."

"Now, look," I began, turning to him, but then realizing that a mirthful smile had appeared on his face. "I suppose you're right," I said.

"It seems to me," he said, his voice dropping and becoming drily sober, "that among your species there are three classes of chronic cultural sentimentalists: those fixated only upon the past, those obsessed only with the future, and those capable of happiness only in the fleeting present. All are deluded. It's a rare anthropine soul indeed that knows how to place his or her hopes and allegiances in the eternal. That's why, for instance, political conservatism is typically so infantile, splenetic, resentful, and petulant a philosophy. It's also why so much *bien pensant* liberalism lapses so effortlessly into inflexibly adolescent sanctimony. And it's why those who live entirely in the fashions of the moment exist in a state of perpetual distraction and anxiety and fascination with the trivial. In every case, though, the atrocious and debilitating vice is the same: a pathetic clinging to impermanence... to *anitya*. It's the malady of your race."

"Surely," I said, turning my head to stare at the sunlight flickering in the trembling leaves of the tallest of the trees beyond the fence, "learning to dwell in the present, properly understood, isn't all that vicious a habit."

"In the proper sense, yes," he replied. "I didn't mean that, though. I specifically spoke of the *fleeting* present. I was speaking of those who are desperate always to be up to date, to be *au fait* with everything... *relevant*, I suppose. I didn't mean those who know truly how to inhabit the present *moment* in its pure nowness, and to see that moment as an image of and participation in eternity... eternity as forever reiterated in the vanishing instant, and so discovered in every instant by those who know how to detach the present from mere... mere contemporaneity."

"I know," I said. "I understood what you meant really."

"It's such a curious thing... at least, to dogs. You might remember we've talked in the past about those poor deluded billionaires who dream of creating a digital platform onto which to download their minds, in the hope of achieving immortality."

"I remember."

"Setting aside the catastrophic philosophical confusions there regarding consciousness, one can only pity a personality so contracted and diminished as to cherish the prospect of eternal virtual existence as something to hope for rather than something to shudder at in horror. That wouldn't be true immortality at all. A real longing for immortality isn't a craving for sheer duration... for the interminable hell of mere existence. It's the search for the intrinsically eternal, intrinsically super-temporal ground and end of being. What would a 'downloaded' mind really be, if such a thing were logically possible? At the last, only a sad, thwarted, tormented self-made Tantalus, whose natural thirst for the pure wellsprings of Being in itself could never be slaked, not once in all the ages. To want that is a sickness worse than death. And to want death rather than that sort of empty persistence is the very heart of wisdom. There's the benign element—the virtuous aspiration—obscurely expressed in the death-instinct, after all."

This last remark I had not expected. "How so?" I asked.

"Well"—he paused to nibble pensively at his own shoulder, shifted his weight slightly, bent forward to sniff at the grass, and then resumed his original position—"what I mean is that software can cease to run, which would be an altogether pathetic conclusion to the story of a virtual consciousness, even if it were deferred to the most extreme possible limit of time, to the very last habitable instant before the eventual thermodynamic collapse of the universe; but only a true self can die, and that's a precious gift—a precious availability to the eternal. To Freudians, of course, the death-instinct could only seem to be a longing for a slackening of the tensions and constant neural stresses of the life-instinct—the *élan vital* seeking to subside again into the blessed oblivion and anonymity of pure matter. But the deeper truth of both instincts, toward life and death both, however disfigured and dissociated from one another they might be by your wounded natures, is a more original longing for the ultimate, for the final divine consummation of spiritual love. Even the darkest impulses of self-destruction, even the pain of suicide—there's a still more primordial innocence in that, one that can never be extinguished, one that makes it impossible for any final culpability to attach to it. It's a damaged but at some level sincere expression of the same love that compels the contemplative to flee from his or her ego into a final *unio mystica*. Or that drives two lov-

354

ers to seek release from themselves in emotional and sexual fusion, each in the other's embrace. Or that prompts parents to have children, and thereby to will their own displacement by a succeeding generation. In either the tenderest or the most tragic surrender of the empirical ego to its own dissolution—in that final fatigue of the *conatus essendi*—there's always the memory, the promise of an eternal longing not for nothingness, but for the whole of being... for liberation from selfishness, union with all... in a God who is all in all. At least, that's how I interpret it. Again, there are mysteries in your kind that even the wisest of dogs can't fathom."

"I find that hard to believe," I said.

"Which is why I speak of the horror of sheer limitless successive existence. The desire simply to perdure forever, the resentful refusal to die—which at a deeper level is also the refusal to die into the now. But that sort of dying, that relinquishing of the past—that's precisely what life is. It's also a matter of relinquishing the self that clings to the future so long as that future is understood only as the ego's mere duration. That's a craving that makes one small, cowardly, greedy for existence even at the expense of others. True life is a dying into the now, and ultimately the fullness of life is a dying into the eternal now. And learning to live is learning the art of dying fruitfully. Unless the grain fall to earth and perish, and all that. To learn to die properly is to learn to live."

The breeze briefly rose, and the leaves of the tall tree momentarily became more frantic in their shaking, and rattled and hissed and whispered together. "I like that way of putting it," I said when the breeze had fallen again, "at least in regard to one's own death. But I'm not sure it makes it easier to face the death of others."

"No," he said quietly. Then, however, a moment later, he added, "But also yes. You know the story of the time Zhuangzi's friends found him, soon after his wife's death, beating a drum and merrily singing, and when they reacted with dismay he told them that he had been about to succumb to grief but then had remembered all the beautiful and wonderful transformations that she would now go through, and so decided to celebrate instead?"

"Of course."

"That wasn't callousness on his part. I wouldn't recommend imi-

355

tating him, even if one could, but I'm sure that in his case it was a gesture of sincere love. I say this even though I know, as a dog, that one must always mourn the lost and howl in inconsolable horror at the ignominy and cruelty of physical death. But I also know that perpetual incarceration in the prison of perishable flesh or of the selfish ego—the part of the *jīva* that's always ensnared in *māyā*, as you Hindus might phrase it—would be a far worse fate. Why would anyone want to persist indefinitely in the minuscule confines of the meager psychological self, with all its failures, resentments, egoism, venality, regrets... all that burden of guilt? The *ātman* is always seeking to die to self so as to know itself in its true nature; and physical death can be mastered only by being accepted as simply the last, best occasion for this higher *art* of dying. And that's just the right word. All the arts are labors of ascent from the illusory to the really real, and that's just as true of the art of dying well."

I breathed deeply, lowered my head, and closed my eyes. "That's all very well," I said, "and very sagacious of you too, I know. But it's not really a very comforting thought. Or, rather, not in every circumstance. I can understand, of course, the occasional impulse to be no more. I even occasionally find the idea of death soothing. I find it appealing as the possibility of escape from myself."

"Are you uniquely loathsome?" he asked mildly.

"Everyone is to himself sometimes," I replied. "But that's as may be. It's all the *others*, you see. We can't not love, and those we love are all always already dying... always being carried away from us. The art of dying... well, maybe even I could master that. But not the art of seeing others die... of letting others die."

"You've had to do so in the past," he said.

"And did it without grace," I replied. "Anyway, I'm thinking right now about one person in particular."

"Who?"

I looked at him. "You," I said, my voice dwindling to a whisper. "I'm terrified by the thought of your death."

Roland stared at me with a gentle expression for a long time before speaking. "Because I'm ten years old, you mean?"

"Well... yes," I said. "I remember the veterinarian years ago telling us that dogs your size live on average eleven years."

GARDEN

The kindness in his eyes somehow mysteriously deepened. "That's a vague estimate," he said. "Have you seen any signs of ill health in me?"

"None," I said.

"Quite so."

"Although…" I hesitated.

"What?"

"Around your eyes… you've gone… very silver."

"Oh," he shook his head dismissively and returned his gaze to the sky. "I think it looks rather distinguished, myself. Anyway, a year, two, maybe four or five for all you know. We've plenty of time yet."

"Not in human terms," I said. "Whichever it is, it'll come too soon for me."

He licked his nose a few times, then sniffed curiously at the air, as if some interesting fragrance were wafting past in the breeze. "It's the richness of experience that determines the real length of life," he said. "Or perhaps I should say the real *depth* of life. To you, a decade seems almost ephemeral, at least by comparison to the long, receding corridor of the remembered life you carry around with you as a middle-aged man. But for a dog every day is so full of the richness of sheer sensibility—so many reflections, so many scents, so many thrills of vitality, such deep communion with the invincible animal energy of life—that ten years is an age."

"Again," I said, "that's all very well for you. But I'll be the one who has to endure the long aftermath."

"I might outlive you, you know," he said. "You've been a bit feeble for some years."

"It's good of you to suggest it," I said, "but it doesn't make it easier to deal with the feeling of inevitability… as the days go by." I looked at him more closely, and as I did so the image of the puppy he had once been—the mottled, speckled, and brindled coat of white, black, brown, light auburn, and gray, the two dark, glossily drooping ears parenthesizing a gentle and pensive face, the limpid brown eyes peering out through a *maschera di Colombina* of burnt umber and dark honey, the milk-white snout dappled with ash, the gleaming coal-black nose—momentarily superimposed itself over the image of the mature dog at my side. Then it faded again. At once, my eyes were filling with tears. "I really can't bear to think about it," I said, hearing my voice break and feeling the tears beginning to spill down my cheeks. "I don't know what I'll do with myself... how I'll possibly get by without you. I'll be so lonely." Now I could see nothing clearly and so closed my eyes tightly.

An instant later, however, I felt Roland's broad, warm tongue avidly licking my face, and heard him snuffling gently about my eyes with his nose. This lasted for several seconds. And, when at last he finished and drew away again, I wiped my cheeks with both my hands and murmured, in a ridiculously apologetic voice, "I'm sorry. I'm very tired. I don't mean to become so emotional. I don't know what's possessed me." I opened my eyes again.

He was looking directly at me with an expression of deep earnestness, but also of strange serenity. "You'll never be without me," he said softly. "You never have been." Once again, he looked away into the sky. "There's nothing to fear. Nothing at all. Over there, across the dark waters, on that far shore, there's only beauty. Dogs can see it, you know. We can peer through the thin places between worlds —even through the veil between this life and the next. And over there you and I are already together, and always have been, and always will be. Part of you remembers. Part of everyone does. Hence those myths we've discussed so often—Eden, for instance."

"It's not a very vivid memory, then," I said.

"Let's see," said Roland, "how does it go...?"

"What?" I asked after a few moments.

"Oh, you know, the bit from the second division, I believe, of the *Aganña Sutta*, in the *Digha Nikāya*, about our existences in the *pralaya* between world-cycles?"

"I'm not sure I do know," I said, composed again and wiping the last of my tears from my face.

"Oh, you know—primordial entities, made from mind, self-moving, feasting on delight, flying through the air, self-luminous, radiant with glory..."

"I suppose I remember," I said. "I mean, remember reading it. I don't actually remember... *it*."

"Well, it's just another way of depicting the universal truth of memory," he said, "appropriate to a Buddhist imaginary. I might just as well say, in Christian terms, that the final reality of all things—the world where the lion and the lamb lie down together—is the real and eternal world of the first creation, the only world really created by God, not contaminated with the illusion and transgression of a fallen cosmos. And, from the perspective of eternity, it's always already been accomplished. We began there together because that's our one true end in the eternal—the ground of spirit where we're all present to one another in unity."

"Dogs," I said. "You're so... *mystical*... so certain of things."

"We're eternal, you and I," Roland continued. "There's a place of light that was there before all things and that will be there after all things and that always *is*. There we've always dwelled together. You remember, we've said as much before: the myth of the celestial twin or double each of us has there above, where we were, will be, and even now are. In the Aeon. In the Dreamtime. Oh, that reminds me!"

The sudden note of urgency in his voice caused me to flinch. "Yes?" I said.

"I've printed out another poem for you to read," he replied, looking into my eyes. "I meant to mention it to you. I typed it up, in fact, so it's a nice new document. A longish poem. It's called 'The Great Voyage.' You may enjoy it."

"What's it about?"

His eyes narrowed. "It's about a great voyage," he said pertly. "The clue's in the title—even if it's a bit subtle."

"All right, all right," I said. "No need to mock. I mean, does it have some great theme? Does it recount some real event?"

His features relaxed into a slight, enigmatic, obviously amused smile. "Oh, by all accounts it concerns the span of mortal life, religion, the search for truth, the search for God... that sort of thing."

"Goodness," I said. "By my great uncle, I presume?"

Roland said nothing.

"That's right, isn't it?" I asked after some moments. "It's by my uncle?"

Still he said nothing. He merely continued to smile at me, now a mite more inscrutably.

"It's not something of mine?" I asked. "Something you found in my papers that I've forgotten, maybe? Something I wrote in one of my… one of my *states*?"

He arched a single eyebrow, even more mysteriously.

I gazed back deeply into his eyes now. "Is it your own composition?" I finally asked. "Did you write it?"

He sighed, somewhat theatrically, looked away again, and then sidled up against my ribs, so that the warmth of his body was immediately communicated to me. "I think I'll withhold the answer for now, to see whether you can guess when you read it. In a sense, I'm not sure it matters."

I considered questioning him further, but knew it would be fruitless. Instead, I simply put my arm around him, and we drew even closer together. He continued to gaze away to the sky and, after a moment, I did the same. "I look forward to it," I said. And then, about a minute later, I added, "I do love you very much."

"And well you should," he replied. "Well you should."

We stayed there, together like that, for quite some time.

CODA

The Great Voyage

So how, my love, did we depart from our own shores?

Ah, my dear, when we set out upon those frigid seas,
The harbor's waters thickly thronged with floating ice
That slapped against our hull and chirred on our sharp keel,
A fine sleet sang upon our sails and glittered on
The glass-gray waves. Our hawsers moaned, drawn taut
   by winds
Too fierce to face, while seagulls raised their raucous plaints.
And how we laughed and strummed our ebon lutes and danced
And doffed cockaded hats to pretty girls who waved
To us along the rime-rimmed docks and blew us kisses!
Then, as the floes were parted by our prow, we glided
Into the ocean's vastness, and its mystery—

On depths as cold, dark, and unfathomable as the mind of God.

And where then shall we go, my love, upon our voyage?

Oh, we shall sail the darkest straits of northern seas,
Out past green glaciated scarps, near shelves of ice,
And through the foaming surf of dim volcanic isles,
Just off their shores of smooth and black obsidian sand,
Below their ceaseless lightnings and skies of fiery ash.
And we shall sail into uncharted waters where
The huge and sagittated spine of dread Leviathan
Is often seen to loom up on perpetual dusk.
And we shall race around the horns of endless storm,

Roland in Moonlight

Or rest becalmed in shadowy gulfs and listen as
The ghosts of shipwrecked men call out to us for rescue
In thin and fading voices from the starlit waves.
Past Scylla and Charybdis we shall sail, and through
The grim Symplegades, and near the sirens' rocks,
Past Maelstrom and insatiate Kraken's gaping maw,
And underneath the brooding brows of snow-glazed peaks
Where gods of tempest hurl their thunderstones, and close
To jagged reefs where monsters keep millennial watch.
And we shall sail to Cumae, to the mouth of Erebus,
Send expeditions to the banks of Acheron,
And sail away again as Evening's Daughters dance
Beneath the purple gloaming and the wind-stirred trees.
And when we reach the Paxian shoals, in fear we shall
Stand on the deck and listen, mystified, and hear
The daemon's voice that echoes from those plangent woods,
Announcing that great Pan is dead, and charging us
To bear these bitter tidings to the Palodes—

Dark tidings, enigmatic and inscrutable, like the will of God.

Where else, my love, shall we be borne upon the waves?

See! We shall sail into those radiant regions where
The sprawling waters shine with gorgeous dazzling blues,
Like tiles of turquoise and of lapis-lazuli,
And sparkle like the facets of ten billion prisms
Spinning in the golden brilliance of the sun.
Warm zephyrs there will fill our sails, and carry us
Atop the crystal skies of kingdoms in the deep,
Above the coral palaces with roofs of pearl
That glow through those translucent billows and enchant
The weary wayfarer with rainbowed reveries.
And we shall sail to all the far-flung, fabled isles—
The Islands of the Blest, the Fairy Isles, the Isles

THE GREAT VOYAGE

Of Orchids, and the far Japans—and farther still:
To atolls ringed by shores whose lambent cream-white sands
Enclose lagoons of sapphire and dark indigo;
To emerald-canopied archipelagoes,
With streams like flowing nectar, and flowering vines,
And rippling grassy meadows, and hills like green billows,
And aromatic spice-trees swaying in salt winds,
And parrots in their sighing forests and dim dells,
And young, brown, lovely girls with mesmerizing eyes
Cooled by the shade of mighty trees, near bright cascades.
And in clear diamond waters we shall spy the frolics
Of nubile mermaids, with their rosy breasts and lips
And tails that shimmer with sleek scales of silver blue,
And hear the trills and tremolos of their quaint songs.
And we shall visit other isles where thrumming bees
Hang lazily upon the air like blazing jewels,
And swarm the glades, and there decoct a honey pale
And amber, headier than wine and sweeter than love,
And where delightful music fills the balmy breeze
And lulls the languid lotos-eaters in the grass.
Then we shall venture on into the holy waters
Of the Cyclades and Delos, womb of Apollo
And of Artemis, then to Delphi's mystic bourn,
And on to countless other legendary lands—

Realms glorious, splendid, ravishing, remote, just like
    the face of God.

What treasures then, my love, shall we bring back for you?

We shall bring you dainties from feasts of ancient kings,
And other gifts more rare and beautiful and strange.
For we shall fill our hold with cinnamon and silks,
With cockle-shells and limes and bluest beetles' husks,
And mangoes, pomegranates from the groves of Hades,

Roland in Moonlight

Black pearls and amethysts, red scarab dust, the wings—
With all their glistening and iridescent sheen—
Of butterflies who perished in pitched ecstasy.
And we shall bring you cardamom from high Nepal,
Samaras from Kyoto's maples, and porcelains
From far Cathay, and leaf of gold, and bright electrum,
And red gold saffron, cochineal, and milky quartz,
And sea-sponges, and carapaces of tortoises
Whose weedy graves the nereids tend with loving hands.
And we shall bring you moonstones, opals, and green jades
Extracted from the hidden vaults of Prester John,
The lustrous bones of titans slain an age ago,
The marble bones of fallen gods, and dragons' teeth,
And polished weights and wheels and springs from antique clocks.
And we shall bring you phoenix feathers bright as fire,
And ash from flames that burned in long-abandoned shrines,
And cobwebs wanly gleaming with the morning's dew,
Enchanted healing water drawn from magic wells,
And fairy liquors made from spume of cataracts,
Anemones from soil where fair Adonis bled,
And asphodels plucked from the moist Elysian fields,
And blossom-petals from the mighty Bodhi-tree,
And peaches from Amida's Western Paradise,
And cherries from the ever-blooming boughs of Eden.
And we shall bring you centuries of tranquil dreams
Left in the cave where once the Seven Sleepers lay,
And secrets whispered by the lips of angels and
Then caught in fragile bottles of deep azure glass,
And goblets filled with clouds from far-off mountain peaks,
And mirrors brimming with the moonlight gathered up
From forest pools and babbling streams in unnamed lands.
And these are but a tiny portion of the riches
That we shall pour out from our treasure trove for you—

A plunder as immense and awful as the holiness of God.

THE GREAT VOYAGE

And how, my love, shall we at last come home again?

Why, we shall journey back again the way we came,
On open seas, through those same terrors and delights,
Through mists that roll like smoke upon the pathless tides,
And nights that linger on the deep as dark as death,
As that once swelling music of our voyage fades
And disappears in faint but keen diminuendos.
But when we reach the port we left so long ago,
And sail once more into that broad, familiar harbor,
No crowds will greet us from the docks, no bells ring out,
For few will still recall the day of our departure.
When we return we shall be old and lean and weary;
The girls who blew us kisses now will have grown children—
Though you, my dear, will still be young and beautiful.
And we shall come like mystics who in raptures scale
The highest heavens and then once again descend
But cannot name the things that they have seen, or say
What they heard told in unintelligible tongues.
Still, we shall give you all those fine, exotic things
That please us and perplex us, and that excite
Such thoughts as leave us desolate with longing for
Some other world, known to us only in our dreams.
And how, my dear, I long to taste your lips again!
For, when at last our hold is emptied of its hoard,
We shall lay down our heads and sink down deep in sleep,
Exhausted, surfeited, and yet not satisfied,
Resolved to sail again before our final days,
But grateful now to rest and think of nothing else
Until the morning light awakens us once more.
And I, my love, will lie beside you through the night—
In bliss, insensate, warm—not seeking any visions,
Not dreaming now of fabulous shores, or of waves
That break upon their strands, and not recalling now
The wonders or the perils met along the way,

Roland in Moonlight

Or those old stirrings of desire to journey forth
Upon the unplumbed deep, but rather drifting down
Into forgetfulness, and floating there, content
To let my will fall dormant for a time, while I
Embrace the emptiness, and sleep well past the dawn—

A sleep—my love, my only love—a sleep as boundless and
  abysmal as the mystery of God.

DAVID BENTLEY HART writes upon too many topics (religion, philosophy, the arts, culture…) and in too many genres (essays, fiction, monographs, satires, screeds…) and lives in hiding, beside a garden.

ROLAND W. HART is a dog and an altogether mysterious and magical presence in this fallen world. He lives beside the same garden.

Made in United States
Troutdale, OR
02/28/2024

18057121R00235